NOBEL PRIZE LIBRARY

SOLZHENITSYN

TAGORE

UNDSET

YEATS

Nobel Prize Library

PUBLISHED UNDER THE SPONSORSHIP OF THE
NOBEL FOUNDATION & THE SWEDISH ACADEMY

Aleksandr Solzhenitsyn

Rabindranath Tagore

Sigrid Undset

William Butler Yeats

ALEXIS GREGORY, *New York,* AND
CRM PUBLISHING, *Del Mar, California*

CONTENTS

CONTENTS

WILLIAM BUTLER YEATS

Aleksandr Solzhenitsyn

1970

"For the ethical force with which he

has pursued the indispensable

traditions of Russian literature"

Illustrated by PIERRE LEROI

PRESENTATION ADDRESS

By *KARL RAGNAR GIEROW*

PERMANENT SECRETARY

OF THE SWEDISH ACADEMY

Our passports show where and when we were born, facts that
are needed to fix our identity. According to a current theory this also
applies to authorship. A literary work belongs to its time and its creator
is a product of his social and political situation. There are weighty
examples to the contrary but these must be jettisoned or the theory will
founder. A case to which it does apply, however, is this year's Nobel
Prizewinner for Literature. This is worth emphasizing because from all
points of the compass, not least the west, people are prone for various
reasons to make exceptions in his case.

Aleksandr Solzhenitsyn's passport—I have in mind the one that will
convey him to posterity—tells us when and where he was born, details
that we need in order to establish his artistic identity. Born in 1918 in
Kislovodsk, he belongs to the first generation of Soviet Russian writers
who grew up with the new form of government, and he is indivisible
from the climate and the time in which he was born. Solzhenitsyn himself has said that he cannot contemplate living anywhere but in his
native land. His books can do so; they are already living all round the
world, now perhaps more than ever before, in the future perhaps more
than now. But their vitality springs not least from the feeling that roots
his being to his country and its destiny.

Here, too, Solzhenitsyn is of the incomparable Russian tradition. The
same background offsets the gigantic predecessors who have derived
from Russia's suffering the compelling strength and inextinguishable
love that permeate their work. There is little room in their descriptions
for idylls according to plan or prescribed information about the future.

But it would be a gross misunderstanding of their quest for the truth not to feel in this their profound decisive identification with the country whose life provided their subject matter and for whose life their works are essential. The central figure in this powerful epic is the invincible Mother Russia. She appears in various guises under diverse names. One is Matryona, the main character in one of Solzhenitsyn's stories. Her lined face recalls the land's constant, indomitable features and recasts the spell of devotion that she is able to offer and which she so proudly deserves.

Love is blind, the saying goes, and if so it signifies love's instinct for self-preservation. Clear-sighted love does not always conjure up an immediate response. Time and distance may be—and have been— necessary for a true appreciation of the depth and warmth of perceptive feeling. This has not been so in Solzhenitsyn's case. When his novel *One Day in the Life of Ivan Denisovich* first appeared eight years ago, it was recognized at once in his own country and soon all over the world that a major new writer had entered the arena. As a *Pravda* writer expressed it, "Solzhenitsyn's narrative is reminiscent at times of Tolstoy's artistic force. An unusually talented author has been added to our literature." It would also be difficult to outdo *Pravda*'s exposé of the power exercised by Solzhenitsyn's narrative art: "Why is it that our heart contracts with pain as we read this remarkable story, at the same time as we feel our spirits soar? The explanation lies in its profound humanity, in the quality of mankind even in the hour of degradation."

A message about special circumstances seldom travels far, and the words that fly round the world are those which appeal to and help us all. Such are the words of Aleksandr Solzhenitsyn. They speak to us of matters that we need to hear more than ever before, of the individual's indestructible dignity. Wherever that dignity is violated, whatever the reason or the means, his message is an accusation but also an assurance: those who commit such a violation are the only ones to be degraded by it. The truth of this is plain to see wherever one travels.

Even the external form which Solzhenitsyn seeks for his work bears witness to his message. This form has been termed the polyphonic or horizontal novel. It might equally be described as a story with no chief character. Which is to say that this is not individualism at the expense of the surroundings. Nor may the gallery of persons act as a collective that smothers the individuals of which it is entirely composed. Solzhenitsyn has explained what he means by polyphonism: each person becomes the chief character whenever the action concerns him. This is not just a technique, it is a creed. The narrative focuses on the only human element in existence, the human individual, with equal status among equals—one destiny among millions, and a million destinies in one. This is the whole of humanism in a nutshell, for the kernel is love of mankind. This year's Nobel Prize for Literature has been awarded to the proclaimer of such a humanism.

As explained in "The 1970 Prize" (page 97), Solzhenitsyn did not feel able to travel to Stockholm for the presentation.

ONE DAY IN THE LIFE OF IVAN DENISOVICH

By ALEKSANDR SOLZHENITSYN

Translated by Ralph Parker

At five o'clock that morning reveille was sounded, as usual, by the blows of a hammer on a length of rail hanging up near the staff quarters. The intermittent sounds barely penetrated the window-panes on which the frost lay two fingers thick, and they ended almost as soon as they'd begun. It was cold outside, and the campguard was reluctant to go on beating out the reveille for long.

The clanging ceased, but everything outside still looked like the middle of the night when Ivan Denisovich Shukhov got up to go to the bucket. It was pitch dark except for the yellow light cast on the window by three lamps—two in the outer zone, one inside the camp itself.

And no one came to unbolt the barracks door; there was no sound of the barrack orderlies pushing a pole into place to lift the barrel of excrement and carry it out.

Shukhov never overslept reveille. He always got up at once, for the next ninety minutes, until they assembled for work, belonged to him, not to the authorities, and any old-timer could always earn a bit—by sewing a pair of mittens for someone out of old sleeve lining; or bringing some rich loafer in the squad his dry valenki[1]—right up to his bunk, so that he wouldn't have to stumble bare-foot round the heap of boots looking for his own pair; or going the rounds of the warehouses, offering to be of service, sweeping up this or fetching that; or going to the mess hall to collect bowls from the tables and bring them stacked to the dishwashers—you're sure to be given something to eat there, though there were plenty of others at that game, more than plenty—and, what's worse, if you found a bowl with something left in it you could hardly resist licking it out. But Shukhov had never forgotten the words of his first squad leader, Kuziomin —a hard-bitten prisoner who had already been in for twelve years by 1943—who told the newcomers, just in from the front, as they sat beside a fire in a deso-late cutting in the forest:

"Here, men, we live by the law of the taiga. But even here people manage to live. The ones that don't make it are those who lick other men's leftovers, those who count on the doctors to pull them through, and those who squeal on their buddies."

---

[1] Knee-length felt boots for winter wear.

As for squealers, he was wrong there. Those people were sure to get through camp all right. Only, they were saving their own skin at the expense of other people's blood.

Shukhov always arose at reveille. But this day he didn't. He had felt strange the evening before, feverish, with pains all over his body. He hadn't been able to get warm all through the night. Even in his sleep he had felt at one moment that he was getting seriously ill, at another that he was getting better. He had wished morning would never come.

But the morning came as usual.

Anyway, where would you get warm in a place like this, with the windows iced over and the white cobwebs of frost all along the huge barracks where the walls joined the ceiling!

He didn't get up. He lay there in his bunk on the top tier, his head buried in a blanket and a coat, both feet stuffed into one tucked-under sleeve of his wadded jacket.

He couldn't see, but his ears told him everything going on in the barrack room and especially in the corner his squad occupied. He heard the heavy tread of the orderlies carrying one of the big barrels of excrement along the passage outside. A light job, that was considered, a job for the infirm, but just you try and carry out the muck without spilling any. He heard some of the 75th slamming bunches of boots onto the floor from the drying shed. Now their own men were doing it (it was their own squad's turn, too, to dry valenki). Tiurin, the squad leader, and his deputy Pavlo put on their valenki without a word but he heard their bunks creaking. Now Pavlo would be going off to the bread-storage and Tiurin to the staff quarters to see the P.P.D.[1]

Ah, but not simply to report as usual to the authorities for the daily assign-

ment. Shukhov remembered that this morning his fate hung in the balance: they wanted to shift the 104th from the building shops to a new site, the "Socialist Way of Life" settlement. It lay in open country covered with snowdrifts, and before anything else could be done there they would have to dig holes and put up posts and attach barbed wire to them. Wire themselves in, so that they wouldn't run away. Only then would they start building.

There wouldn't be a warm corner for a whole month. Not even a doghouse. And fires were out of the question. There was nothing to build them with. Let your work warm you up, that was your only salvation.

No wonder the squad leader looked so worried, that was his job—to elbow some other squad, some bunch of suckers, into the assignment instead of the 104th. Of course with empty hands you got nowhere. He'd have to take a pound of salt pork to the senior official there, if not a couple of pounds.

There's never any harm in trying, so why not have a go at the dispensary and get a few days off if you can? After all, he did feel as though every limb was out of joint.

Then Shukhov wondered which of the campguards was on duty that morning. It was "One-and-a-half" Ivan's turn, he recalled. Ivan was a thin, weedy, dark-eyed sergeant. At first sight he looked like a real bastard, but when you got to know him he turned out to be the most good-natured of the guards on duty: he didn't put you in the guardhouse, he didn't haul you off before the authorities. So Shukhov decided he could lie in his bunk a little longer, at least while Barracks 9 was at the mess hall.

The whole four-bunk frame began to shake and sway. Two of its occupants were getting up at the same time: Shukhov's top-tier neighbor, Alyosha the

---

[1] Production Planning Department.

Baptist, and Buinovsky, the ex-naval captain down below.

The orderlies, after removing both barrels of excrement, began to quarrel about which of them should go for hot water. They quarreled naggingly, like old women.

"Hey you, cackling like a couple of hens!" bellowed the electric welder in the 20th squad. "Get going." He flung a boot at them.

The boot thudded against a post. The squabbling stopped.

In the next squad the deputy squad leader growled quietly: "Vasily Fyodorovich, they've cheated us again at the supply depot, the dirty rats. They should have given us four twenty-five-ounce loaves and I've only got three. Who's going to go short?"

He kept his voice down, but of course everyone in the squad heard him and waited fearfully to learn who would be losing a slice of bread that evening.

Shukhov went on lying on his sawdust mattress, as hard as a board from long wear. If only it could be one thing or the other—let him fall into a real fever or let his aching joints ease up.

Meanwhile Alyosha was murmuring his prayers and Buinovsky had returned from the latrines, announcing to no one in particular but with a sort of malicious glee: "Well, sailors, grit your teeth. It's twenty below, for sure."

Shukhov decided to report sick.

At that very moment his blanket and jacket were imperiously jerked off him. He flung his coat away from his face and sat up. Looking up at him, his head level with the top bunk, was the lean figure of The Tartar.

So the fellow was on duty out of turn and had stolen up.

"S 854," The Tartar read from the white strip that had been stitched to the back of his black jacket. "Three days' penalty with work."

The moment they heard that peculiar choking voice of his, everyone who wasn't up yet in the whole dimly lit barracks, where two hundred men slept in bug-ridden bunks, stirred to life and began dressing in a hurry.

"What for, citizen[1] chief?" asked Shukhov with more chagrin than he felt in his voice.

With work—that wasn't half so bad. They gave you hot food and you had no time to start thinking. Real jail was when you were kept back from work.

"Failing to get up at reveille. Follow me to the camp commandant's office," said The Tartar lazily.

His crumpled, hairless face was imperturbable. He turned, looking around for another victim, but now everybody, in dim corners and under the lights, in upper bunks and in lower, had thrust their legs into their black wadded trousers or, already dressed, had wrapped their coats around themselves and hurried to the door to get out of the way until The Tartar had left.

Had Shukhov been punished for something he deserved he wouldn't have felt so resentful. What hurt him was that he was always one of the first to be up. But he knew he couldn't plead with The Tartar. And, protesting merely for the sake of form, he hitched up his trousers (a bedraggled scrap of cloth had been sewn on them, just above the left knee, with a faded black number), slipped on his jacket (here the same digits appeared twice—on the chest and on the back), fished his valenki from the heap on the floor, put his hat on (with his number on a patch of cloth at the front), and followed The Tartar out of the barrack room.

The whole 104th saw him go, but no one said a word—what was the use, and

_____

[1] Prisoners were not allowed to use the word comrade.

[9]

anyway what could they say? The squad leader might have tried to do something, but he wasn't there. And Shukhov said nothing to anyone. He didn't want to irritate The Tartar. Anyway he could rely on the others in his squad to keep his breakfast for him.

The two men left the barracks. The cold made Shukhov gasp.

Two powerful searchlights swept the camp from the farthest watchtowers. The border lights, as well as those inside the camp, were on. There were so many of them that they outshone the stars.

With the snow creaking under their boots, the prisoners hurried away, each on his own business, some to the parcels office, some to hand in cereals to be cooked in the "individual" kitchen. All kept their heads down, buried in their buttoned-up coats, and all were chilled to the bone, not so much from the actual cold as from the prospect of having to spend the whole day in it. But The Tartar in his old army coat with the greasy blue tabs walked at a steady pace, as though the cold meant nothing to him.

They walked past the high wooden fence around the guardhouse, the only brick building in the camp; past the barbed wire that protected the camp bakery from the prisoners; past the corner of the staff quarters where the length of frosted rail hung on thick strands of wire; past another pole with a thermometer hanging on it (in a sheltered spot, so that the registered temperature shouldn't drop too low). Shukhov looked hopefully out of the corner of an eye at the milk-white tube—if it had shown −41° they ought not to be sent out to work. But today it was nowhere near −41°.

They walked into the staff quarters and The Tartar led him straight to the guardroom; and Shukhov realized, as he had guessed on the way there, that he wasn't being sent to the guardhouse at all—it was simply that the guardroom floor needed scrubbing. The Tartar told him he was going to let him off, and ordered him to scrub the floor.

Scrubbing the guardroom floor had been the job of a special prisoner who wasn't sent to work outside the camp—a staff orderly. The fellow had long ago made himself at home in the staff quarters; he had access to the offices of the camp commandant, the man in charge of discipline, and the security officer (the Father Confessor, they called him). When working for them he sometimes heard things that even the guards didn't know, and after a time he got a big head and came to consider scrubbing the floor for rank-and-file campguards a bit beneath him. Having sent for him once or twice, the guards discovered what was in the wind and began to pick on other prisoners for the floor-scrubbing.

In the guardroom the stove was throwing out a fierce heat. Two guards in grubby tunics were playing checkers, and a third, who had not bothered to remove his sheepskin and valenki, lay snoring on a narrow bench. In one corner of the room stood an empty pail with a rag inside.

Shukhov was delighted. He thanked The Tartar for letting him off and said: "From now on I'll never get up late again."

The rule in this place was a simple one: when you'd finished you left. And now that he'd been given work to do, Shukhov's aches and pains seemed to have gone. He picked up the pail and, bare-handed—in his hurry he'd forgotten to take his mittens from under his pillow—went to the well.

Several of the squad leaders who were on their way to the P.P.D. had gathered near the pole with the thermometer, and one of the younger ones, a former Hero of the Soviet Union, shinnied up it and wiped off the instrument.

The others shouted advice from below:

"See you don't breathe on it. It'll push up the temperature."

"Push it up? Not fucking likely. *My* breath won't have any effect."

Tiurin of the 104th—Shukhov's squad —was not among them. Shukhov put down the pail, tucked his hands into his sleeves, and watched with interest.

The man up the pole shouted hoarsely: "Seventeen and a half. Not a damn bit more."

And, taking another look to be sure, slid down.

"Oh, it's cockeyed. It always lies," someone said. "Do you think they'd ever hang one up that gave the true temperature?"

The squad leaders scattered. Shukhov ran to the well. The frost was trying to nip his ears under his earflaps, which he had lowered but not tied.

The top of the well was so thickly coated with ice that he only just managed to slip the bucket into the hole. The rope hung stiff as a ramrod.

With numb hands he carried the dripping bucket back to the guardroom and plunged his hands into the water. It felt warm.

The Tartar was no longer there. The guards—there were four now—stood in a group. They'd given up their checkers and their nap and were arguing about how much cereal they were going to get in January (food was in short supply at the settlement, and although rationing had long since come to an end, certain articles were sold to them, at a discount, which were not available to the civilian inhabitants).

"Shut that door, you scum. There's a draft," said one of the guards.

No sense in getting your boots wet in the morning. Even if Shukhov had dashed back to his barracks he wouldn't have found another pair to change into.

During eight years' imprisonment he had known various systems for allocating footwear: there'd been times when he'd gone through the winter without valenki at all, or leather boots either, and had had to make shift with rope sandals or a sort of galoshes made of scraps of motor tires—"Chetezes" they called them, after the Cheliabinsk tractor works. Now the footwear situation seemed better; in October Shukhov had received (thanks to Pavlo, whom he trailed to the warehouse) a pair of ordinary, hard-wearing leather boots, big enough for a double thickness of rags inside. For a week he went about as though he'd been given a birthday present, kicking his new heels. Then in December the valenki arrived, and, oh, wasn't life wonderful?

But some devil in the bookkeeper's office had whispered in the commandant's ear that valenki should be issued only to those who surrendered their boots. It was against the rules for a prisoner to possess two pairs of footwear at the same time. So Shukhov had to choose. Either he'd have to wear leather throughout the winter, or surrender the boots and wear valenki even in the thaw. He'd taken such good care of his new boots, softening the leather with grease! Ah, nothing had been so hard to part with in all his eight years in camps as that pair of boots! They were tossed into a common heap. Not a hope of finding your own pair in the spring.

Now Shukhov knew what he had to do. He dexterously pulled his feet out of the valenki, put the valenki in a corner, stuffed his foot rags into them (his spoon tinkled on the floor—though he'd made himself ready for the guardhouse in a hurry, he hadn't forgotten his spoon), and, barefoot, sloshed the water right under the guards' valenki.

"Hey there, you slob, take it easy," one of the guards shouted, putting his feet on a chair.

"Rice?" another went on. "Rice is in a different category. You can't compare cereal with rice."

"How much water are you going to use, idiot? Who on earth washes like that?"

"I'll never get it clean otherwise, citizen chief. It's thick with mud."

"Didn't you ever watch your wife scrub the floor, pig?"

Shukhov drew himself up, the dripping rag in his hand. He smiled ingenuously, revealing the gaps in his teeth, the result of a touch of scurvy at Ust-Izhma in 1943. And what a touch it was—his exhausted stomach wouldn't hold any kind of food, and his bowels could move nothing but a bloody fluid. But now only a lisp remained from that old trouble.

"I was taken away from my wife in forty-one, citizen chief. I've forgotten what she was like."

"That's the way the scum wash. . . . They don't know how to do a fucking thing and don't want to learn. They're not worth the bread we give them. We ought to feed them on shit."

"Anyway, what's the fucking sense in washing it every day? Who can stand the damp? Look here, you, 854. Just wipe it over lightly to make it moist and then fuck off."

"No, you can't compare cereal with rice."

Shukhov knew how to manage anything.

Work was like a stick. It had two ends. When you worked for the knowing you gave them quality; when you worked for a fool you simply gave him eyewash.

Otherwise, everybody would have croaked long ago. They all knew that.

Shukhov wiped the floorboards with a damp rag so that no dry patches remained, tossed the rag behind the stove without wringing it out, pulled on his valenki near the door, threw out the rest of the water onto the path used by the camp authorities, and, taking short cuts, made a dash past the bathhouse and the dark, cold club to the mess hall.

He still had to fit in a visit to the dispensary. He ached all over. And there was that guard outside the mess hall to be dodged—the camp commandant had issued strict orders that prisoners on their own were to be picked up and thrown into the guardhouse.

That morning—a stroke of luck—there was no crowd, no lines, outside the mess. Walk in.

The air was as thick as in a Turkish bath. An icy wave blew in through the door and met the steam rising from the stew. The squads sat at tables or crowded the aisles in between, waiting for places to be freed. Shouting to each other through the crush, two or three men from each squad carried bowls of stew and oatmeal on wooden trays and tried to find room for them on the tables. Look at that damn stiff-necked fool. He doesn't hear, he's bumped a tray. Splash, splash! You've a hand free, hit him on the back of the neck. That's the way. Don't stand there blocking the aisle, looking for something to swipe!

There at the table, before dipping his spoon in, a young man crossed himself. A West Ukrainian, that meant, and a new arrival, too.

As for the Russians, they'd forgotten which hand to cross themselves with.

They sat in the cold mess hall, most of them eating with their hats on, eating slowly, picking out putrid little fish from under leaves of boiled black cabbage and spitting the bones out on the table. When the bones formed a heap and it was the turn of another squad, someone would sweep them off and they'd be trodden into a mush on the floor. But it was considered bad manners to spit the fishbones straight out on the floor.

Two rows of trestles ran down the middle of the hall and near one of them sat Fetiukov of the 104th. It was he who was keeping Shukhov's breakfast for him. Fetiukov had the last place in his squad, lower than Shukhov's. From the outside, everyone in the squad looked the same—their numbered black coats were identical—but within the squad there were great distinctions. Everyone had his grade. Buinovsky, for instance, was not the sort to sit keeping another zek's[1] bowl for him. And Shukhov wouldn't take on any old job either. There were others lower than him.

Fetiukov caught sight of Shukhov and with a sigh surrendered his place.

"It's all cold. I was just going to eat your helping. Thought you were in the guardhouse."

He didn't hang around—no hope for any leftovers to scrape out of Shukhov's bowl.

Shukhov pulled his spoon out of his boot. His little baby. It had been with him his whole time in the North, he'd cast it with his own hands in sand out of aluminum wire, and it was embossed with the words "Ust-Izhma 1944."

Then he removed his hat from his clean-shaven head—however cold it might be, he could never bring himself to eat with his hat on—and stirred the cold stew, taking a quick look to see what kind of helping they'd given him. An average one. They hadn't ladled it from the top of the kettle, but they hadn't ladled it from the bottom either. Fetiukov was the sort who when he was looking after someone else's bowl took the potatoes from it.

The only good thing about stew was that it was hot, but Shukhov's portion had grown quite cold. However, he ate it with his usual slow concentration. No

_____
[1] Abbreviation of Russian for prisoner.

need to hurry, not even for a house on fire. Apart from sleep, the only time a prisoner lives for himself is ten minutes in the morning at breakfast, five minutes over dinner, and five at supper.

The stew was the same every day. Its composition depended on the kind of vegetable provided that winter. Nothing but salted carrots last year, which meant that from September to June the stew was plain carrot. This year it was black cabbage. The most nourishing time of the year was June; then all vegetables came to an end and were replaced by grits. The worst time was July—then they shredded nettles into the pot.

The little fish were more bone than flesh; the flesh had been boiled off the bone and had disintegrated, leaving a few remnants on head and tail. Without neglecting a single fish scale or particle of flesh on the brittle skeleton, Shukhov went on chomping his teeth and sucking the bones, spitting the remains on the table. He ate everything—the gills, the tail, the eyes when they were still in their sockets but not when they'd been boiled out and floated in the bowl separately—big fish-eyes. Not then. The others laughed at him for that.

This morning Shukhov economized. Since he hadn't returned to the barracks he hadn't drawn his rations, so he ate his breakfast without bread. He'd eat the bread later. Might be even better that way.

After the vegetable stew there was _magara_, that damned "Chinese" oatmeal. It had grown cold too, and had set into a solid lump. Shukhov broke it up into pieces. It wasn't only that the oatmeal was cold—it was tasteless even when hot, and left you no sense of having filled your belly. Just grass, except that it was yellow, and looked like cereal. They'd got the idea of serving it instead of cereals from the Chinese, it was said. When boiled, a bowlful of it weighed nearly a pound. Not much of an oatmeal but that was what it passed for.

Licking his spoon and tucking it back into his boot, Shukhov put on his hat and went to the dispensary.

The sky was still quite dark. The camp lights drove away the stars. The broad beams of the two searchlights were still sweeping the zone. When this camp, this "special" (forced-labor) camp, had been organized, the security forces had a lot of flares left over from the war, and whenever there was a power failure they shot up flares over the zone—white, green, and red—just like real war. Later they stopped using them. To save money, maybe.

It seemed just as dark as at reveille but the experienced eye could easily distinguish, by various small signs, that soon the order to go to work would be given. Khromoi's assistant (Khromoi, the mess orderly, had an assistant whom he fed) went off to summon Barracks 6 to breakfast. This was the building occupied by the infirm, who did not leave the zone. An old, bearded artist shuffled off to the C.E.D.[1] for the brush and paint he needed to touch up the numbers on the prisoners' uniforms. The Tartar was there again, cutting across the parade ground with long, rapid strides in the direction of the staff quarters. In general there were fewer people about, which meant that everyone had gone off to some corner or other to get warm during those last precious minutes.

Shukhov was smart enough to hide from The Tartar around a corner of the barracks—the guard would stick to him if he caught him again. Anyway, you should never be conspicuous. The main thing was never to be seen by a camp-guard on your own, only in a group. Who knows whether the guy wasn't looking for someone to saddle with a job, or

wouldn't jump on a man just for spite? Hadn't they been around the barracks and read them that new regulation? You had to take off your hat to a guard five paces before passing him, and replace it two paces after. There were guards who slopped past as if blind, not caring a damn, but for others the new rule was a godsend. How many prisoners had been thrown in the guardhouse because of that hat business? Oh no, better to stand around the corner.

The Tartar passed by, and now Shukhov finally decided to go to the dispensary. But suddenly he remembered that the tall Lett in Barracks 7 had told him to come and buy a couple of glasses of home-grown tobacco that morning before they went out to work, something Shukhov had clean forgotten in all the excitement. The Lett had received a parcel the previous evening, and who knew but that by tomorrow none of the tobacco would be left, and then he'd have to wait a month for another parcel. The Lett's tobacco was good stuff, strong and fragrant, grayish-brown.

Shukhov stamped his feet in vexation. Should he turn back and go to the Lett? But it was such a short distance to the dispensary and he jogged on. The snow creaked audibly underfoot as he approached the door.

Inside, the corridor was, as usual, so clean that he felt quite scared to step on the floor. And the walls were painted with white enamel. And all the furniture was white.

The surgery doors were all shut. The doctors must still be in bed. The man on duty was a medical assistant—a young man called Kolya Vdovushkin. He was seated at a clean little table, wearing a small white cap and a snow-white smock. Writing something.

There was no one else in sight.

Shukhov took off his hat as if in the presence of one of the authorities and,

---

[1] Culture and Education Department.

letting his eyes shift, in the camp manner, where they had no business to shift, he noticed that Kolya was writing in even, neatly spaced lines and that each line, starting a little way from the edge of the page, began with a capital letter. He realized at once, of course, that Kolya was not doing official work but something on the side. But that was none of his business.

"Well, Nikolai Semyonich, it's like this. . . . I'm feeling sort of . . . rotten . . . ," said Shukhov shamefacedly, as if coveting something that didn't belong to him.

Kolya Vdovushkin raised his big placid eyes from his work. His number was covered up by his smock.

"Why've you come so late? Why didn't you report sick last night? You know very well there's no sick call in the morning. The sick list has already been sent to the planning department."

Shukhov knew all this. He knew too that it was even harder to get on the sick list in the evening.

"But after all, Kolya . . . You see, when I should have come . . . last night . . . it didn't ache."

"And now it does? And what is it?"

"Well, if you stop to think of it, nothing aches, but I feel ill all over."

Shukhov was not one of those who hung around the dispensary. Vdovushkin knew this. But in the morning he had the right to exempt from work two men only, and he'd already exempted them—their names were written down under the glass —it was greenish—on his desk, and he'd drawn a line across the page.

"Well, you ought to have considered that earlier. What are you thinking about? Reporting sick just before roll call. Come on, take this."

He pulled a thermometer out of one of the jars where they stood in holes cut in pieces of gauze, wiped it dry, and handed it to Shukhov, who put it in his armpit.

Shukhov sat on a bench near the wall, right at the very end, so that he nearly tipped it up. He sat in that uncomfortable way, involuntarily emphasizing that he was unfamiliar with the place and that he'd come there on some minor matter.

Vdovushkin went on writing.

The dispensary lay in the most remote and deserted corner of the zone, where no sounds of any sort reached it. No clocks or watches ticked there—prisoners were not allowed to carry watches; the authorities knew the time for them. Even mice didn't scratch there; they'd all been dealt with by the hospital cat, placed there for the purpose.

For Shukhov it was a strange experience to sit in that spick-and-span room, in such quietness, to sit under the bright lamps for five long minutes doing nothing. He cast his eyes around the walls and found them empty. He looked at his jacket—the number on the chest was almost rubbed off. That might be noticed. He ought to have it touched up. He ran his free hand over his chin and felt the stubble. His beard had grown fast since his last bath, over ten days back. But that didn't worry him. Next bath day was about three days off and he'd have a shave then. What was the sense in lining up at the barber's? Who did he have to doll himself up for?

Then as he eyed Vdovushkin's snow-white cap he remembered the hospital on the banks of the River Lovat where he'd been taken with a smashed jaw, and then—what a dope he was!—volunteered for the front again, though he could have lain there in bed for five days.

And now here he was dreaming of being ill for two or three weeks, not dangerously ill, of course, not so bad that they'd have to operate, yet bad enough to go to the hospital and lie in bed for three weeks without stirring; and let them feed him on nothing but that clear soup of theirs, he wouldn't mind.

But, he recalled, now they didn't let you lie in bed even in the camp infirmary. A new doctor had arrived with one of the latest replacements—Stepan Grigorych, a fussy, loud-voiced fellow who gave neither himself nor his patients any peace. He invented jobs in and around the infirmary for all the patients who could stand on their feet—fencing the garden, laying paths, bringing soil to the flowerbeds, and, in wintertime, erecting snow barriers. Work, he said, was a first-rate medicine for any illness.

You can overwork a horse to death. That the doctor ought to understand. If *he*'d been sweating blood laying blocks he'd quiet down, you could be sure of that.

Vdovushkin went on with his writing. He was, indeed, doing some work "on the side," but it was something beyond Shukhov's understanding. He was making a fair copy of a long new poem that he'd finished the previous evening and had promised to show that day to Stepan Grigorych, the doctor who advocated work therapy.

As can happen only in camps, Stepan Grigorych had advised Vdovushkin to describe himself as a medical assistant, and had taken him on at the infirmary and taught him to make intravenous injections on ignorant prisoners, to whose innocent minds it could never occur that Vdovushkin wasn't a medical assistant at all. Vdovushkin had been a university student of literature, arrested while still in his second year. The doctor wanted him to write when in prison what he'd been given no opportunity to write in freedom.

The signal for the roll call was barely audible through the double-paned, frost-blurred windows. Shukhov heaved a sigh and stood up. He still had that feverish chill but evidently he wouldn't be able to skip work.

Vdovushkin reached for the thermometer and read it.

"H'm, neither one thing nor the other. Ninety-nine point two. If it had been a hundred it would have been clear to anyone. I can't exempt you. Stay behind at your own risk, if you like. The doctor will examine you. If he considers you're ill, he'll exempt you. If he finds you fit, he won't. Then you'll be locked up. You'd better go back to work."

Shukhov said nothing. He didn't even nod. Pulling his hat over his eyes, he walked out.

How can you expect a man who's warm to understand a man who's cold?

The cold stung. A murky fog wrapped itself around Shukhov and made him cough painfully. The temperature out there was −17°; Shukhov's temperature was +99°. The fight was on.

He ran at a jog trot to his barracks. The whole parade ground was deserted, the camp looked empty. It was that brief moment of relaxation when, although everything has been decided, everyone is pretending to himself that there will be no march to work. The sentries sit in warm quarters, their sleepy heads propped against their rifles—it's not all milk and honey for them either, lounging on the watchtowers in such cold. The guards at the main gate tossed coal into the stove. The campguards in their room smoked a last cigarette before searching the barracks. And the prisoners, now clad in all their rags, a rope around their waists, their faces bound from chin to eyes with bits of cloth against the cold, lay on their bunks with their boots on and waited, eyes shut, hearts aquake, for their squad leader to yell: "Out you go."

The 104th were with the rest in Barracks 7—all except Pavlo, the deputy squad leader, who moved his lips as he totted something up with a pencil, and Alyosha, Shukhov's clean and tidy neighbor, who was reading from a notebook in which he'd copied out half the New Testament.

Shukhov ran headlong, but without making any noise, straight to Pavlo's bunk.

Pavlo looked up.

"So they didn't put you in the guardhouse, Ivan Denisovich? All right?" he asked with a marked Ukrainian accent, rolling out the name and patronymic in the way West Ukrainians did even in prison.

Picking up Shukhov's bread ration he handed it to him. A spoonful of granulated sugar lay in a small mound on top of the hunk. Shukhov had no time to spare but he answered properly (the deputy squad leader was also one of the authorities, and even more depended on him than on the camp commandant). And, though he was in a hurry, he sucked the sugar from the bread with his lips, licked it under his tongue as he put his foot on a support to climb up to make his bed, and took a look at his ration, weighing it in his hand and hastily calculating whether it reached the regulation sixteen ounces. He had drawn many a thousand of these rations in prisons and camps, and though he'd never had an opportunity to weigh them on scales, and although, being a man of timid nature, he knew no way of standing up for his rights, he, like every other prisoner, had discovered long ago that honest weight was never to be found in the bread-cutting. There was short weight in every ration. The only point was how short. So every day you took a look to soothe your soul—today, maybe, they haven't snitched any.

He decided he was half an ounce short as he broke the bread in two. One half he stuck into a little clean pocket he'd specially sewn under his jacket (at the factory they make jackets for prisoners without pockets). The other half, which he'd saved by going without at breakfast, he considered eating on the spot. But food gulped down is no food at all; it's wasted; it gives you no feeling of fullness. He started to put the bread into his locker but again thought better of it—he recalled that two barrack orderlies had been beaten up for stealing. The barracks was a big place, like a public yard.

And so, still clutching the hunk of bread, he drew his feet out of his valenki, deftly leaving inside them his foot rags and spoon, crawled barefoot up to his bunk, widened a little hole in the mattress, and there, amidst the sawdust, concealed his half-ration. He pulled off his hat, drew out of it a needle and thread (hidden deeply, for they fingered the hats when they frisked you; once a guard had pricked his finger and almost broken Shukhov's skull in his rage). Stitch, stitch, stitch, and the little tear in the mattress was mended, with the bread concealed under it. Meanwhile the sugar in his mouth had melted. Every nerve was strained to breaking point. At any moment the roster guard would begin shouting at the door. Shukhov's fingers worked fast but his mind, planning the next move, worked faster.

Alyosha the Baptist was reading the Testament under his breath (perhaps especially for Shukhov—those fellows were fond of recruiting).

"If you suffer, it must not be for murder, theft, or sorcery, nor for infringing the rights of others. But if anyone suffers as a Christian, he should feel it no disgrace, but confess that name to the honor of God."

Alyosha was smart—he'd made a chink in the wall and hidden the little book in it, and it had survived every search.

With the same rapid movements as before, Shukhov hung up his coat on a crossbeam and pulled what he wanted from under the mattress: a pair of mittens, a second pair of old foot rags, a length of rope, and a piece of cloth with tapes at each end. He smoothed the sawdust in the mattress (it was lumpy and dense), tucked in the blanket, arranged the pillow, and slid down onto his bare feet and started binding them with the rags, first with the good ones, then, on top, with the torn.

Just then Tiurin stood up and barked: "Sleep's over, One hundred and fourth! Out you go."

And at once the entire squad, drowsing or not, got up, yawned, and went to the door. Tiurin had been in for nineteen years and never turned his men out for the roll call a moment too soon. When he said, "Out you go," it meant you'd better.

And while the men with heavy tread and tight lips walked into the corridor one by one and then onto the porch, and the leader of the 20th, following Tiurin's example, called in turn "Out you go," Shukhov drew his valenki over the double thickness of foot rags, slipped his coat over his wadded jacket, and fastened a rope tightly around him (leather belts had been removed from zeks who had them—leather belts weren't allowed in "special" camps).

So Shukhov managed to get everything done and to catch up with the last of his companions, just as their numbered backs were passing through the door onto the porch. Looking rather bulky, for they had wrapped themselves up in every garment they possessed, the men shuffled diagonally toward the parade ground in single file, making no attempt to overtake one another. The only sound was the crunch of their heavy tread on the snow.

It was still dark, though in the east the sky was beginning to glow with a greenish tint. A light but piercing breeze came to meet them from the rising sun.

There is nothing as bitter as this moment when you go out to the morning roll call—in the dark, in the cold, with a hungry belly, to face a whole day of work. You lose your tongue. You lose all desire to speak to anyone.

A junior guard was rushing around the parade ground.

"Well, Tiurin, how long do we have to wait for you? Late again?"

Maybe Shukhov might get scared of him but not Tiurin, oh no. He wouldn't waste breath on him in the cold. Just stomped on in silence.

And the squad followed him through the snow. Shuffle, shuffle, squeak, squeak.

Tiurin must have greased them with that pound of salt pork, for the 104th had gone back to its old place in the column—that could be seen from the neighboring squads. So one of the poorer and stupider squads was being sent to the "Socialist Way of Life" settlement. Oh, it'd be cruel there today: seventeen degrees below zero, and windy. No shelter. No fire.

A squad leader needs a lot of salt pork—to take to the planning department, and to satisfy his own belly too. Tiurin received no parcels but he didn't go short of pork. No one in the squad who received any lost a moment in taking him some as a gift.

Otherwise you'd never survive.

The senior roster guard glanced at a small piece of board.

"You have one away on sick leave today, Tiurin. Twenty-three present?"

"Twenty-three," said Tiurin with a nod.

Who was missing? Panteleyev wasn't there. But surely he wasn't ill.

And at once a whisper ran through the squad: Panteleyev, that son of a bitch, was staying behind again. Oh no, he wasn't ill, the security boys were keeping him back. He'd be squealing on someone.

They would send for him during the day, on the quiet, and keep him two or three hours. No one would see, no one would hear.

And they'd fix it all up with the medical authorities.

The whole parade ground was black with coats as the squads drifted forward to be searched. Shukhov remembered he wanted to have the numbers on his jacket touched up, and elbowed his way through the crowd to the side. Two or three prisoners stood waiting their turn with the artist. He joined them. They spelled nothing but trouble, those numbers: if they were distinct the guards could identify you from any distance, but if you neglected to have them repainted in time you'd be sure to land in the guardhouse for not taking care of your number.

There were three artists in the camp. They painted pictures for the authorities free of charge, and in addition took turns appearing at roll call to touch up the numbers. Today it was the turn of an old man with a gray beard. When he painted the number on your hat with his brush it was just like a priest anointing your brow.

The old man painted on and on, blowing from time to time into his glove. It was a thin, knitted glove. His hand grew stiff with cold. He only just managed to paint the numbers.

He touched up the S 854 on Shukhov's jacket, and Shukhov, holding his rope belt in his hand and without bothering to pull his coat around him—very soon he'd be frisked—caught up with the squad. At once he noticed that his fellow squad member Tsezar was smoking, and smoking a cigarette, not a pipe. That meant he might be able to cadge a smoke. But he didn't ask straight away; he stood quite close up to Tsezar and, half turning, looked past him.

He looked past him and seemed in-different, but he noticed that after each puff (Tsezar inhaled at rare intervals, thoughtfully) a thin ring of glowing ash crept down the cigarette, reducing its length as it moved stealthily to the cigarette holder.

Fetiukov, that jackal, had come up closer too and now stood opposite Tsezar, watching his mouth with blazing eyes.

Shukhov had finished his last pinch of tobacco and saw no prospects of acquiring any more before evening. Every nerve in his body was taut, all his longing was concentrated in that cigarette butt—which meant more to him now, it seemed, than freedom itself—but he would never lower himself like that Fetiukov, he would never look at a man's mouth.

Tsezar was a hodgepodge of nationalities: Greek, Jew, Gypsy—you couldn't make out which. He was still young. He'd made films. But he hadn't finished his first when they arrested him. He wore a dark, thick, tangled mustache. They hadn't shaved it off in the camp because that was the way he looked in the photograph in his dossier.

"Tsezar Markovich," slobbered Fetiukov, unable to restrain himself. "Give us a puff."

His face twitched with greedy desire.

Tsezar slightly raised the lids that drooped low over his black eyes and looked at Fetiukov. It was because he didn't want to be interrupted while smoking and asked for a puff that he had taken up a pipe. He didn't begrudge the tobacco; he resented the interruption in his chain of thought. He smoked to stimulate his mind and to set his ideas flowing. But the moment he lighted a cigarette he read in several pairs of eyes an unspoken plea for the butt.

Tsezar turned to Shukhov and said: "Take it, Ivan Denisovich."

And with his thumb he pushed the

smoldering cigarette butt out of the short amber holder.

Shukhov started (though it was exactly what he had expected of Tsezar) and gratefully hurried to take the butt with one hand, while slipping the other hand under it to prevent it from dropping. He didn't resent the fact that Tsezar felt squeamish about letting him finish the cigarette in the holder (some had clean mouths, some had foul) and he didn't burn his hardened fingers as they touched the glowing end. The main thing was, he had cut out that jackal Fetiukov, and now could go on drawing in smoke until his lips were scorched. Mmm. The smoke crept and flowed through his whole hungry body, making his head and feet respond to it.

Just at that blissful moment he heard a shout:

"They're stripping our undershirts off us."

Such was a prisoner's life. Shukhov had grown accustomed to it. All you could do was to look out they didn't leap at your throat.

But why the undershirts? The camp commandant himself had issued them. No, something was wrong.

There were still squads ahead of them before it was their turn to be frisked. Everyone in the 104th looked about. They saw Lieutenant Volkovoi, the security chief, stride out of the staff quarters and shout something to the guards. And the guards who, when Volkovoi wasn't around, carried out the frisking perfunctorily, now flung themselves into their work with savage zeal.

"Unbutton your shirts," the sergeant shouted.

Volkovoi was as unpopular with the prisoners as with the guards—even the camp commandant was said to be afraid of him. God had named the bastard appropriately.[1] He was a wolf indeed, and looked it. He was dark, tall, with a scowl, very quick in his movements. He'd turn up from behind a barracks with a "What's going on here?" There was no hiding from him. At first, in '49, he'd been in the habit of carrying a whip of plaited leather, as thick as his forearm. He was said to have used it for flogging in the cells. Or when the prisoners would be standing in a group near a barracks at the evening count, he'd slink up from behind and lash out at someone's neck with a "Why aren't you standing in line, slobs?" The men would dash away in a wave. Stung by the blow, his victim would put a hand to his neck and wipe away the blood, but he'd hold his tongue, for fear of the cells.

Now, for some reason, Volkovoi had stopped carrying his whip.

When the weather was cold the guards were fairly lenient in the morning, though not in the evening. The prisoners untied their belts, and flung their coats wide open. They advanced five abreast, and five guards stood waiting to frisk them. The guards slapped their hands down the belted jackets, ran over the right pants pocket, the only one permitted by regulation, and, reluctant to pull off their gloves, felt any object that puzzled them, asking lazily: "What's that?"

What was there to look for on a prisoner at the morning roll call? A knife? But knives weren't taken out of the camp, they were brought into it. In the morning they had to make certain a prisoner wasn't taking six pounds of bread with him, meaning to escape with it. There was a time when they were so scared of the quarter-pound hunks the prisoners took to eat with their dinner

---

[1] *Volk* means wolf in Russian.

that each of the squads had to make a wooden case for carrying the whole ration, after collecting it, piece by piece, from the men. What they reckoned to gain by this stupidity was beyond imagining. More likely it was just another way of tormenting people, giving them something extra to worry about. It meant taking a nibble at your hunk, making your mark on it, so to speak, and then putting it in the case; but anyway the pieces were as alike as two peas—they were all off the same loaf. During the march it preyed on your mind: you tortured yourself by imagining that somebody else's bit of the ration might be substituted for yours. Why, good friends quarreled about it, even to the point of fighting! But one day three prisoners escaped in a truck from the work site and took one of those cases of bread with them. That brought the authorities to their senses—they chopped up all the boxes in the guardroom. Everyone carry his own hunk, they said.

At this first search they also had to make sure that no one was wearing civvies under the camp outfit. But, after all, every prisoner had had his civvies removed from him down to the very last garment, and they wouldn't be returned, they were told, until they'd served their terms. No one had served his term in this camp.

Sometimes the guards frisked you for letters that might have been sent through civilians. But if they were going to search every prisoner for letters they'd be fussing around till dinnertime.

Volkovoi, however, had shouted that they were to search for something, and so the guards peeled off their gloves, ordered everyone to pull up his jacket (where every little bit of barrack-room warmth was treasured) and unbutton his shirt. Then they strode up to run their paws over the zeks and find out whether any of them might have slipped on something against the rules. A prisoner was allowed to wear a shirt and an undershirt —he was to be stripped of anything else: such were Volkovoi's instructions, passed down the ranks by the prisoners. The squads that had been frisked earlier were in luck. Some of them had already been passed through the gates. But the rest had to bare their chests. And anyone who had slipped on an extra garment had to take it off on the spot, out there in the cold.

That's how it started, but it resulted in a fine mix-up—a gap formed in the column, and at the gates the escort began shouting, "Get a move on, get a move on." So when it was the turn of the 104th to be frisked they had to ease up a bit: Volkovoi told the guards to take the name of anyone who might be wearing extra garments—the culprits were to surrender them in person to personal property that evening with a written explanation of how and why they had hidden the garments.

Shukhov was in regulation dress. Come on, paw me as hard as you like. There's nothing but my soul in my chest. But they made a note that Tsezar was wearing a flannel vest and that Buinovsky, it seemed, had put on a vest or a cummerbund or something. Buinovsky protested—he'd been in the camp less, than three months, a former Navy commander who still couldn't get his destroyer out of his system.

"You've no right to strip men in the cold. You don't know Article Nine of the Criminal Code."

But they did have the right. They knew the code. You, friend, are the one who doesn't know it.

"You're not behaving like Soviet people," Buinovsky went on saying. "You're not behaving like communists."

Volkovoi had put up with the reference to the criminal code but this made him wince and, like black lightning, he flashed: "Ten days in the guardhouse."

And aside to the sergeant: "Starting from this evening."

They didn't like putting a man in the cells in the morning—it meant the loss of his work for a whole day. Let him sweat blood in the meantime and be put in the cells in the evening.

The prison lay just over there, to the left of the parade ground. A brick building with two wings. The second wing had been added that autumn—there wasn't room enough in the first. The prison had eighteen cells besides those for solitary confinement, which were fenced off. The entire camp was log-built except for that brick prison.

The cold had got under the men's shirts and now it was there to stay. All that wrapping-up had been in vain.

Shukhov's back was giving him hell. How he longed to be in bed in the infirmary, fast asleep! He wanted nothing else. Under the heaviest of blankets.

The zeks stood in front of the gates, buttoning their coats, tying a rope around their bellies. And from outside the escort shouted: "Come on. Come on."

And from behind, the guard urged them on: "Move along. Move along."

The first gate. The border zone. The second gate. Railings along each side near the gatehouse.

"Halt!" shouted a sentry. Like a flock of sheep. "Form fives."

It was growing light. The escort's fire was burning itself out behind the gatehouse. They always lit a fire before the prisoners were sent out to work—to keep themselves warm and be able to see more clearly while counting.

One of the gate guards counted in a loud brisk voice: "First. Second. Third . . ."

And the prisoners, in ranks of five, separated from the rest and marched ahead, so that they could be watched from front and behind: five heads, five backs, ten legs.

A second gate guard—a checker—stood at the next rail in silence verifying the count.

And, in addition, a lieutenant stood watching.

That was from the camp side.

A man is worth more than gold. If there was one head short when they got past the barbed wire you had to replace it with your own.

Once more the squad came together.

And now it was the turn of the sergeant of the escort to count.

"First. Second. Third."

And each rank of five drew away and marched forward separately.

And on the other side of the wire the assistant head guard verified the count.

And another lieutenant stood by and watched.

That was from the side of the escort.

No one dared make a mistake. If you signed for one head too many, you filled the gap with your own.

There were escort guards all over the place. They flung a semicircle around the column on its way to the power station, their machine guns sticking out and pointing right at your face. And there were guards with gray dogs. One dog bared its fangs as if laughing at the prisoners. The escorts all wore short sheepskins, except for a half a dozen whose coats trailed the ground. The long sheepskins were interchangeable: they were worn by anyone whose turn had come to man the watchtowers.

And once again as they brought the squads together the escort recounted the entire power-station column by fives.

"You always get the sharpest frost at sunrise," said Buinovsky. "You see, it's the coldest point of the night."

Captain Buinovsky was fond of explaining things. The state of the moon—whether it was old or young—he could calculate it for any day of the year.

He was fading away under your very eyes, the captain, his cheeks were falling in. But he had guts.

Out beyond the camp boundary the intense cold, accompanied by a head wind, stung even Shukhov's face, which was used to every kind of unpleasantness. Realizing that he would have the wind in his face all the way to the power station, he decided to make use of his bit of rag. To meet the contingency of a head wind he, like many other prisoners, had got himself a cloth with a long tape at each end. The prisoners admitted that these helped a bit. Shukhov covered his face up to the eyes, brought the tapes around below his ears, and fastened the ends together at the back of his neck. Then he covered his nape with the flap of his hat and raised his coat collar. The next thing was to pull the front flap of the hat down onto his brow. Thus in front only his eyes remained unprotected. He fixed his coat tightly at the waist with the rope. Now everything was in order except for his hands, which were already stiff with cold (his mittens were worthless). He rubbed them, he clapped them together, for he knew that in a moment he'd have to put them behind his back and keep them there for the entire march.

The chief of the escort guard recited the "morning prayer," which every prisoner was heartily sick of:

"Attention, prisoners. Marching orders must be strictly obeyed. Keep to your ranks. No hurrying, keep a steady pace. No talking. Keep your eyes fixed ahead and your hands behind your backs. A step to right or left is considered an attempt to escape and the escort has orders to shoot without warning. Leading guards, on the double."

The two guards in the lead of the escort must have set out along the road.

The column heaved forward, shoulders swaying, and the escorts, some twenty paces to the right and left of the column, each man at a distance of ten paces from the next, machine guns held at the ready, set off too.

It hadn't snowed for a week and the road was worn hard and smooth. They skirted the camp and the wind caught their faces sideways. Hands clasped behind their backs, heads lowered, the column of prisoners moved on, as though at a funeral. All you saw was the feet of two or three men ahead of you and the patch of trodden ground where your own feet were stepping. From time to time one of the escorts would cry: "U 48. Hands behind back," or "B 502. Keep up." But they shouted less and less; the slashing wind made it difficult to see. The guards weren't allowed to tie cloth over their faces. Theirs was not much of a job either.

In warmer weather everybody in the column talked, no matter how much the escort might shout at them. But today every prisoner hunched his shoulders, hid behind the back of the man in front of him, and plunged into his own thoughts.

The thoughts of a prisoner—they're not free either. They kept returning to the same things. A single idea keeps stirring. Would they feel that piece of bread in the mattress? Would he have any luck at the dispensary that evening? Would they put Buinovsky in the cells? And how did Tsezar get his hands on that warm vest? He'd probably greased a palm or two in the warehouse for people's private belongings. How else?

Because he had breakfasted without bread and eaten his food cold, Shukhov's belly felt unsatisfied that morning. And to prevent it complaining and begging for food, he stopped thinking about the camp and let his mind dwell on the letter he'd soon be writing home.

The column passed the wood-process-

[23]

ing factory, built by prison labor, the workers' settlement (the huts had been assembled by prisoners too, but the inhabitants were civilians), the new club (convict-built in entirety, from the foundations to the mural decorations—but it wasn't they who saw the films there), and then moved out into the steppe, straight into the wind heading for the reddening dawn. Bare white snow stretched to the horizon, to the left, to the right, and not a single tree could be seen on the whole expanse of steppe.

A new year, 1951, had begun, and Shukhov had the right to two letters that year. He had sent his last letter in July and got an answer to it in October. At Ust-Izhma the rules had been different: you could write once a month. But what was the sense of writing? He'd written no more often then than now.

Ivan Shukhov had left home on June 23, 1941. On the previous Sunday the people who'd been to Polomnya to attend Mass had said: *War!* At Polomnya they'd learned it at the post office but at Temgenovo no one had a radio in those days. Now, they wrote, the radio roared in every cottage—it was piped in. There was little sense in writing. Writing now was like dropping stones in some deep, bottomless pool. They drop; they sink—but there is no answer. You couldn't write and describe the squad you were working with and what kind of squad leader Andrei Prokofievich was. Just now he had a good deal more to talk about with Kilgas the Lett than with his family at home.

Neither did the two letters a year they sent him throw much light on the way they were living. The kolkhoz had a new chairman—as if that hadn't happened regularly! It'd been amalgamated with neighboring farms—that'd happened before, too, but afterward they'd reduced it to its former condition. And what else? The farmers were failing to fulfill their quota of work days—or the individual plots had been cut down to one-third acre, and some people's right back to the cottage walls.

What he couldn't take in was the fact that, as his wife wrote, the number of people in the kolkhoz hadn't grown by a single soul since the war. All the young men and women, without exception, had managed to get away to work in factories or in the peat-processing works. Half the men hadn't come back from the war at all and, among those who had, were some who cold-shouldered the kolkhoz. They lived in the village and worked on the side. The only men on the farm were Zakhar Vasilych, the manager, and Tikhon, the carpenter, who was turned eighty-four, had married recently, and already had children. The kolkhoz was kept going by the women who'd been there since 1930.

There was something about this that Shukhov couldn't understand—"living in the village and working on the side." He'd seen life in the days of private farming and in the days of the kolkhozes too, but that men weren't working in their own villages—this he couldn't swallow. Sort of seasonal workers, were they? Going out traveling? But then how did the village manage with the haymaking?

They'd given up seasonal work a long time back, his wife had replied. They didn't go out carpentering, for which that part of the country was famous; they didn't make osier baskets, for no one wanted them these days. But they did have a craft, a wonderful new craft— carpet painting. Someone had brought stencils back from the war and from that time it had become so popular that the number of those carpet painters grew and grew. They had no steady jobs, they didn't work anywhere, they helped the kolkhoz for a month or so, just at the haymaking or the harvesting, and for that the kolkhoz gave them a chit saying that so-and-so, a member of the kolkhoz, had been released to carry on his work and that the kolkhoz had no claim on him. And they traveled all over the country, they even flew in airplanes to save time, and they piled up rubles by the thousand and painted carpets all over the place. Fifty rubles a carpet made out of any old sheet you could spare—and it didn't seem to take them more than an hour to make a carpet of it. And Shukhov's wife nursed the strong hope that when Ivan returned he too would become one of those painters. Then they'd raise themselves out of the poverty in which she was living and they'd send the children to a technical school and build a new cottage instead of the old broken-down one. All the carpet painters were building new cottages and now, near the railway station, the cottages had gone up in price from five thousand to all of twenty-five.

Then Shukhov asked his wife to explain to him how he, who'd never been able to draw in his life, was going to become a painter. And what were those beautiful carpets like? What did they have on them? His wife answered that you'd have to be an utter fool not to be able to paint the patterns; all you had to do was to put the stencil on and paint through the little holes with a brush. There were three sorts of carpets, she wrote: the "Troika," an officer of the hussars driving a beautiful troika; the "Reindeer"; and a third with a Persian-style pattern. They had no other designs, but people all over the country were glad to get these and snatch them out of the painters' hands. Because a real carpet cost not fifty but thousands of rubles.

How Shukhov longed to see just one of those carpets!

During his years in prisons and camps he'd lost the habit of planning for the next day, for a year ahead, for supporting his family. The authorities did his

thinking for him about everything—it was somehow easier that way. He still had another two winters, another two summers to serve. But those carpets preyed on his mind. . . .

There was easy money to be made, you see, and made fast. And somehow it seemed a pity to lag behind his fellow villagers. . . . But, frankly, he didn't want to turn carpet painter. For that a man needed to be free and easy with people, to be brash, to know how to grease a palm or two. And although Shukhov had trodden the earth for forty years, though he'd lost half his teeth and his head was growing bald, he'd never either given or taken a bribe, nor had he learned to do so in camp.

Easy money weighs light in the hand and doesn't give you the feeling you've earned it. There was truth in the old saying: pay short money and get short value. He still had a good pair of hands, capable hands. Surely, when he was out, he'd find work as a plumber, a carpenter, or a repairman.

Only if they deprived him of his civil rights and he couldn't be taken on anywhere, or if they wouldn't let him go home, would he turn to those carpets for a spell.

Meanwhile the column had come to a halt before the gatehouse of the sprawling site on which the power station stood. While the column was still on the move, two of the escort, clad in ankle-length sheepskins, had left their places and wandered across open country to their distant watchtowers. Until all the towers were manned the site was forbidden territory. The head guard, a machine gun slung over his shoulder, advanced to the gatehouse. Smoke, a great cloud of it, belched from its chimney—a civilian watchman sat there all night to prevent anyone stealing lumber or cement.

Far in the distance, on the other side of the site, the sun, red and enormous, was rising in haze, its beams cutting obliquely through the gates, the whole building site, and the fence. Alyosha, who was standing next to Shukhov, gazed at the sun and looked happy, a smile on his lips. What had he to be happy about? His cheeks were sunken, he lived strictly on his rations, he earned nothing. He spent all his Sundays muttering with the other Baptists. They shed the hardships of camp life like water off a duck's back.

During the march, Shukhov's face cloth had grown quite wet from his breath. In some spots the frost had caught it and formed an icy crust. He drew it down from his face to his neck and stood with his back to the wind. He'd managed to keep the cold out in most places though his hands were numb in his worn mittens. The toes of his left foot were numb too—that left boot was badly worn. The sole had been repaired twice.

The small of his back ached, and so did the rest of it, all the way up to his shoulders. Ached and throbbed. How could he work?

He looked around, and his eyes fell on the face of the squad leader, who had marched among the last five. Tiurin was a broad-shouldered man, broad in the face too. He looked morose as he stood there. He had no jokes or smiles for his squad, but he took pains to see they got better rations. He was serving his second term; he was a true son of the GULAG[1] and knew camp ways through and through.

In camp the squad leader is everything: a good one will give you a second life; a bad one will put you in your coffin. Shukhov had known Andrei Tiurin since the time they met at Ust-Izhma, though he hadn't been in his squad then. And when the prisoners who were in under Article 58[2] were transferred from general camps to "special" ones, Tiurin had immediately picked him out for his squad. Shukhov had no dealings with the camp commandant or the P.P.D., with foremen or engineers—that was the squad leader's job: he'd protect him with his own chest of steel. In return, Tiurin had only to lift an eyebrow or beckon with a finger—and you ran and did what he wanted. You can cheat anyone you like in camp, but not your squad leader. Then you'll live.

Shukhov would have liked to ask Tiurin whether they were to work at the same place as the day before or go somewhere else, but he was afraid to interrupt his lofty thoughts. He'd only just averted the danger of the squad being sent to work at the Socialist Way of Life settlement, and now he was probably deliberating over the "percentage"[3] on which the squad's rations for the next five days depended.

Tiurin was heavily pockmarked. He was facing the wind but not a muscle moved—his skin was as tough as the bark of an oak.

In the column the prisoners were clapping their hands and stamping their feet. The wind was nasty. It looked now as if the sentries, known to the prisoners as "parrots," were perched in all six watchtowers, but still they weren't letting the column in. They tormented the life out of you with their vigilance.

Here they are. The head guard came out of the gatehouse with the work checker. They posted themselves on each side of the gate. The gates swung wide open.

"Form fives. First. Second. Third . . ."

---

[1] Central Camp Administration: here used to mean camps in general.

[2] For political crimes.

[3] A paper stating the amount of work done and the percentage of the plan it amounts to.

The prisoners marched as though on parade, almost in step. To get inside, that was all they wanted—there no one had to teach them what to do.

Just beyond the gatehouse was the office; near it stood the work superintendent, beckoning the squad leaders to turn in there, not that they didn't head that way anyway. Der, too, was there, a convict himself but a foreman, the swine, who treated his fellow prisoners worse than dogs.

Eight o'clock. Five minutes past (the whistle had just sounded the hour). The authorities were afraid that the prisoners might waste time and scatter into warm corners—and the prisoners had a long day ahead of them, there was time enough for everything. Everyone who steps onto the building site bends to pick up a scrap of firewood here and there—fuel for the stove. And they hoard it away in nooks and crannies.

Tiurin ordered Pavlo to go with him to the office. Tsezar turned in there too. Tsezar was well off. Two parcels a month. He greased every palm that had to be greased, and worked in the office in a cushy job, as assistant to the rate inspector.

The rest of the squad at once turned off to the side and vanished.

The sun rose red and hazy over the deserted area. At one place the panels of the prefabs lay under the snow; at another a start had been made on the brickwork, and abandoned when no higher than the foundations. Here lay a broken steam shovel, there a dredge, farther on a pile of scrap metal. A network of ditches and trenches crisscrossed the site with a hole or two here and there. The building of the automobile repair shop was ready for roofing. On a rise stood the power station itself, built up to the second story.

Now there was not a soul in sight. Only the six sentries on their watchtowers were visible—and some people bustling around the office. That moment belonged to the prisoners. The senior work superintendent, it was said, had long been threatening to save time by giving the squads their work assignments the evening before, but for all his efforts they never got around to it—because between the evening and the following morning all their plans turned upside down.

So that moment still belonged to the prisoners. While the authorities were sorting things out you stuck to the warmest place you could find. Sit down, take a rest, you'll have time enough to sweat blood. Good if you can get near a stove. Unwrap your footrags and warm them a little. Then your feet will keep warm all day. And even without a stove it's good to sit down.

The 104th went into a big room in the repair shop where the windows had been glazed during the autumn and the 38th were pouring slabs of concrete. Some of the slabs lay in wooden forms, others, with mesh reinforcement, were stood up on end. The ceiling was high, the floor was of bare earth: a cold place it would've been if they hadn't heated it with lots of coal—not for the sake of the men working there, of course, but to help the slabs set faster. There was even a thermometer, and on Sundays, if for some reason or other no one was sent from the camp to work there, a civilian kept the stove going.

The 38th, naturally, wouldn't let any stranger near their stove. Their own men sat around it, drying their footrags. Never mind, we'll sit here in the corner, it's not so bad.

Shukhov found a place for the seat of his wadded trousers—where hadn't they sat?—on the edge of a wooden form, and leaned against the wall. When he did so his coat and jacket tightened, and he felt something sharp pressing against the left side of his chest, near his heart. It was the edge of the hunk of bread in his little inner pocket—that half of his morning ration which he'd taken with him for dinner. He always brought the same amount with him to work and never touched it till dinnertime. But usually he ate the other half at breakfast. This time he hadn't. But he realized he had gained nothing by economizing—his belly called out to him to eat the bread at once, in the warmth. Dinner was five hours off— and time dragged.

And that nagging pain had now moved down to his legs, which felt quite weak. Oh, if he could only get to the stove!

He laid his mittens on his knees, un-buttoned his coat, untied the tapes of his face cloth, stiff with cold, folded it sev-eral times over, and put it away in his pants pocket. Then he reached for the hunk of bread, wrapped in a piece of clean cloth, and, holding the cloth at chest level so that not a crumb should fall to the ground, began to nibble and chew at the bread. The bread, which he had carried under two garments, had been warmed by his body. The frost hadn't caught it at all.

More than once during his life in the camps, Shukhov had recalled the way they used to eat in his village: whole pots full of potatoes, pans of oatmeal, and, in the early days, big chunks of meat. And milk enough to bust their guts. That wasn't the way to eat, he learned in camp. You had to eat with all your mind on the food—like now, nibbling the bread bit by bit, working the crumbs up into a paste with your tongue and suck-ing it into your cheeks. And how good it tasted—that soggy black bread! What had he eaten for eight, no, more than eight years? Next to nothing. But how much work had he done? Ah!

· So he sat there, occupying himself

with his hunk of bread, while near him on the same side of the room sat the rest of the 104th.

Two Estonians, close as brothers, sat on a flat concrete slab taking turns smok-ing half a cigarette from the same holder. These Estonians were equally fair, equally tall, equally lean, and had equally long noses and big eyes. They hung onto each other so closely that you'd think one would suffocate unless he breathed the same air as the other. Tiurin never separated them. They shared their food, they slept in adjacent bunks in the top row. And when they stood in the col-umn, waiting for work to start, or turned in for the night, they went on talking to each other in their quiet, deliberate man-ner. In fact they weren't brothers at all. They first met here in the 104th. One of them, they explained, had been a fisher-man on the coast; the other had been taken as a child to Sweden by his parents when the Soviets were established in Estonia. But he'd grown up with a mind of his own and returned to Estonia to complete his education.

Well, it's said that nationality doesn't mean anything and that every nation has its bad eggs. But among all the Estonians Shukhov had known he'd never met a bad one.

The prisoners sat around, some on the slabs, some on forms, some straight on the ground. A tongue doesn't wag in the morning; everyone sat silent, locked in thought. Fetiukov, the jackal, had been collecting cigarette butts (he even fished them out of the spitoons, he wasn't fussy), and now he was breaking them up and filtering the unsmoked tobacco onto a piece of paper. Fetiukov had three children at home but when he was sen-tenced they'd disclaimed him and his wife had married again. So he got no help from anywhere.

Buinovsky, who kept stealing glances

at him, finally barked: "Hey, you, what do you think you're doing? Picking up all kinds of diseases? You'll get a syphilitic lip that way. Stop it."

The captain was used to giving orders. He spoke to everyone as if in command.

But Fetiukov didn't give a damn for him—the captain got no parcels either. And with a malicious grin on his drooling lips he replied: "You wait, captain. When you've been in for eight years you'll be picking them up yourself. We've seen bigger men than you in the camp. . . ."

Fetiukov was judging by his own standards. Perhaps the captain would stand up to camp life.

"What? What?" asked Senka Klevshin, missing the point. Senka was deaf and thought they were talking about Buinovsky's bad luck during the frisking. "You shouldn't have shown your pride so much," he said, shaking his head in commiseration. "It could all have blown over."

Senka was a quiet, luckless fellow. One of his eardrums had been smashed in '41. Then he was captured; he escaped, was recaptured, and was sent to Buchenwald. There he evaded death by a miracle and now he was serving his time here quietly. If you show your pride too much, he said, you're lost.

There was truth in that. Better to growl and submit. If you were stubborn they broke you.

Alyosha sat silent, his face buried in his hands. Praying.

Shukhov ate his bread down to his very fingers, keeping only a little bit of bare crust, the half-moon-shaped top of the loaf—because no spoon is as good for scraping a bowl of cereal clean as a bread crust. He wrapped the crust in his cloth again and slipped it into his inside pocket for dinner, buttoned himself up against the cold, and prepared for work.

Let them send him out now! Though, of course, it would be better if they'd wait a bit longer.

The 38th stood up and scattered—some to the concrete mixer, some to fetch water, some to the mesh reinforcements.

But neither Pavlo nor Tiurin came back to their squad. And although the 104th had been sitting there barely twenty minutes and the working day—curtailed because it was winter—didn't end till six, everyone felt already they'd had a rare stroke of luck—now evening didn't seem so far off.

"Damn it, it's a long time since we had a snowstorm," said Kilgas, a plump, red-faced Lett, gesturing. "Not one snowstorm all winter. What sort of winter do you call this?"

"Yes . . . a snowstorm . . . a snowstorm," the squad sighed in response.

When there was a snowstorm in those parts no one was taken out to work—they were afraid of letting the prisoners leave the barracks. They could get lost between the barrack room and the mess hall if you didn't put up a guide rope. No one would care if a prisoner froze to death, but what if he tried to escape? There had been instances. During the storms the snow was as fine as dust but the drifts were as firm as ice. Prisoners had escaped over them when they topped the barbed wire. True, they hadn't got far.

Come to think of it, a snowstorm was no use to anyone. The prisoners sat locked in; the coal was delivered late and all the warmth was blown out of the barracks. Flour didn't reach the camp, so there was no bread; and more often than not there was no hot food either. And as long as the storm lasted—three days, four days, even a week—those days were counted as holidays and had to be made up for by work on Sunday.

All the same, the prisoners loved snowstorms and prayed for them. Whenever the wind rose a little, every face was turned up to the sky. Let the stuff come! The more the merrier.

Snow, they meant. With only a ground wind, it never really got going.

Someone edged up to the stove of the 38th, only to be ousted.

Just then Tiurin walked in. He looked gloomy. His squad understood that there was something to be done, and quickly.

"H'm," said Tiurin, looking around. "All present, hundred and fourth?"

He didn't verify or count them because none of Tiurin's men could have gone anywhere. Without wasting time he gave his men their assignments. The two Estonians, Senka, and Gopchik were sent to pick up a big wooden box for mixing mortar nearby and carry it to the power station. They all immediately knew that they were being transferred to the half-completed building where work had been halted in late autumn. The other men were sent with Pavlo to get tools. Four were ordered to shovel snow near the power station and the entrance to the machine room, and inside and on the ramps. A couple of men were sent to light the stove in the machine room, using coal and such lumber as they could swipe and chop up. Another was to drag cement there on a sled. Two were sent to fetch water, two for sand, and yet another to sweep the snow off the sand and break it up with a crowbar.

The only two left without assignments were Shukhov and Kilgas, the leading workers of the squad. Calling them over, Tiurin said:

"Well, look here, boys—" he was no older than they were but he had the habit of addressing them like that—"after dinner you'll be laying cement blocks on the second-story walls, over there where the sixth stopped work last autumn. Now we have to figure how to make the machine room warmer. It has three big windows and the first thing to do is to board them up somehow. I'll give you people to help, but you must figure out what to board them up with. We're going to use the machine room for mixing the mortar, and for warming ourselves too. Unless we keep warm we'll freeze like dogs, understand?"

He'd have said more, maybe, but up came Gopchik, a Ukrainian lad, pink as a suckling pig, to complain that the other squad wouldn't give them the box. There was a scrap going on over it. So off went Tiurin.

Difficult as it was to start working in such cold, the important thing was to get going.

Shukhov and Kilgas exchanged looks. They'd worked as a team more than once as carpenter and mason, and had come to respect one another.

It was no easy matter to find something to board up those windows with in the bare expanse of snow. But Kilgas said: "Vanya, I know a little place over there where those prefabs are going up, with a fine roll of roofing felt. I put it aside with my own hands. Let's go and scrounge it."

Kilgas was a Lett but he spoke Russian like a native. There'd been a settlement of Old Believers near his village and he'd learned Russian from childhood. He'd been in the camp only two years but already he understood everything: if you don't use your teeth you get nothing. His name was Johann and Shukhov called him Vanya.

They decided to go for the roll, but first Shukhov ran over to where a new wing of the repair shops was under construction. He had to get his trowel. For a mason a trowel is a serious matter—if it's light and easy to handle. But there was a rule that wherever you worked you had to turn in every evening the tools you'd been issued that morning; and which tool you would get the next day was a matter of chance. One evening, though, Shukhov had fooled the man in the tool store and pocketed the best trowel; and now he kept it hidden in a different place every evening, and every morning, if he was put to laying blocks, he recovered it. If the 104th had been sent to the Socialist Way of Life settlement that morning, Shukhov would of course have been without a trowel again. But now he had only to push aside a brick, dig his fingers into the chink—and presto! there it was.

Shukhov and Kilgas left the repair shops and walked over toward the prefabs. Their breath formed thick clouds of vapor. The sun was now some way above the horizon but it cast no rays, as in a fog. On each side of it rose pillars of light.

"Like poles, eh?" Shukhov said with a nod.

"It's not poles we have to worry about," said Kilgas casually, "so long as they don't put any barbed wire between them."

He never spoke without making a joke, that Kilgas, and was popular with the whole squad for it. And what a reputation he had already won for himself among the Letts in the camp! Of course, it was true he ate properly—he received two food parcels a month—and looked as ruddy as if he wasn't in camp at all. *You'd* make jokes if you were in his shoes!

This construction site covered an immense area. It took quite a long time to cross it. On their way they ran into men from the 82nd. Again they'd been given the job of chopping out holes in the ground. The holes were small enough—one-and-a-half feet by one-and-a-half feet and about the same in depth—but the ground, stone-hard even in summer, was

now in the grip of frost. Just try and gnaw it! They went for it with picks—the picks slipped, scattering showers of sparks, but not a bit of earth was dislodged. The men stood there, one to a hole, and looked about them—nowhere to warm up, they were forbidden to budge a step—so back to the pick. The only way to keep warm.

Shukhov recognized one of them, a fellow from Viatka.

"Listen," he advised him. "You'd do better to light a fire over each hole. The ground would thaw out then."

"It's forbidden," said the man. "They don't give us any firewood."

"Scrounge some then."

Kilgas merely spat.

"How do you figure it, Vanya! If the authorities had any guts do you think they'd have men pounding away at the ground with pickaxes in a frost like this?"

He muttered a few indistinguishable oaths and fell silent. You don't talk much in such cold. They walked on and on till they reached the spot where the panels of the prefabs lay buried under snow.

Shukhov liked to work with Kilgas. The only bad thing about him was that he didn't smoke and there was never any tobacco in his parcels.

Kilgas was right: together they lifted a couple of planks and there lay the roll of roofing felt.

They lugged it out. Now, how were they going to carry it? They'd be spotted from the watchtowers, but that didn't matter: the "parrot's" only concern was that the prisoners shouldn't escape. Inside, you could chop up all those panels into firewood for all they cared. Nor would it matter if they happened to meet one of the guards. He'd be looking about like the others to see what he could scrounge. As for the prisoners, they didn't give a damn for those prefabs, and neither did the squad leaders. The only people who kept an eye on them were the superintendent, who was a civilian, that bastard Der, and the lanky Shkuropatenko, a mere goose egg, a trusty who'd been given the temporary job of guarding the prefabs from any stealing by the prisoners. Yes, it was Shkuropatenko who was most likely to spot them on the open ground.

"Look here, Vanya," said Shukhov, "we mustn't carry it lengthwise. Let's take it up on end with our arms around it. It'll be easy to carry and our bodies will hide it. They won't spot it from a distance."

It was a good idea. To carry the roll lengthwise would have been awkward, so they held it upright in between them and set off. From a distance it would look as if there were three of them, rather close to one another.

"But when Der notices the felt on the windows he'll guess where it came from," said Shukhov.

"What's it got to do with us?" asked Kilgas, in surprise. "We'll say it was there before. Were we to pull it down or what?"

That was true.

Shukhov's fingers were numb with cold under his worn mittens. He'd lost all sense of touch. But his left boot was holding—that was the main thing. The numbness would go out of his fingers when he started to work.

They crossed the stretch of virgin snow and reached a sled trail running from the tool store to the power station. Their men must have brought the cement along there.

The power station stood on a rise at the edge of the site. No one had been near the place for weeks and the approaches to it lay under a smooth blanket of snow; the sled tracks, and the fresh trails that had been left by the deep footsteps of the 104th, stood out boldly. The

men were already clearing away the snow from around the building with wooden shovels and making a road for the trucks to drive up on.

It would have been good if the mechanical lift in the power station had been in order. But the motor had burned out, and no one had bothered to repair it. This meant that everything would have to be carried by hand to the second story —the mortar and the blocks.

For two months the unfinished structure had stood in the snow like a gray skeleton, just as it had been left. And now the 104th had arrived. What was it that kept their spirits up? Empty bellies, fastened tight with belts of rope! A splitting frost! Not a warm corner, not a spark of fire! But the 104th had arrived —and life had come back to the building.

Right at the entrance to the machine room the trough for mixing mortar fell apart. It was a makeshift affair, and Shukhov hadn't expected it to last the journey in one piece. Tiurin swore at his men just for form's sake, for he saw that no one was to blame. At that moment Kilgas and Shukhov turned up with their roll of roofing felt. Tiurin was delighted, and at once worked out a new arrangement: Shukhov was put to fixing the stovepipe, so that a fire could be quickly kindled; Kilgas was to repair the mixing trough, with the two Estonians to help him; and Senka was given an ax to chop long laths with—felt could then be tacked to them, two widths for each window. Where were the laths to come from? Tiurin looked around. Everybody looked around. There was only one solution: to remove a couple of planks that served as a sort of handrail on the ramp leading up to the second story. You'd have to keep your eyes peeled going up and down; otherwise you'd be over the edge. But where else were the laths to come from?

Why, you might wonder, should prisoners wear themselves out, working hard, ten years on end, in the camps? You'd think they'd say: No thank you, and that's that. We'll drag ourselves through the day till evening, and then the night is ours.

But that didn't work. To outsmart you they thought up work squads—but not squads like the ones outside the camps, where every man is paid his separate wage. Everything was so arranged in the camp that the prisoners egged one another on. It was like this: either you all got a bit extra or you all croaked. You're loafing, you bastard—do you think I'm willing to go hungry just because of you? Put your guts into it, slob.

And if a situation like this one turned up there was all the more reason for resisting any temptation to slack. Regardless, you put your back into the work. For unless you could manage to provide yourself with the means of warming up, you and everyone else would give out on the spot.

Pavlo brought the tools. Now use them. A few lengths of stovepipe, too. True, there were no tinsmith's tools, but there was a little hammer and a light ax. One could manage.

Shukhov clapped his mittens together, joined up the lengths, and hammered the ends into the joints. He clapped his hands together again and repeated his hammering. (He'd hidden his trowel in a nearby crack in the wall. Although he was among his own men, one of them might swap it for his own. That applied to Kilgas too.)

And then every thought was swept out of his head. All his memories and worries faded. He had only one idea—to fix the bend in the stovepipe and hang it up to prevent it smoking. He sent Gopchik for a length of wire—hang up the pipe near the window with it; that would be best.

In the corner there was another stove, a squat one with a brick chimney. It had an iron plate on top that grew red-hot, and sand was to be thawed and dried on it. This stove had already been lit, and the captain and Fetiukov were bringing up barrows of sand. You don't have to be very bright to carry a handbarrow. So the squad leader gave such work to people who'd been in positions of authority. Fetiukov had been a big-shot in some office, with a car at his disposal.

At first Fetiukov had spat on the captain, bawled at him. But one punch on the jaw was enough. They got on all right after that.

The men bringing in the sand were edging over to the stove to warm up, but Tiurin drove them off.

"Look out, one of you is going to catch it in a hurry. Wait till we've got the place fixed up."

You've only to show a whip to a beaten dog. The frost was severe, but not as severe as the squad leader. The men scattered and went back to their jobs.

And Shukhov heard Tiurin say to Pavlo: "Stay here and keep them at it. I'm going to hand in the work report."

More depended on the work report than on the work itself. A clever squad leader was one who concentrated on the work report. That was what kept the men fed. He had to prove that work which hadn't been done had been done, to turn jobs that were rated low into ones that were rated high. For this a squad leader had to have his head screwed on, and to be on the right side of the inspectors. Their palms had to be greased, too. But who benefited, then, from all those work reports? Let's be clear about it. The camp. The camp got thousands of extra rubles from the building organization and so could give higher bonuses to its guard-lieutenants, such as to Volkovoi for using his whip. And you? You got an extra six ounces of bread for your supper. A couple of ounces ruled your life.

[33]

Two buckets of water were carried in, but they had frozen on the way. Palvo decided that there was no sense in doing it like this. Quicker to melt snow. They stood the buckets on the stove.

Gopchik brought along some new aluminum wire, used for electric leads.

"Ivan Denisovich," he said, as he turned it over to Shukhov, "it's good for making spoons. Teach me how to cast them."

Shukhov was fond of the kid. His own son had died young, and the two daughters he had left at home were grown up. Gopchik had been arrested for taking milk to the forest for Bendera's men,[1] and had been given an adult's term of imprisonment. He was like a puppy and he fawned on everyone. But he'd already learned cunning: he ate the contents of his food packages alone, sometimes during the night.

After all, you couldn't feed everyone.

They broke off a length of wire for the spoons and hid it in a corner. Shukhov knocked together a couple of planks into a stepladder and sent Gopshik up to hang the stovepipe. The boy, as nimble as a squirrel, climbed up into the beams, pounded in a nail or two, slipped the wire around them, and passed it under the pipe. Shukhov didn't begrudge him his energy; he made another bend in the pipe close to the end. Though there was little wind that day, there might be plenty tomorrow, and this bend would prevent the pipe from smoking. They mustn't forget that it was for themselves that they were fixing the stove.

Meanwhile, Senka had finished making the laths, and Gopchik was again given the job of nailing them up. The little devil crawled about up there, shouting down to the men.

[1] General in the Soviet Army who betrayed his country in World War II.

The sun had risen higher, dispersing the haze. The two bright columns had gone. It was reddish inside the room. And now someone had got the stove going with the stolen wood. Made you feel a bit more cheerful.

"In January the sun warmed the flanks of the cow," Shukhov chanted.

Kilgas finished nailing the mortar trough together and, giving it an extra smash with his ax, shouted: "Listen, Pavlo, I won't take less than a hundred rubles from Tiurin for this job."

"You get three ounces," said Pavlo with a laugh.

"The prosecutor will make up the difference," shouted Gopchik from above.

"Stop that," Shukhov shouted, "stop." That wasn't the way to cut the roofing felt.

He showed them how to do it.

The men crept up to the stove, only to be chased away by Pavlo. He gave Kilgas some wood to make hods, for carrying the mortar up to the second story. He put on a couple more men to bring up the sand, others to sweep the snow off the scaffolding where the blocks were to be put, and another to take the hot sand off the top of the stove and throw it into the mortar trough.

A truck engine snorted outside. They were beginning to deliver the blocks. The first truck had got through. Pavlo hurried out and waved on the driver to where the blocks were to be dumped.

They put up one thickness of roofing felt, then a second. What protection could you expect from it? It was paper, just paper. All the same, it looked like a kind of solid wall. The room became darker, and this brightened the stove up.

Alyosha brought in some coal. Some of them shouted to tip it onto the stove, others not to. They wanted to warm up with the flames. Alyosha hesitated, not knowing whom to obey.

Fetiukov had found himself a cozy corner near the stove and, the fool, was holding his boots right up to the flames. The captain took him by the scruff of the neck and lugged him off to the barrow.

"You haul sand, you bastard."

The captain might still have been on board ship—if you were told to do something you did it. He had grown haggard during the past month, but he kept his bearing.

In the end, all three windows were covered. Now the only light came through the door. And with it came the cold. So Pavlo had the upper half of the doorway boarded up but the lower left free, so that the men, by stooping, could get through it.

Meanwhile three trucks had driven up and dumped their loads of blocks. Now the problem was how to get the blocks up without the mechanical lift.

"Masons, let's go and look around," Pavlo called.

It was a job to be respected. Shukhov and Kilgas went up with Pavlo. The ramp was narrow enough anyhow, but now that Senka had robbed it of its rails you had to make sure you pressed close to the wall if you weren't going to fall off it. And still worse—the snow had frozen to the treads and rounded them; they offered no grip to your feet. How would they bring up the mortar?

They looked all around to find where the blocks should be laid. The men Pavlo had sent up were shoveling the snow from the top of the walls. Here was the place. You had to take an ax to the ice on the old workings, and then sweep them clean.

They figured out how best to bring up the blocks. They looked down. They decided that, rather than carry them up the ramp, four men would be posted down below to heave the blocks up to that platform over there, that another couple would move them on, and that two more would hand them up to the second story. That would be quicker than carrying them up the ramp.

The wind wasn't strong but you felt it. It would pierce them all right when they started laying. They'd have to keep behind the bit of wall that the old crew had begun on; it would give them some shelter. Not too bad—it'd be warmer that way.

Shukhov looked up at the sky and gasped—the sun had climbed almost to the dinner hour. Wonder of wonders! How time flew when you were working! That was something he'd often noticed. The days rolled by in the camp—they were over before you could say "knife." But the years, they never rolled by; they never moved by a second.

When they went down, they found that everyone had settled around the stove except the captain and Fetiukov, who were still hauling sand. Pavlo flew into a rage and sent eight men out at once to move blocks, two to pour cement into the box and mix it with sand, another for water, another for coal. But Kilgas gave his own orders:

"Well, men, we must finish with the barrows."

"Shall I give 'em a hand?" Shukhov volunteered.

"Yes, help them out," said Pavlo with a nod.

Just then they brought in a tank for melting snow. Someone had told the men that it was already noon.

Shukhov confirmed this.

"The sun's already reached its peak," he announced.

"If it's reached its peak," said the captain reflectively, "it's one o'clock, not noon."

"What do you mean?" Shukhov demurred. "Every old-timer knows that the sun stands highest at dinnertime."

"Old-timers, maybe," snapped the captain. "But since their day a new decree has been passed, and now the sun stands highest at one."

"Who passed that decree?"

"Soviet power."

The captain went out with a barrow. Anyway, Shukhov wouldn't have argued with him. Mean to say that the sun up in the sky must bow down to decrees, too?

The sound of hammering continued as the men knocked together four hods.

"All right, sit down awhile and warm yourselves," said Pavlo to the two masons. "And you too, Senka. You can join them up there after dinner. Sit down."

So now they had a right to sit by the stove. Anyway they couldn't start laying the blocks before dinner and there was no point in carrying the mortar up there —it would freeze.

The coals were gradually glowing red-hot and throwing out a steady heat. But you felt it only when you were near them—everywhere else the shop was as cold as ever.

They took off their mittens. All four men held their hands up to the stove.

But you never put your feet near the flame if you're wearing boots. You have to remember that. If they're leather boots the leather cracks, and if they're valenki the felt becomes sodden and begins to steam and you don't feel any warmer. And if you hold them still nearer the flame then they scorch, and you'll have to drag along till the spring with a hole in your boot—getting another pair can't be counted on.

"What does Shukhov care?" Kilgas said. "Shukhov has one foot almost home."

"The bare one," said someone. They laughed (Shukhov had taken his mended boot off and was warming his footrags).

"Shukhov's term's nearly up."

They'd given Kilgas twenty-five years. Earlier there'd been a spell when people were lucky: everyone to a man got ten years. But from '49 onward the standard sentence was twenty-five, irrespective. A man can survive ten years—but twenty-five, who can get through alive?

Shukhov rather enjoyed having everybody poke a finger at him as if to say: Look at him, his term's nearly up. But he had his doubts about it. Those zeks who finished their time during the war had all been "retained pending special instructions" and had been released only in '46. Even those serving three-year sentences were kept for another five. The law can be stood on its head. When your ten years are up they can say, "Here's another ten for you." Or exile you.

Yet there were times when you thought about it and you almost choked with excitement. Yes, your term really *is* coming to an end; the spool is unwinding. . . . Good God! To step out to freedom, just walk out on your own two feet.

But it wasn't right for an old-timer to talk about it aloud, and Shukhov said to Kilgas: "Don't you worry about those twenty-five years of yours. It's not a fact you'll be in all that time. But that I've been in eight full years—now that is a fact."

Yes, you live with your feet in the mud and there's no time to be thinking about how you got in or how you're going to get out.

According to his dossier, Ivan Denisovich Shukhov had been sentenced for high treason. He had testified to it himself. Yes, he'd surrendered to the Germans with the intention of betraying his country and he'd returned from captivity to carry out a mission for German intelligence. What sort of mission neither Shukhov nor the interrogator could say. So it had been left at that—a mission.

Shukhov had figured it all out. If he didn't sign he'd be shot. If he signed he'd still get a chance to live. So he signed.

But what really happened was this. In February 1942 their whole army was surrounded on the northwest front. No food was parachuted to them. There were no planes. Things got so bad that they were scraping the hooves of dead horses —the horn could be soaked in water and eaten. Their ammunition was gone. So the Germans rounded them up in the forest, a few at a time. Shukhov was in one of these groups, and remained in German captivity for a day or two. Then five of them managed to escape. They stole through the forest and marshes again, and, by a miracle, reached their own lines. A machine gunner shot two of them on the spot, a third died of his wounds, but two got through. Had they been wiser they'd have said they'd been wandering in the forest, and then nothing would have happened. But they told the truth: they said they were escaped POW's. POW's, you fuckers! If all five of them had got through, their statements could have been found to tally and they might have been believed. But with two it was hopeless. You've put your damned heads together and cooked up that escape story, they were told.

Deaf though he was, Senka caught on that they were talking about escaping from the Germans, and said in a loud voice: "Three times I escaped, and three times they caught me."

Senka, who had suffered so much, was usually silent: he didn't hear what people said and didn't mix in their conversation. Little was known about him— only that he'd been in Buchenwald, where he'd worked with the underground and smuggled in arms for the mutiny; and how the Germans had punished him by tying his wrists behind his back, hanging him up by them, and whipping him.

"You've been in for eight years, Vanya," Kilgas argued. "But what camps? Not 'specials.' You had broads to sleep with. You didn't wear numbers. But try and spend eight years in a 'special'— doing hard labor. No one's come out of a 'special' alive."

"Broads! Boards you mean, not broads."

Shukhov stared at the coals in the stove and remembered his seven years in the North. And how he worked for three years hauling logs—for packing cases and railroad ties.

The flames in the campfires had danced up there, too—at timber-felling during the night. Their chief made it a rule that any squad that had failed to meet its quota had to stay in the forest after dark.

They'd dragged themselves back to the camp in the early hours but had to be in the forest again next morning.

"N-no, brothers, . . . I think we have a quieter life here," he said with his lisp. "Here, when the shift's over, we go back to the camp whether our job's done or not. That's a law. And bread—three ounces more, at least, than up there. Here a man can live. All right, it's a 'special' camp. So what? Does it bother you to wear a number? They don't weigh anything, those numbers."

"A quieter life, do you call it?" Fetiukov hissed (the dinner break was getting near and everyone was huddling around the stove). "Men having their throats cut, in their bunks! And you call it quieter!"

"Not men—squealers." Pavlo raised a threatening finger at Fetiukov.

True enough, something new had started up. Two men, known to be squealers, had been found in their bunks one morning with their throats cut; and, a few days later, the same thing had happened to an innocent zek—someone must have gone to the wrong bunk. And one squealer had run off on his own to the head of the guardhouse and they'd put him inside for safety. Amazing. . . . Nothing like that had happened in the ordinary camps. Nor here, either, up till then.

Suddenly the whistle blew. It never began at full blast. It started hoarsely, as though clearing its throat.

Midday. Lay down tools. The dinner break.

Damn it, they'd waited too long. They should have gone off to the canteen long ago and taken their places in the line. There were eleven squads at work at the power station and there was room in the canteen for only two at a time.

Tiurin was still missing. Pavlo cast a rapid glance around the shop and said: "Shukhov and Gopchik, you come with me. Kilgas, as soon as I send Gopchik to you, bring the whole squad along."

Others took their places at the stove the moment any were vacated. The men surrounded it as though it was a pretty broad. They all crept up to embrace it.

"Come on, don't spend all night with her!" others shouted. "Let's smoke."

They looked at one another to see who was going to light up. No one did. Either they had no tobacco or they were holding onto it, unwilling to let it be seen.

Shukhov went out with Pavlo. Gopchik loped behind like a hare.

"It's gotten warmer," Shukhov said at once. "Zero, no lower. Fine for laying the blocks."

They stole a glance at those blocks. The men had already thrown a lot of them up to the platform and quite a number had been shifted to the floor above.

Screwing up his eyes at the sun, Shukhov checked its position. He was thinking of the captain's "decree."

Out in the open the wind was still having its way and the cold was still fierce. Don't forget, it was telling them, this is January.

The zeks' canteen was no more than a shanty made of boards nailed together around a stove, with some rusty metal strips over the cracks. Inside, it was partitioned into a kitchen and an eating room. In neither was there a wood floor; it was pitted with the lumps and hollows that the men's feet had trodden into it. All that the kitchen consisted of was a square stove with a soup kettle stuck on top.

The kitchen was run by two men—a cook and a sanitation inspector. Every morning as he left the camp the cook drew an issue of grits from the main kitchen: about one-and-a-half ounces a head, probably. That made two pounds a squad, a little less than a pood[1] for the whole column. The cook didn't much like carrying the sack of grits the two miles himself, so he got a "helper" to carry it for him—better to give the "helper" an extra portion at the zeks' expense than burden his own back. There was water to be carried, too, and firewood for the stove, and these were jobs the cook didn't much like either; so he found zeks to do them instead, for extra helpings at others' expense. What did it matter to him?

Then there was a rule that food must be eaten in the canteen; but the bowls couldn't be left there overnight, they'd have been swiped by civilians, so about fifty, not more, had to be brought in, and quickly washed after use and turned over to the next diners (an extra helping for the man who carried the bowls). To make sure that no one took bowls from the canteen, a man had to be posted at the door; but however careful he might be people took them just the same, either by distracting his attention or talking him into it. So someone else had to go over

_____
[1] Thirty-six pounds.

the whole site to collect the dirty bowls and bring them back to the kitchen. And *he* got an extra helping. And many others got one too.

All the cook himself did was this: he poured the grits into the pot, adding salt; he divided the fat between the pot and himself (good fat didn't reach the zeks, and the rancid all went into the soup kettle, so when there was an issue of rancid fat from the warehouse, the zeks welcomed it as an extra). Another thing he did: he stirred the kasha[1] when it was boiling.

The sanitation inspector had even less to do—he sat and watched: but when the oatmeal was ready he got his helping, as much as his belly would hold. And the cook too. Then the duty-squad leader arrived—the squad was changed every day—to have a taste and decide whether the stuff was good enough for the workers. He received a double portion.

The whistle sounded again. The squad leaders at once lined up, and the cook handed them bowls through the serving window. In the bottom of the bowls lay some oatmeal, how much you didn't ask, or try to judge by the weight. All you got if you opened your mouth was a bunch of swear words.

The steppe was barren and windswept, with a dry wind in the summer and a freezing one in winter. Nothing could ever grow in that steppe, less than nothing behind four barriers of barbed wire. Bread comes only from the bread cutter; oats are threshed only in the warehouse. And however much blood you sweat at work, however much you grovel on your belly, you'll force no food out of that earth; you'll get no more than the damned authorities give you. And you don't even get that—because of the cook and the "help" and all the other trusties

---
1 Oatmeal.

in soft jobs. They rob you here, they rob you in camp, they rob you even earlier— in the warehouse. And those who do the robbing don't swing picks. But you—you swing a pick and take what they give you. And get away from the serving window!

Pavlo and Shukhov, with Gopchik bringing up the rear, walked into the canteen. The men stood there so close to one another that you couldn't see either tables or benches. Some ate sitting down but most stood. The men of the 82nd, who'd been digging those holes half a day without a chance of getting warm, had been the first to get in after the whistle; now even after they'd finished eating they didn't leave. Where else could they warm up? The swearing fell off them like water off a duck's back—it was so much more comfortable here than in the cold. Pavlo and Shukhov elbowed their way in. They'd arrived at a good moment: one squad was being served, another was awaiting its turn, and there was only one deputy squad leader near the window. So, they were well ahead of the rest.

"Bowls, bowls," the cook shouted through the window and people hurriedly handed them over. Shukhov was collecting another lot and turning them in, not to get extra oatmeal but to get what was coming to him quicker.

Behind the partition some "helpers" were already washing bowls—for extra oatmeal.

The cook began to serve the deputy squad leaders who stood ahead of Pavlo in the line.

"Gopchik," Pavlo shouted, over the heads of the men behind him.

"Here I am," came Gopchik's thin goatlike bleat from the door.

"Call the squad."

Off he went.

The main thing today was that the oatmeal was good—real oatmeal, the best sort. It wasn't often they had it. More often they got *magara* twice a day. But real oatmeal is filling, it's good.

How often had Shukhov in his youth fed oats to horses! Never had it occurred to him that there'd come a time when his whole soul would yearn for a handful of them.

"Bowls, bowls," shouted the cook.

Now the 104th was in line. That squad leader's deputy, up ahead, got his double helping and bounced away from the window.

This extra helping, too, was at the zeks' expense—but no one objected. The cook gave double helpings to all the squad leaders, and they either ate the extra helping themselves or gave it to their deputies. Tiurin gave his to Pavlo.

Shukhov's job now was to wedge himself in behind a table, oust two loafers, politely ask another prisoner to move, and clear a little space in front of him—for twelve bowls (to stand close together), with a second row of six, and two more on top. Next he had to take the bowls from Pavlo, repeating the number as he did so and keeping his eyes peeled—in case some outsider should grab a bowl from the table. And he had to see he wasn't bumped by someone's elbow so as to upset a bowl—right beside him people were leaving the table, stepping over the benches or squeezing in to eat. Yes, you had to keep your eyes peeled—was that fellow eating out of his own bowl? Or had he wormed his way up to one of the 104th's?

"Two, four, six," the cook counted at the window. He handed out the bowls two at a time—it was easier for him that way; otherwise he might count wrong.

"Two, four, six," Pavlo repeated quietly to himself, there at the window, in Ukrainian, and at once gave the bowls, in pairs, to Shukhov, who put them on the table. Shukhov didn't repeat the numbers aloud—but he counted more sharply than anyone.

"Eight, ten."

Why wasn't Gopchik bringing in the squad?

"Twelve, fourteen," the counting continued.

The kitchen ran out of bowls. Shukhov had a clear view through the window past Pavlo's head and shoulders. The cook put two bowls down on the counter and, keeping his hands on them, paused as though thinking. Must be bawling out the dishwashers. But just then another bunch of dirty bowls was pushed onto the counter. The cook let go of the two clean ones he'd filled and pushed back the pile of dirty ones.

Shukhov left the fourteen bowls he'd already stacked on the table, straddled a bench, took the two filled ones from the counter, and said quietly to Pavlo rather than to the cook: "Fourteen."

"Stop! Where are you taking those bowls?" shouted the cook.

"He's from our squad," Pavlo confirmed.

" 'Our squad,' but he's mixed up the count."

"Fourteen," Pavlo said with a shrug. Himself, he wouldn't have swiped the extra bowls, for as deputy squad leader he had to maintain his dignity; but now he was simply repeating what Shukhov had said—he could always blame him for the mistake.

"I've already counted fourteen," the cook expostulated.

"So you did, but you didn't pass them out. You kept your hands on them," Shukhov shouted. "Come and count for yourself if you don't believe us. Look, they're all here on the table."

As he spoke he'd noticed the two Estonians pushing through to him, and he shoved the two bowls into their hands as they passed. And he'd managed to get back to the table to see that all the bowls were in place—the next table hadn't swiped any, though they'd had plenty of opportunity to do so.

The cook's red face loomed large in the window.

"Where are those bowls?" he asked sternly.

"Here they are, at your service," yelled Shukhov. "Move along, scum, you're spoiling his view," he said to someone, giving him a shove. "Here they are, the pair of them." He picked up two bowls from the second row. "Here we have three rows of four, all nice and neat. Count them."

"Hasn't your squad come?" the cook asked, looking suspiciously around the small segment of the canteen he could see through the window—it had been kept narrow to prevent anyone looking into the kitchen and seeing how much was left in the kettle.

"No, none of 'em are here yet," said Pavlo, shaking his head.

"Then why the hell are you taking bowls when the squad's not here?"

"Here they come," yelled Shukhov.

And everyone heard the peremptory shouts of the captain at the door: "Why are you hanging around here?" he yelled, in his best quarter-deck voice. "If you've eaten, beat it and let others in."

The cook muttered something through the serving window. Then he drew himself up, and his hands could again be seen giving out the bowls: "Sixteen, eighteen."

Then he ladled the last portion, a double helping: "Twenty-three. That's all. Next squad."

The men of the 104th pushed through. Pavlo handed them bowls, passing them over the heads of the prisoners sitting at the second table.

In summer five could have sat on a bench, but now, as everyone was wearing thick clothes, four could barely fit in, and even they found it awkward to move their spoons.

Figuring that of the two bowls of oatmeal that had been swiped one at least would be his, Shukhov lost no time in applying himself to his first bowl. He drew his right knee up to his stomach, pulled his spoon ("Ust-Izhma, 1944") from under his boot top, removed his hat, put it in his left armpit, and ran his spoon under the edge of the kasha.

This is a moment that demands complete concentration, as you remove some of the scanty kasha from the bottom of the bowl, put it carefully into your mouth, and swirl it around there with your tongue. But Shukhov had to hurry, to show Pavlo he'd already finished and was waiting to be offered a second bowl. And there was Fetiukov to be dealt with. He had come into the canteen with the two Estonians and had witnessed the whole affair of the two extra bowls. Now he stood there, straight in front of Pavlo, eying the four undistributed helpings as if to say that he ought to be given at least half a helping too.

Young swarthy Pavlo, however, went calmly on with his double portion, and there was no way of telling whether he noticed anyone standing there, or even remembered those extra bowls at all.

Shukhov finished his kasha. He had promised his belly two helpings, so one wasn't enough now to give him the full feeling he normally got from real oatmeal kasha.

He groped in his inside pocket for the scrap of clean rag, found the unfrozen crescent of crust, and meticulously used it to wipe off the last remnant of mush from the bottom of the bowl and any that still clung to the brim. Then he licked the crust clean; then repeated the whole process. The bowl looked now as if it had been washed, with a dull film, nothing more, on the inside surface. He handed it over his shoulder to one of the dish-collectors and sat on, without replacing his hat.

Though it was Shukhov who had swindled the extra bowls, it was for Pavlo to distribute them.

Pavlo prolonged the agony a little longer while emptying his own bowl. He didn't lick it clean; he merely gave a lick to his spoon, tucked it away, and crossed himself. And then, very lightly, he touched—there wasn't room to move—two of the remaining four bowls. It meant he was giving them to Shukhov.

"Ivan Denisovich, take one for yourself and give the other to Tsezar."

Shukhov knew one of the bowls had to be taken to the office of Tsezar, who would never lower himself by going to the canteen or, for that matter, to the mess hall in camp. He knew it, but, all the same, when Pavlo touched the bowls his heart contracted. Could Pavlo be giving him both? And now, as Pavlo spoke, his heartbeat went back to normal.

Without losing any time he leaned over his lawful spoil and began to eat with deliberation, insensitive to the thumps on his back that the zeks in the next squad were dealing him. The only thing that vexed him was that the second bowl might still go to Fetiukov. Fetiukov was a past master at cadging, but he lacked the courage to swipe anything.

Nearby sat Captain Buinovsky. He had long finished his kasha. He didn't know the squad had two extra portions to dispose of. He didn't look around to see how much Pavlo still had left to hand out. He was simply relaxing, warming up. He was not strong enough to rise to his feet and go out into the cold or into that icy warming-up spot. He, like the very people he had just hounded out of the canteen with his rasping voice, was occupying a place he had no right to and

getting in the way of the next squad. He was a newcomer. He was unused to the hard life of the zeks. Though he didn't know it, moments like this were particularly important to him, for they were transforming him from an eager, confident naval officer with a ringing voice into an inert, though wary, zek. And only in that inertness lay the chance of surviving the twenty-five years of imprisonment he'd been sentenced to.

People were already shouting at him and nudging him in the back to make him give up his place.

"Captain!" said Pavlo. "Hey, captain."

Buinovsky shuddered as though he was being jerked out of a dream. He looked around.

Pavlo handed him a bowl of kasha. He didn't ask him whether he wanted it.

The captain's eyebrows shot up. He looked at the bowl as at something miraculous.

"Take it, take it," said Pavlo reassuringly, and picking up the last bowl—for the squad leader—went out.

An apologetic smile fitted over the captain's chapped lips. And this man, who had sailed around Europe and navigated the Great Northern Route, leaned happily over half a ladleful of thin oatmeal kasha, cooked entirely without fat —just oats and water.

Fetiukov cast angry looks at Shukhov and the captain and left the canteen.

But Shukhov thought Pavlo had been right. In time the captain would learn the ropes. Meanwhile, he didn't know how to live.

Shukhov still nursed a faint hope that Tsezar would give him his bowl of kasha. But it seemed unlikely, for more than two weeks had passed since Tsezar had received his last package.

After scraping the bottom and rim of the second bowl in the same way as the first, then licking the crust, Shukhov finally ate the crust itself. Then he picked up Tsezar's bowl of cold kasha and went out.

"It's for the office," he said, as he pushed past the man at the door who tried to stop him taking the bowl out.

The office was in a log cabin near the sentry house. As in the morning, smoke was curling out of the chimney. The stove was kept going by an orderly who worked as an errand boy too, picking up a few kopecks here and there. They didn't begrudge him shavings or even logs for the office stove.

The outer door creaked as Shukhov opened it. Then came another door, calked with oakum. Bringing with him a cloud of frosty vapor, he went in and quickly pulled the door shut (so that they wouldn't yell at him: "Hey, you bastard, shut the door").

The office was as hot as a Turkish bath, it seemed to Shukhov. The sun, coming in through the icy windowpanes, played gaily in the room, not angrily as it did at the power station; and, spreading across the broad sunbeam, the smoke of Tsezar's pipe looked like incense in church. The stove glowed red right through. How they piled it on, the devils! Even the stovepipe was red-hot.

In an oven like that you only have to sit down a minute and you're fast asleep.

The office had two rooms. The door into the second one, occupied by the superintendent, was not quite closed, and through it the superintendent's voice was thundering:

"There's an overdraft on the expenses for labor and building materials. Right under your noses prisoners are chopping up valuable lumber, not to mention prefabricated panels, and using them for firewood at their warming-up spots. The other day the prisoners unloaded cement near the warehouse in a high wind. What's more, they carried it up to ten yards on barrows. As a result the whole area around the warehouse is ankle-deep

in cement and the men are smothered in it. Just figure the waste!"

Obviously a conference was going on in there. With the foremen.

In a corner near the door an orderly sat lazing on a stool. Beyond him, like a bent pole, stooped Shkuropatenko—B 219. That fathead—staring out of the window, trying to see, even now, whether anyone was pinching some of his precious prefabs! You didn't spot us *that* time, you snoop!

The bookkeepers, also zeks, were toasting bread at the stove. To prevent it from burning they'd fixed up a grill out of wire.

Tsezar was sprawling over his desk, smoking a pipe. His back was to Shukhov and he didn't notice him come in.

Opposite him sat X 123, a stringy old man who was serving a twenty-year sentence. He was eating kasha.

"No, my friend," Tsezar was saying in a gentle, casual way. "If one is to be objective one must acknowledge that Eisenstein is a genius. *Ivan the Terrible*, isn't that a work of genius? The dance of Ivan's guards, the masked *oprichniki!* The scene in the cathedral!"

"Ham," said X 123 angrily, stopping his spoon in front of his lips. "It's all so arty there's no art left in it. Spice and poppyseed instead of everyday bread and butter! And then, the vicious political idea—the justification of personal tyranny. A mockery of the memory of three generations of Russian intelligentsia."

He ate as if his lips were made of wood. The kasha would do him no good.

"But what other interpretation could he have gotten away with?"

"Gotten away with? Ugh! Then don't call him a genius! Call him an ass-kisser, obeying a vicious dog's order. Geniuses don't adjust their interpretations to suit the taste of tyrants!"

"Hm, hm!" Shukhov cleared his

throat. He hadn't the nerve to interrupt such a learned conversation. But there wasn't any sense in standing there, either.

Tsezar swung around and held out his hand for the bowl, not even looking at Shukhov, as though the kasha had materialized out of thin air.

"But listen," he resumed. "Art isn't a matter of *what* but of *how*."

X 123 struck the table angrily with the edge of his hand.

"To hell with your 'how' if it doesn't arouse any worthwhile feeling in me."

Shukhov stood there just as long as was decent for a man who had brought a bowl of kasha. After all, Tsezar might offer him a smoke. But Tsezar had quite forgotten his presence.

So Shukhov turned on his heel and went quietly out. The cold was bearable, he decided. The block-laying wouldn't go too badly.

As he walked along the path he caught sight in the snow of a short length of steel—a bit of a hacksaw blade.

He could conceive of no immediate use for it, but then you can never tell what you might need in the future. So he picked it up and slipped it into his pants pocket. He'd hide it at the power station. Waste not, want not.

The first thing he did on reaching the power station was to take his trowel out of its hiding place and slip it under the length of rope he wore around his waist. Then he took off for the machine shop.

After the sunlight the shop seemed quite dark and no warmer than outside. Sort of clammy.

All the men had crowded near the round iron stove that Shukhov had fixed, or near the one where the sand was steaming as it dried. Those who could find no room around the stoves sat on the edge of the mortar trough. Tiurin was seated against the stove, finishing the kasha that Pavlo had warmed up for him on it. The men were whispering to one another. They were in high spirits. One of them passed the news on to Shukhov: the squad leader had been successful in fixing the work report. He'd come back in a good mood.

What sort of work he'd found and how it had been rated was Tiurin's own business. What in fact had the squad done that first half of the day? Not a thing. They weren't paid for fixing the stoves, they weren't paid for arranging a place to warm up in—they had done that for themselves, not for the building site. But something had to be written in the report. Perhaps Tsezar was helping the squad leader to fix it up properly. It wasn't for nothing that Tiurin looked up to him. A cleverly fixed work report meant good rations for five days. Well, say four. Out of the five the authorities would wangle one for themselves by putting the whole camp onto the guaranteed minimum—the same for all, the best and the worst. Seems to be fair enough: equal rations for all. But it's an economy at the expense of our bellies. Well, a zek's belly can stand anything. Scrape through today somehow and hope for tomorrow.

This was the hope they all went to sleep with on the days they got only the guaranteed minimum.

But when you thought about it, it was five days' work for four days' food.

The shop was quiet. Zeks who had tobacco were smoking. The light was dim, and the men sat gazing into the fire. Like a big family. It was a family, the squad. They were listening to Tiurin as he talked to two or three of the men by the stove. Tiurin never wasted his words, and if he permitted himself to talk, then he was in a good humor.

He too hadn't learned to eat with his hat on, and when his head was bared he looked old. He was close-cropped like all of them, but in the light of the flames you could see how many white hairs he had.

"I'd be shaking in my boots before a battalion commander and here was the regimental commander himself. 'Red Army man Tiurin at your service,' I reported. The commander looked at me hard from under his beetle brows as he asked me my full name. I told him. Year of birth. I told him. It was in the thirties and I was, let's see, just twenty-two then, just a kid. 'Well, Tiurin, who are you serving?' 'I serve the working people,' I replied, with a salute. He blew up and banged both fists on the desk, bang! 'You're serving the working people, you bastard, but what are you yourself?' I froze inside but I kept a grip on myself. 'Machine-gunner, first-class. Excellent marks in military training and polit. . . .' 'First-class! What are you talking about, you shit? Your father's a kulak. Look, this document has come from Kamen. Your father's a kulak and you've been hiding. They've been looking for you for two years.' I turned pale and kept my mouth shut. I hadn't written a line home for a year, to keep them from tracing me. I had no idea how they were living at home, and they knew nothing about me. 'Where's your conscience?' he shouted at me, all four bars on his collar shaking. 'Aren't you ashamed of yourself for deceiving the Soviet Power?' I thought he was going to hit me. But he didn't. He wrote out an order. To have me thrown out of the army at six o'clock that very day. It was November. They stripped me of my winter uniform and issued me a summer one, a third-hand one it must've been, and a short, tight jacket. I didn't know at the time that I didn't have to give up my winter uniform, just send it to them. . . . So they packed me off with a slip of paper: 'Discharged from the ranks . . . as a kulak's son.' A fine reference for a job! I had a four-day train journey ahead of me to get home. They didn't give me a free pass, they didn't provide me with even one day's rations. Just gave me dinner for the last time and threw me off the post.

"Incidentally, in thirty-eight, at the Kotlas deportation point, I met my former squadron commander. He'd been given ten years too. I learned from him that the regimental commander and the commissar were both shot in thirty-seven, no matter whether they were of proletarian or kulak stock, whether they had the conscience or not. So I crossed myself and said: 'So, after all, Creator, You do exist up there in heaven. Your patience is long-suffering but You strike hard.' "

After two bowls of kasha Shukhov so longed to smoke he felt he'd die if he didn't. And, reckoning he could buy those two glassfuls of home-grown tobacco from the Lett in Barracks 7, he said in a low voice to the Estonian fisherman: "Listen, Eino, lend me some for a cigarette till tomorrow. You know I won't let you down."

Eino gave him a hard look and then slowly turned his eyes to his "brother." They shared everything—one of them wouldn't spend even a pinch of tobacco without consulting the other. They muttered something together and Eino reached for his pink-embroidered pouch. Out of it he extracted a pinch of tobacco, factory-cut, placed it in Shukhov's palm, measured it with his eye, and added a few more strands. Just enough for one cigarette, no more.

Shukhov had a piece of newspaper ready. He tore off a scrap, rolled the cigarette, picked up a glowing coal from where it lay at Tiurin's feet—and drew and drew. A sweet dizziness went all through his body, to his head, to his feet, as if he had downed a glass of vodka.

The moment he began to smoke he felt, blazing at him from across the length of the shop, a pair of green eyes— Fetiukov's. He might have relented and given him a drag, the jackal, but he'd seen him pulling one of his fast ones already that day. No—better leave something for Senka instead. Senka hadn't heard the squad leader's tale and sat in front of the fire, poor guy, his head on one side.

Tiurin's pockmarked face was lit up by the flames. He spoke calmly, as if he were telling someone else's story:

"What rags I had, I sold for a quarter of their value. I bought a couple of loaves from under the counter—they'd already started bread rationing. I'd thought of hopping onto a freight train, but they'd just introduced some stiff penalties for that. And, if you remember, you couldn't buy tickets even if you had the money; you had to produce special little books or show travel documents. There was no getting onto the platform either—militiamen at the barrier, and guards wandering up and down the lines at both ends of the station. It was a cold sunset and the puddles were freezing over. Where was I going to spend the night? I straddled a brick wall, jumped over with my two loaves, and slipped into the public toilet. I waited in there for a while. No one was after me. I came out as though I were a soldier-passenger. The Vladivostok-Moscow was standing in the station. There was a crowd around the hot-water faucet, people banging each other's heads with their teakettles. On the edge of the crowd I noticed a girl in a blue jersey—her kettle was a big one. She was scared of pushing through to the faucet. Didn't want her little feet stepped on or scalded. 'Look,' I said to her, 'hang onto these loaves and I'll get your kettle filled fast.' While I was doing so, off went the train. She was holding the loaves. She burst into tears. What was she going to do with them? She didn't mind losing the kettle. 'Run,' I called to her. 'I'll follow you.' Off she went, with me at her heels. I caught up

with her and hoisted her onto the train with one arm. The train was going quite fast. I had a foot on it too. The conductor didn't slash at my fingers or shove me in the chest—there were other soldiers in the carriage and he took me for one of them."

Shukhov nudged Senka in the ribs—come on, finish this, you poor slob. He handed him the cigarette in his wooden holder. Let him take a drag, he's all right. Senka, the chump, accepted it like an actor, pressed one hand to his heart, and bowed his head. But, after all, he was deaf.

Tiurin went on:

"There were six, all girls, in a compartment to themselves—Leningrad students traveling back from technical courses. A lovely spread on their little table; raincoats swinging from coat hangers; expensive suitcases. They were going through life happily. All clear ahead for them. We talked and joked and drank tea together.

"They asked me what coach I was in. I sighed and told them the truth. 'I'm in a special coach, girls, heading straight for death.'"

There was silence in the shop. All you could hear was the stove roaring.

"Well, they gasped and moaned and put their heads together. And the result was they covered me with their raincoats on the top berth. They hid me all the way to Novosibirsk. By the way, I was able to show my gratitude to one of them later—she was swept up by the Kirov wave in thirty-five. She had just about had it, working in a hard-labor team, and I got her fixed up in the tailoring shop."

"Shall we mix the mortar?" Pavlo asked Tiurin in a whisper.

Tiurin didn't hear him.

"I came up to our house at night, through the back garden. I left the same night. I took my little brother with me, took him to warmer parts, to Frunze. I'd nothing to give him to eat, and nothing for myself either. In Frunze some road workers were boiling asphalt in a pot, with all kinds of bums and stray kids sitting around. I sat down among them and said: 'Hey, you guys, take on my little brother as a learner. Teach him how to live.' They took him. I'm only sorry I didn't join the crooks myself."

"And you never saw your brother again?" asked the captain.

Tiurin yawned. "Never again."

He yawned once more. "Well, don't let it get you down, men," he said. "We'll live through it, even in this power station. Get going, mortar mixers. Don't wait for the whistle."

That's what a squad is. A guard can't get people to budge even in working hours, but a squad leader can tell his men to get on with the job even during the break, and they'll do it. Because he's the one who feeds them. And he'd never make them work for nothing.

If they were going to start mixing the mortar only when the whistle blew, then the masons would have to hang around waiting for it.

Shukhov drew a deep breath and got to his feet.

"I'll go up and chip the ice off."

He took with him a small hatchet and a brush and, for the laying, a mason's hammer, a leveling rod, a plumb, and a length of string.

Kilgas looked at him, a wry expression on his ruddy-cheeked face. Why should *he* jump up before his squad leader told him to? But after all, thought Shukhov, Kilgas didn't have to worry about feeding the squad. It was all the same to him if he got a couple of ounces less—he'd manage on his parcels.

Even so, Kilgas stirred himself—you can't keep the squad waiting, he understood, just because of *you*.

"Wait a minute, Vanya, I'm coming too," he said.

"There you go, fathead. If you'd been working for yourself you'd have been on your feet in a hurry."

(There was another reason why Shukhov hurried—he wanted to lay his hands on that plumb before Kilgas. They'd drawn only one from the tool store.)

"Sure three are enough for the blocklaying?" Pavlo asked Tiurin. "Shouldn't we send another man up? Or won't there be enough mortar?"

Tiurin knitted his brows and thought.

"I'll be the fourth man myself, Pavlo. You work here on the mortar. It's a big box, we'll put six on the job. Work like this—take the mortar out from one end when it's ready and use the other for mixing some more. And see there's a steady supply. Not a moment's break."

"Ugh!" Pavlo sprang to his feet. He was young, his blood was fresh, camp life hadn't as yet worn him out. His face had been fattened on Ukrainian dumplings. "If *you're* going to lay blocks, I'll make the mortar for you myself. We'll see who's working hardest. Hey, where's the longest spade?"

That's what a squad leader is too. Pavlo had been a forest sniper, he'd even been on night raids. Try and make *him* break his back in a camp! But to work for the squad leader—that was different.

Shukhov and Kilgas came out onto the second story. They heard Senka creaking up the ramp behind them. So poor deaf Senka had guessed where they would be.

Only a start had been made with laying the blocks on the second-story walls. Three rows all around, a bit higher here and there. That was when the laying went fastest. From the knee to the chest, without the help of a scaffold.

All the platforms and trestles that had been there had been swiped by the zeks —some had been carried off to other buildings, some had been burned. Anything to prevent another squad getting them. But now everything had to be done right. Tomorrow they'd have to nail some trestles together; otherwise the work would be held up.

You could see a long way from up there—the whole snowclad, deserted expanse of the site (the zeks were hidden away, warming up before the dinner break ended), the dark watchtowers and the sharp-tipped poles for the barbed wire. You couldn't see the barbed wire itself except when you looked into the sun. The sun was very bright; it made you blink.

And also, not far away, you could see the portable generator smoking away, blackening the sky. And wheezing, too. It always made that hoarse, sickly noise before it whistled. There it went. So they hadn't, after all, cut too much off the dinner break.

"Hey, Stakhanovite! Hurry up with that plumb," Kilgas shouted.

"Look how much ice you've got left on your wall! See if you can chip it off before evening," Shukhov said derisively. *"You* didn't have to bring your trowel up with you!"

They'd intended to start with the walls they'd been allocated before dinner, but Tiurin called from below: "Hey, men! We'll work in pairs, so that the mortar doesn't freeze in the hods. You take Senka with you on your wall, and I'll work with Kilgas. But to start with, you stand in for me, Gopchik, and clean up Kilgas's wall."

Shukhov and Kilgas looked at one another. Correct. Quicker that way.

They grabbed their axes.

And now Shukhov was no longer seeing that distant view where sun gleamed on snow. He was no longer seeing the prisoners as they wandered from the warming-up places all over the site, some to hack away at the holes they hadn't finished that morning, some to fix the mesh reinforcement, some to put up beams in the workshops. Shukhov was seeing only his wall—from the junction at the left where the blocks rose in steps, higher than his waist, to the right to the corner where it met Kilgas's. He showed Senka where to remove ice and chopped at it energetically himself with the back and blade of his ax, so that splinters of ice flew all about and into his face. He worked with drive, but his thoughts were elsewhere. His thoughts and his eyes were feeling their way under the ice to the wall itself, the outer façade of the power station, two blocks thick. At the spot he was working on, the wall had previously been laid by some mason who was either incompetent or had stunk up the job. But now Shukhov tackled the wall as if it was his own handiwork. There, he saw, was a cavity that couldn't be leveled up in one row; he'd have to do it in three, adding a little more mortar each time. And here the outer wall bellied a bit—it would take two rows to straighten that. He divided the wall mentally into the place where he would lay blocks, starting at the point where they rose in steps, and the place where Senka was working, on the right, up to Kilgas's section. There in the corner, he figured, Kilgas wouldn't hold back; he would lay a few blocks for Senka, to make things easier for him. And, while they were puttering around in the corner, Shukhov would forge ahead and have half the wall built, so that his pair wouldn't be behindhand. He noted how many blocks he'd require for each of the places. And the moment the carriers brought the blocks up he shouted at Alyosha: "Bring 'em to me. Put 'em here. And here."

Senka had finished chipping off the ice, and Shukhov picked up a wire brush, gripped it in both hands, and went along the wall swishing it—to and fro, to and fro—cleaning up the top row, especially the joints, till only a snowy film was left on it.

Tiurin climbed up up and, while Shukhov was still busy with his brush, fixed up a leveling rod in the corner. Shukhov and Kilgas had already placed theirs on the edges of their walls.

"Hey," called Pavlo from below. "Anyone alive up there? Take the mortar."

Shukhov broke into a sweat—he hadn't stretched his string over the blocks yet. He was rushing. He decided to stretch it for three rows at once, and make the necessary allowance. He decided also to take over a little of the outer wall from Senka and give him some of the inside instead; things would be easier for him that way.

Stretching his string along the top edge, he explained to Senka, with mouthings and gestures, where he was to work. Senka understood, for all his deafness. He bit his lips and glanced aside with a nod at Tiurin's wall. "Shall we make it hot for him?" his look said. We won't fall behind. He laughed.

Now the mortar was being brought up the ramp. Tiurin decided not to have any of it dumped beside the masons—it would only freeze while being shifted onto the hods. The men were to put down their barrows; the masons would take the mortar straight from them and get on with the laying. Meanwhile the carriers, not to waste time, would bring on the blocks that other prisoners were heaving up from below. As soon as the mortar had been scooped up from one pair of barrows, another pair would be coming and the first would go down. At the stove in the machine room, the carriers would thaw out any mortar that had frozen to their barrows—and themselves too, while they were at it.

The barrows came up two at a time—one for Kilgas's wall, one for Shukhov's. The mortar steamed in the frost but held no real warmth in it. You slapped it on

the wall with your trowel and if you slowed down it would freeze, and then you'd have to hit it with the side of a hammer—you couldn't scrape it off with a trowel. And if you laid a block a bit out of true, it would immediately freeze too and set crooked; then you'd need the back of your ax to knock it off and chip away the mortar.

But Shukhov made no mistakes. The blocks varied. If any had chipped corners or broken edges or lumps on their sides, he noticed it at once and saw which way up to lay them and where they would fit best on the wall.

Here was one. Shukhov took up some of the steaming mortar on his trowel and slapped it into the appropriate place, with his mind on the joint below (this would have to come right in the middle of the block he was going to lay). He slapped on just enough mortar to go under the one block. He snatched it from the pile—carefully, though, so as not to tear his mittens, for with cement blocks you can do that in no time. He smoothed the mortar with his trowel and then—down with the block! And without losing a moment he leveled it, patting it with the side of the trowel—it wasn't lying exactly right—so that the wall would be truly in line and the block lie level both lengthwise and across. The mortar was already freezing.

Now if some mortar had oozed out to the side, you had to chop it off as quickly as possible with the edge of your trowel and fling it over the wall (in summer it would go under the next brick, but now that was impossible). Next you took another look at the joint below, for there were times when the block was not completely intact but had partially crumbled. In that event, you slapped in some extra mortar where the defect was, and you didn't lay the block flat—you slid it from side to side, squeezing out the extra mortar between it and its neighbor. An eye on the plumb. An eye on the surface. Set. Next.

The work went with a rhythm. Once two rows were laid and the old faults leveled up it would go quite smoothly. But now was the time to keep your eyes peeled.

Shukhov forged ahead; he pressed along the outside wall to meet Senka. Senka had parted with Tiurin in the corner and was now working along the wall to meet him.

Shukhov winked at the mortar carriers. Bring it up, bring it up. Steady. That's the ticket. He was working so fast he had no time to wipe his nose.

He and Senka met and began to scoop out of the same mortar hod. It didn't take them long to scrape it to the bottom.

"Mortar!" Shukhov shouted over the wall.

"Coming up!" shouted Pavlo.

Another load arrived. They emptied that one too—all the liquid mortar in it, anyhow. The rest had already frozen to the sides. Scrape it off yourselves! If you don't, you're the ones who'll be taking it up and down again. Get going! Next!

And now Shukhov and the other masons felt the cold no longer. Thanks to the urgent work, the first wave of heat had come over them—when you feel wet under your coat, under your jacket, under your shirt and your vest. But they didn't stop for a moment; they hurried on with the laying. And after about an hour they had their second flush of heat, the one that dries up the sweat. Their feet didn't feel cold, that was the main thing. Nothing else mattered. Even the breeze, light but piercing, couldn't distract them from the work. Only Senka stamped his feet—he had enormous ones, poor slob, and they'd given him a pair of valenki too tight for him.

From time to time Tiurin would shout

"Mo-o-rtar," and Shukhov would shout "Mo-o-rtar"—he was shouting to his own men. When you're working all out, you're a sort of squad leader to your neighbors yourself. It was up to Shukhov to keep up with the other pair. Now, he'd have made his own brother sweat to hurry up with the mortar.

At first, after dinner, Buinovsky had carried mortar with Fetiukov. But the ramp was steep and dangerous, and the captain dragged his feet to begin with. Shukhov urged him on gently: "Quicker, captain. Blocks, captain."

Every time Buinovsky came up he worked faster. Fetiukov, on the other hand, grew lazier and lazier. He'd tilt the barrow as he came up, the lousy bastard, so that the mortar would slop out of it and then it'd be lighter to carry.

Shukhov poked him in the back: "Hey, you damn bastard. When you were an overseer I'll bet you made your men sweat."

Buinovsky appealed to the squad leader: "Give me a man to work with. I won't go on working with this shit."

Tiurin agreed. He sent Fetiukov to heave up blocks from below; and made him work, on top of that, where the number of blocks he handled was counted separately. He told Alyosha to work with the captain. Alyosha was a quiet man; anyone could order him about.

"It's all hands on deck, sailor," the captain urged. "See how fast they're laying blocks?"

Alyosha smiled meekly. "If we have to work faster then let's work faster. Anything you say."

And tramped down for the next load.

Thank God for the man who does his job and keeps his mouth shut!

Tiurin shouted to someone down below. Another truckload of blocks had apparently arrived. Not one had been brought here for six months; now they were pouring in. You could work really fast as long as the trucks brought blocks. But this wouldn't go on. Later there'd be a hold-up in the delivery and then you'd stand idle yourself.

Tiurin was bawling out someone else down below. Something about the lift. Shukhov would have liked to know what was up but he'd no time to find out—he was leveling his wall. The carriers came up and told him: a mechanic had come to repair the motor of the lift, and the superintendent of electrical repairs, a civilian, was with him. The mechanic was tinkering with the motor; the superintendent watched.

That was according to the rules: one man works, one man watches.

Good if they fixed the lift now. It could be used for both blocks and mortar.

Shukhov was laying his third row (Kilgas too was on his third), when up the ramp came yet another snoop, another chief—building-foreman Der. A Muscovite. Used to work in some ministry, so they said.

Shukhov was standing close to Kilgas, and drew his attention to Der.

"Pfah!" said Kilgas contemptuously. "I don't usually have anything to do with the bigshots. But you call me if he falls off the ramp."

And now Der took up his post behind the masons and watched them work. Shukhov hated these snoops like poison. Trying to make himself into an engineer, the fathead! Once he'd shown Shukhov how to lay bricks—and given him a belly laugh. A man should build a house with his own hands before he calls himself an engineer.

At Shukhov's village of Temgenovo there were no brick houses. All the cottages were built of wood. The school too was a wooden building, made from six-

foot logs. But the camp needed masons and Shukhov, glad to oblige, became a mason. A man with two trades to his credit can easily learn another ten.

No, Der didn't fall off the ramp, though once he stumbled. He came up almost on the double.

"Tiu-u-urin," he shouted, his eyes popping out of his head. "Tiu-u-urin."

At his heels came Pavlo. He was carrying the spade he'd been working with.

Der was wearing a regulation camp coat but it was new and clean. His hat was stylish, made of leather, though, like everyone else's, it bore a number—B 731.

"Well?" Tiurin went up to him trowel in hand, his hat tilted over one eye.

Something out of the ordinary was brewing. Something not to be missed. Yet the mortar was growing cold in the barrows. Shukhov went on working—working and listening.

"What do you think you're doing?" Der spluttered. "This isn't a matter for the guardhouse. This is a criminal offense, Tiurin. You'll get a third term for this."

Only then did Shukhov catch on to what was up. He glanced at Kilgas. He'd understood, too. The roofing felt. Der had spotted it on the windows.

Shukhov feared nothing for himself. His squad leader would never give him away. He was afraid for Tiurin. To the squad Tiurin was a father; for *them* he was a pawn. Up in the North they readily gave squad leaders a second term for a thing like this.

Ugh, what a face Tiurin made. He threw down his trowel and took a step toward Der. Der looked around. Pavlo lifted his spade.

He hadn't grabbed it for nothing.

And Senka, for all his deafness, had understood. He came up, hands on hips. And Senka was built solid.

[51]

Der blinked, gave a sort of twitch, and looked around for a way of escape.

Tiurin leaned up against him and said quite softly, though distinctly enough for everyone to hear: "Your time for giving terms has passed, you bastard. If you say one word, you blood-sucker, it'll be your last day on earth. Remember that."

Tiurin shook, shook uncontrollably.

Hatchet-faced Pavlo looked Der straight in the eyes. A look as sharp as a razor.

"Now, men, take it easy." Der turned pale and edged away from the ramp.

Without another word Tiurin straightened his hat, picked up his trowel, and walked back to his wall.

Pavlo, very slowly, went down the ramp with his spade.

Slo-o-owly.

Der was as scared to stay as to leave. He took shelter behind Kilgas and stood there.

Kilgas went on laying blocks, the way they count out pills at a drugstore—like a doctor, measuring everything so carefully—his back to Der, as if he didn't even know he was there.

Der stole up to Tiurin. Where was all his arrogance?

"But what shall I tell the superintendent, Tiurin?"

Tiurin went on working. He said, without turning his head: "You will tell him it was like that when we arrived. We came and that's how it was."

Der waited a little longer. They weren't going to bump him off now, he saw. He took a few steps and put his hands in his pockets.

"Hey, S 854," he muttered. "Why are you using such a thin layer of mortar?"

He had to get back at someone. He couldn't find fault with Shukhov for his joints or for the straightness of his line, so he decided he was laying the mortar too thin.

"Permit me to point out," Shukhov lisped derisively, "that if the mortar is laid on thick in weather like this, the place will be like a sieve in the spring."

"You're a mason. Listen to what a foreman has to tell you," Der said with a frown, puffing out his cheeks.

Well, here and there it might be a bit on the thin side. He could have used a little more—but only, after all, if he'd been laying the blocks in decent conditions, not in winter. The man ought to have a heart. You've got to show some results. But what was the good of trying to explain? He didn't want to understand.

Der went quietly down the ramp.

"You get me that lift repaired," Tiurin sang out after him. "What do you think we are—pack horses? Carrying blocks up to the second story by hand."

"They'll pay you for taking them up," Der called back from the ramp, quite humbly.

"At the wheelbarrow rate? Child's play, pushing up a wheelbarrow. We've got to be paid for carrying them up by hand."

"Don't think I'm against it. But the bookkeepers won't agree to the higher rate."

"The bookkeepers! I've got a whole squad sweating to keep those four masons at work. How much do you think we'll earn?" Tiurin shouted, pressing on without a break.

"Mort-ar," he called down.

"Mort-ar," echoed Shukhov. They'd leveled off the whole of the third row. On the fourth they'd really get going. Time to stretch the string for the next row, but he could manage this way too.

Der went off across the open ground, looking haggard. To warm up in the office. Something must have been eating him. But he should have thought a bit before taking on a wolf like Tiurin. He should keep pleasant with squad leaders like that; then he'd have nothing to worry about. The camp authorities didn't insist on his doing any real hard work, he received top-level rations, he lived in a separate cabin—what else did he want? Giving himself airs, trying to be smart.

The men coming up with the mortar said the mechanic and superintendent had left. The motor was past repair.

Very well, haul 'em up by hand.

For as long as Shukhov had worked with machinery the machines had either broken down or been smashed by the zeks. He'd seen them wreck a log conveyer by shoving a beam under the chain and leaning hard on it, to give themselves a breather; they were stacking log by log with never a moment to stretch their backs.

"Damn the whole fucking lot of you!" shouted Tiurin, warming up.

"Pavlo's asking how you're fixed for mortar," someone called from below.

"Mix some more."

"We've got half a box mixed."

"Mix another."

What a pace they set! They were driving along the fifth row now. They'd had to bend over double when they were working on the first row, but now the wall had risen shoulder-high. And why shouldn't they race on? There were no windows or doors to allow for—just a couple of adjoining blank walls and plenty of blocks. Shukhov should have stretched a string higher but there was no time for it.

"The eighty-second have gone off to hand in their tools," Gopchik reported.

Tiurin looked at him witheringly. "Mind your own business, squirt. Bring some blocks."

Shukhov looked about. Yes, the sun was beginning to set. It had a grayish appearance as it sank in a red haze. And they'd got into the swing—couldn't be better. They'd started on the fifth row now. Ought to finish it today. Level it off.

The mortar carriers were snorting like winded horses. Buinovsky was quite gray in the face. He might not be forty but he wasn't far off it.

The cold was growing keener. Busy as were Shukhov's hands, the frost nipped his fingers through the shabby mittens. And it was piercing his left boot too. He stamped his foot. Thud, thud.

By now he needn't stoop to the wall, but he still had to bend his aching back for each block and each scoop of mortar.

"Hey, boys!" he pestered the men handling the blocks. "You'd better put them on the wall for me. Heave 'em up here."

The captain would gladly have obliged but lacked the strength. He wasn't used to the work. But Alyosha said: "All right, Ivan Denisovich. Show me where to put them."

You could count on Alyosha. Did whatever was asked of him. If everybody in the world was like that, Shukhov would have done likewise. If a man asks for help why not help him? Those Baptists had something there.

The rail changed. The signal went dinning all over the site and reached the power station. They'd been caught with some unused mortar. Ugh, just when they'd got into the swing of it!

"Mortar! Mortar!" Tiurin shouted.

A new boxful had only just been mixed. They had to go on laying; there was no other way. If they left anything in the box, next morning they could throw the whole lot of it to hell—the mortar would have petrified; it wouldn't yield to a pickax.

"Don't let me down, brothers," Shukhov shouted.

Kilgas was fuming. He didn't like speed-ups. But he pressed on all the same. What else could he do?

Pavlo ran up with a barrow, a trowel in his belt, and began laying himself. Five trowels on the job now.

Now look out for where the rows meet. Shukhov visualized what shape of block was needed there, and shoving a hammer into Alyosha's hand egged him on: "Knock a bit off this one."

Haste makes waste. Now that all of them were racing one another Shukhov bided his time, keeping an eye on the wall. He pushed Senka to the left and took over the laying himself toward the main corner on the right. It would be a disaster if the walls overlapped or if the corner wasn't level. Cost him half a day's work tomorrow.

"Stop!" He shoved Pavlo away from a block and leveled it himself. And from his place in the corner he noticed that Senka's section was sagging. He hurried over to Senka and leveled it out with two blocks.

The captain brought up a load of mortar, enough for a good horse.

"Another two barrowsful," he said.

The captain was tottering. But he went on sweating away. Shukhov had had a horse like that once. He'd thought a lot of that horse but then they'd driven it to death. They'd worked the hide off it.

The top rim of the sun dipped below the horizon. Now, without Gopchik having to tell them, they saw that the squads had not only turned in their tools but were pouring up to the gates. No one came out into the open immediately after the signal—only a fool would go and freeze out there. They sat in the warmth. But the moment came, by agreement between the squad leaders, when all the squads poured out together. Without this agreement, the zeks, a stubborn lot, would have sat each other out in the warmth till midnight.

Tiurin himself realized that he'd cut things too fine. The man in charge of the tool store must be cursing him out.

"Hey," he shouted, "use enough of that shit! Carriers! Go and scrape the big box. Throw what's left into that hole there and scatter some snow on it to keep it hidden. You, Pavlo, take a couple of

men, collect the tools, and hand them in. I'll send Gopchik after you with the three trowels. We'll use up the last two loads of mortar before we knock off."

Everyone dashed to his job. They took Shukhov's hammer from him and wound up his string. The mortar carriers and the block lifters hurried down into the machine room. They'd nothing more to do up there. Three masons remained on top—Kilgas, Senka, and Shukhov. Tiurin walked around to see how much wall they'd built. He was pleased. "Not bad, eh? In half a day. Without any fucking lift."

Shukhov noticed there was a little mortar left in Kilgas's hod. He didn't want to waste it, but was worried that the squad leader might be reprimanded if the trowels were handed in late.

"Listen, men," he said, "give your trowels to Gopchik. Mine's not on the list. So I won't have to hand it in. I'll keep going."

Tiurin said with a laugh: "How can we ever let you out? We just can't do without you."

Shukhov laughed too, and went on working.

Kilgas took the trowels. Senka went on handing blocks to Shukhov. They poured Kilgas's mortar into Shukhov's hod.

Gopchik ran across to the tool store, to overtake Pavlo. The rest were just as anxious to be in time, and hurried over to the gates, without Tiurin. A squad leader is a power, but the escort is a greater power still. They list latecomers, and that means the guardhouse for you.

There was a terrible crowd near the gates now. Everyone had collected there. It looked as if the escort had come out and started counting.

(They counted the prisoners twice on the way out: once before they unbolted the gates, to make sure they were safe in opening them, and again when the gates had been opened and the prisoners were passing through. And if they thought they'd miscounted, they recounted outside the gates.)

"To hell with the mortar," said Tiurin, with a gesture of impatience. "Sling it over the wall."

"Don't wait, leader. Go ahead, you're needed there. (Shukhov usually addressed Tiurin, more respectfully, as Andrei Prokofievich, but now, after working like that, he felt equal to the squad leader. He didn't put it to himself, "Look, I'm your equal," he just knew it.) And as Tiurin strode down the ramp he called after him, jokingly: "Why do these bastards make the work day so short? We were just getting into our stride when they call it off."

Shukhov was left alone now with Senka. You couldn't say much to him. Besides, you didn't have to tell him things: he was the wisest of them all; he understood without need of words.

Slap on the mortar. Down with the block. Press it home. See it's straight. Mortar. Block. Mortar. Block. . . .

Wasn't it enough that Tiurin had told them himself not to bother about the mortar? Just throw it over the wall and fuck off. But Shukhov wasn't made that way—eight years in a camp couldn't change his nature. He worried about anything he could make use of, about every scrap of work he could do—nothing must be wasted without good reason.

Mortar. Block. Mortar. Block. . . .

"Finish, fuck you," shouted Senka. "Let's get out of here."

He picked up a barrow and ran down the ramp.

But Shukhov—and if the guards had put the dogs on him it would have made no difference—ran to the back and looked about. Not bad. Then he ran and gave the wall a good look over, to the left, to the right. His eye was as accurate as a carpenter's level. Straight and even. His hands were as young as ever.

He dashed down the ramp.

Senka was already out of the machine shop and running down the slope.

"Come on, come on," he shouted over his shoulder.

"Run ahead. I'll catch up," Shukhov gestured.

But he went into the machine shop. He couldn't simply throw his trowel down. He might not be there the next day. They might send the squad off to the Socialist Way of Life settlement. It could be six months before he returned to the power station. But did that mean he was to throw down his trowel? If he'd swiped it he had to hang on to it.

Both the stoves had been doused. It was dark, frightening. Frightening not because it was dark but because everyone had left, because he alone might be missing at the count by the gates, and the guards would beat him.

Yet his eyes darted here, darted there, and, spotting a big stone in the corner, he pulled it aside, slipped his trowel under it, and hid it. So that's that.

Now to catch up with Senka. Senka had stopped after running a hundred paces or so. Senka would never leave anyone in a jam. Pay for it? Then together.

They ran neck and neck, the tall and the short. Senka was a head taller than Shukhov, and a big head it was too.

There are loafers who race one another of their own free will around a stadium. Those devils should be running after a full day's work, with aching back and wet mittens and worn-out valenki— and in the cold too.

They panted like mad dogs. All you could hear was their hoarse breathing.

Well, Tiurin was at the gates. He'd explain.

They were running straight into the crowd. It scared you.

Hundreds of throats booing you at once, and cursing you up and down.

Wouldn't *you* be scared if you had five hundred men blowing their tops at you?

But what about the guards? That was the chief thing.

No. No trouble with them. Tiurin was there, in the last row. He must have explained. Taken the blame on his own shoulders.

But the men yelled, the men swore. And what swearing! Even Senka couldn't help hearing and, drawing a deep breath, gave back as good as he got. He'd kept quiet all his life—but now, how he bellowed! Raised his fists too, ready to pick a fight right away. The men fell silent. Someone laughed.

"Hey, one hundred and fourth," came a shout. "Your deaf guy's a fake. We just tested him."

Everyone laughed. The guards too.

"Form fives."

They didn't open the gates. They didn't trust themselves. They pushed the crowd back from the gates (everyone stuck to the gates like idiots—as if they'd get out quicker that way!).

"Form fives. First. Second. Third . . ."

Each five, as it was called, took a few paces forward.

While Shukhov was recovering his breath he looked up. The moon had risen and was frowning, crimson-faced. Yesterday at this hour it had stood much higher.

Pleased that everything had gone so smoothly, Shukhov nudged the captain in the ribs and said: "Listen, captain, where does this science of yours say the old moon goes afterward?"

"Where does it go? What do you mean? What stupidity! It's simply not visible."

Shukhov shook his head and laughed. "Well, if it's not visible, how d'you know it's there?"

"So, according to you," said the captain, unable to believe his ears, "it's another moon every month."

"What's strange about that? People are born every day. Why not a moon every four weeks?"

"Phaugh!" said the captain and spat. "I've never met a sailor as stupid as you in my life. So where do *you* think the old moon goes?"

"That's what I'm asking you. Where does it go?" Shukhov showed his teeth in a smile.

"Well, tell me. Where does it go?"

Shukhov sighed and said with a slight lisp: "In our village, folk say God crumbles up the old moon into stars."

"What savages!" The captain laughed. "I've never heard that one. Then you believe in God, Shukhov?"

"Why not?" asked Shukhov, surprised. "Hear Him thunder and try not to believe in Him."

"But why does God do it?"

"Do what?"

"Crumble the moon into stars. Why?"

"Well, can't you understand?" said Shukhov. "The stars fall down now and then. The gaps have to be filled."

"Turn around, you slob," a guard shouted. "Get in line."

The count had almost reached them. The twelfth five of the fifth hundred had moved ahead, leaving only Buinovsky and Shukhov at the back.

The escort was worried. There was a discussion over the counting boards. Somebody missing. Again somebody missing. Why the hell can't they learn to count?

They'd counted 462. Ought to be 463.

Once more they pushed everybody back from the gates (the zeks had crowded forward again).

"Form fives. First. Second. . . ."

What made this recounting so infuriating was that the time wasted on it was the zeks' own, not the authorities'. They would still have to cross the steppe, get to the camp, and line up there to be searched. The columns would come in from all sides on the double, trying to be first at the frisking and into the camp. The column that was back first was top dog in the camp that evening—the mess hall was theirs, they were first in line to get their packages, first at the private kitchen, first at the C.E.D. to pick up letters or hand in their own to be censored, first at the dispensary, the barber's, the baths—first everywhere.

And the escort too is in a hurry to get the zeks in and be off for the night. A soldier's life isn't much fun either—a lot of work, little time.

And now the count had come out wrong.

As the last few fives were called forward Shukhov began to hope that there were going to be three in the last row after all. No, damn it, two again.

The tellers went to the head guard with their tally boards. There was a consultation. The head guard shouted: "Squad leader of the hundred and fourth."

Tiurin took half a pace forward. "Here."

"Did you leave anyone behind in the power station? Think."

"No."

"Think again. I'll knock your head off. . . ."

"No, I'm quite sure."

But he stole a glance at Pavlo. Could anyone have dropped off to sleep in the machine shop?

"Form squads," the head guard shouted.

They had formed the groups of five just as they happened to be standing. Now they began to shift about. Voices boomed out: "Seventy-fifth over here," "This way, thirteenth," "Thirty-second here."

The 104th, being all in the rear, formed there too. They were empty-handed to a man, Shukhov noticed; like idiots, they'd worked on so late they'd collected no firewood. Only two of them were carrying small bundles.

This game was played every evening: before the job was over the workers would gather chips, sticks, and broken laths, and tie them together with bits of string or ragged tapes to carry back with them. The first raid on their bundles would take place near the gates to the work site. If either the superintendent or one of the foremen was standing there, he'd order the prisoners to throw down their firewood (millions of rubles had gone up in smoke, yet there they were thinking they'd make up the losses with kindling). But a zek calculated his own way: if everyone brought even a few sticks back with them the barracks would be warmer. Barrack orderlies were issued ten pounds of coal dust a stove and little heat could be squeezed out of that. So the men would break up sticks or saw them short and slip them under their coats.

The escort never made the zeks drop their firewood at the gates to the work site. For one thing, it would have been an offense to the uniform; and secondly they had their hands on machine guns, ready to shoot. But just before entering the zone several ranks in the column were ordered to throw their stuff down. The escort, however, robbed mercifully—they had to leave something for the guards, and for the zeks themselves, who otherwise wouldn't bring any with them.

So every zek brought some firewood along with him every evening. You never knew when you might get it through or when they'd grab it.

While Shukhov was scouring the ground in search of a few chips, Tiurin had finished counting the squad.

"One hundred and fourth all present," he reported to the head guard.

Just then Tsezar rejoined his own squad from the group of office workers. His pipe was glowing as he puffed away at it; his dark mustache was tipped with frost.

"Well, captain, how'd it go?" he asked.

A man who's warm can't understand a man who's freezing. "How'd it go?" What a damn fool question!

"If you really want to know," said the captain, his shoulders sagging, "worked so hard I can hardly straighten my back."

You might give me something to smoke was what he meant.

Tsezar gave him something to smoke. The captain was the only man in the squad he stuck to. He could unburden his heart to him—to no one else.

"There's a man missing from the thirty-second. From the thirty-second," everybody began to mutter.

The deputy squad leader of the 32nd scurried off with another young fellow to search the repair shops. And in the crowd people kept asking: Who? How? Where? Soon it reached Shukhov's ears that it was the dark little Moldavian who was missing. The Moldavian? Not the one who, it was said, had been a Rumanian spy, a real spy?

You could find up to five spies in each squad. But they were fakes, prison-made spies. They passed as spies in their dossiers, but really they were simply ex-POW's. Shukhov himself was one of these "spies."

But the Moldavian was genuine.

The head of the escort ran his eye down the list and grew black in the face. After all, if the spy were to escape what would happen to the head of the escort?

In the crowd everybody, including Shukhov, flew into a rage. Were they going through all this for that shit, that slimy little snake, that stinking worm? The sky was already quite dark; what light there was came from the moon. You could see the stars—this meant the frost was gathering strength for the night—and that runty bastard was missing. What, haven't you had your bellyful of work, you miserable idiot? Isn't the official spell of eleven hours, dawn to dusk, long enough for you? Just you wait, the prosecutor will add something.

Odd that anyone could work so hard as to ignore the signal to knock off.

He completely forgot that he'd been working like that himself only an hour ago—that he'd been annoyed with the others for assembling at the gate too early. Now he was chilled to the bone and his fury mounted with everyone else's; were they to be kept waiting another half hour by that Moldavian? If the guards handed him over to the zeks they'd tear him apart, like wolves with a lamb.

Yes, the cold was coming into its own now. No one stood quiet. They either stamped their feet where they stood or walked two or three paces back and forth.

People were discussing whether the Moldavian could have escaped. Well, if he'd fled during the day that was one thing, but if he'd hidden and was simply waiting for the sentries to go off the watchtowers he hadn't a chance. Unless he'd left a trail through the wire the sentries wouldn't be allowed back in camp for at least three days. They'd have to go on manning the towers for a week, if necessary. That was in the regulations, as the oldtimers knew. In short, if someone escaped, the guards had had it; they were hounded, without sleep or food. Sometimes they were roused to such fury that the runaway wouldn't get back alive.

Tsezar was arguing with the captain: "For instance, when he hung his pince-nez on the ship's rigging. D'you remember?"

"Hm, yes," the captain said as he smoked.

"Or the baby carriage on the steps. Bumping down and down."

"Yes. . . . But the scenes on board are somewhat artificial."

"Well, you see, we've been spoiled by modern camera technique."

"And the maggots in the meat, they crawl about like angleworms. Surely they weren't that size?"

"What do you expect of the movies? You can't show them smaller."

"Well, if they'd bring that meat here to camp instead of the fish they feed us and dumped it straight into the kettle, we'd be only too . . ."

The prisoners howled.

Three small figures were bursting out of the repair shop. So they'd found the Moldavian.

"Boooo!" went the crowd at the gates.

And they yelled, as the group drew nearer: "Bastard! Shit! Idiot! Cow's twat! Lousy son-of-a-bitch!"

And Shukhov joined in: "Rat!"

It's no joke to rob five hundred men of over half an hour.

Ducking his head, the Moldavian ran like a mouse.

"Halt!" a guard shouted. And, noting down "K 460," said: "Where were you?"

He strode over to the man and turned the butt of his rifle at him.

In the crowd people were still hurling curses: "Ass! Louse! Pig!"

But others, seeing the guard make ready to swing his rifle, held their tongues.

The Moldavian could hardly keep on his feet. He backed away from the guard.

The deputy squad leader of the 32nd advanced.

"The damned fool crawled up to do some plastering. Trying to hide from me! Warmed up there and fell asleep."

And he hit the man hard in the face and on the neck, pushing him farther from the guard.

The Moldavian reeled back, and as he did so a Hungarian, one of his own squad, leaped up at him and kicked him hard from behind.

That wasn't like spying. Any fool can spy. A spy has a clean, exciting life. But try and spend ten years in a hard-labor camp!

The guard lowered his rifle.

The head of the escort shouted: "Back from the gates. Form fives."

Another recount, the dogs. Why should they count us now that everything's clear? The prisoners began to boo. All their anger switched from the Moldavian to the escort. They booed and didn't move.

"W-wha-a-at?" shouted the head of the escort. "Want to sit down on the snow? All right, I'll have you down in a minute I'll keep you here till dawn."

He was quite capable of doing it, too. He'd had them on the snow many a time. "Down on your faces!" And, to the escort: "Release safety-catches!" The zeks knew all about that. They drew back from the gates.

"Back, back!" yelled the escort.

"What's the sense of shoving up to the gates anyhow, you crappers?" men barked from the rear at the men in front as they were shoved back.

"Form fives. First. Second. Third . . ."

Now the moon was shining full. It cast its light all around and the crimson tint had gone. It had climbed a quarter of the way up the sky. The evening was lost. That damned Moldavian. Those damned guards. This damned life.

As the prisoners in front were counted they turned and stood on tiptoe to see whether there were two men or three in the back row. It was a matter of life or death to them now.

Shukhov had the feeling that there were going to be four. He was numb with fear. One extra. Another recount. But it turned out that Fetiukov, after cadging a butt from the captain, had been wandering around and had failed to get into his five in time. So now he'd turned up in the back row as if he were an extra.

A guard struck Fetiukov angrily on the back of the neck.

Serve him right.

So they counted three in the back row. The count had come out right, thank God.

"Back from the gates," shouted a guard at the top of his voice. But this time the zeks didn't mutter—they'd noticed soldiers coming out of the gatehouse and forming a cordon on the other side of the gates.

So they were going to be let out.

None of the foremen was in sight, nor the superintendent, so the prisoners kept their firewood.

The gates swung open. And now the head of the escort, accompanied by a checker, came and stood on the other side, near some wooden railings.

"First. Second. Third . . ."

If the numbers tallied again the sentries would be removed from the watchtowers.

But what a distance they had to tramp along the edge of the site to reach the towers at the far end of it! Only when the last prisoner had been led off the site and the numbers had been found to agree would they telephone all the towers and relieve the sentries. If the head of the escort had his wits about him he'd put the column on the move right away, for he knew the zeks had nowhere to run to and the sentries would overtake the column. But some of the guards were so foolish, they feared they didn't have enough troops to handle the zeks; so they waited.

They had one of those idiots this evening.

A whole day in that freezing cold! The zeks were already chilled to the marrow; and now to stand around another shivering hour, when work was over! Yet it wasn't so much the cold and the fact that they'd lost an evening that infuriated them; the point was, there'd be no time now to do anything of their own in the camp.

"How is it you happen to know life in the British Navy so well?" Shukhov heard someone in the next five asking.

"Well, you see, I spent nearly a month on board a British cruiser. Had my own cabin. I was attached to a convoy as liaison officer. And imagine—after the war the British admiral—only the devil could have put the idea into his head—sent me a gift, a souvenir as 'a token of gratitude,' damn him! I was absolutely horrified. And now here we are, all lumped together. It's pretty hard to take, being imprisoned here with Bendera's men. . . ."

Strange! Yes, a strange sight indeed: the naked steppe, the empty building site, the snow gleaming in the moonlight. And the escort guards: they'd gone to their posts, ten paces apart, guns at the ready. And the black herd of prisoners; and among them, in a black coat like all the rest, a man, S 311, who'd never imagined life without gold shoulder straps, who had hobnobbed with a British admiral and now sweated at the barrow with Fetiukov.

You can push a man this way, and you can push a man that way.

Now the escort was ready. This time without any "prayer" the head guard barked at them: "Double time! Get a move on!"

To hell with your "Get a move on!" All the other columns were ahead of them. What sense was there in hurrying? The prisoners didn't have to be in league with one another to figure the score: You kept us back; now it's our turn. The escort too, after all, was dying for a warm corner.

"Step lively!" shouted the guard. "Step lively, you in front."

To hell with your "Step lively." The zeks marched with measured tread, hanging their heads as at a funeral. Now we've nothing to lose—we'd be the last back anyhow. He wouldn't treat us like human beings; now let him burst himself shouting.

On he went, "Step lively! Step lively!" But he realized it was futile. He couldn't order his men to shoot either. The prisoners were marching in fives, keeping in line, all correct. He had no power to hound them faster. (When they marched out to work in the morning the zeks walked slowly, to spare themselves. A man who's in a hurry won't live to see the end of his stretch—he'll tire and be done for.)

So on with regular, deliberate steps. The snow crunched under their boots. Some of them talked in low voices; others walked in silence. Shukhov asked himself whether there was anything he'd left undone in the camp that morning. Ah, the dispensary. Funny, he'd forgotten all about the dispensary while he'd been working.

This must be around the consulting hour. He'd manage it if he skipped his supper. But now somehow his back wasn't aching. And his temperature wouldn't be high enough. A waste of time. He'd pull through without benefit of the doctor. The only cure those docs know is to put you in your grave.

It wasn't the dispensary that appealed to him now; it was the prospect of adding something to his supper. His hopes were all pinned on that long-overdue parcel of Tsezar's.

A sudden change came over the column. It began to sway, to break out of its regular stride. The prisoners heaved forward with a buzz of excitement. And now the last five, which included Shukhov, were no longer treading on the heels of the five in front; they had to run to keep up. A few more paces, and again they were running.

When the rear of the column spilled over a rise Shukhov saw to the right, far away across the steppe, another dark column on the move, marching diagonally across their course. They, too, seemed to be forcing their pace.

It must be from the machine works, that column; there were about three hundred men in it. Another bunch with bad luck! Must have been held up—Shukhov wondered why. To finish assembling some piece of machinery? They could be kept after work hours for that. But what did it matter to them? They worked all day in the warmth.

Who'd get in first? The men ran, just ran. Even the escort broke into a jog trot: only the head guard remembered to shout, "Don't fall back. Keep up there, you in the rear. Keep up."

Oh, shut your trap. . . . What are you yapping about? As if we wouldn't keep up!

They forgot to talk; they forgot to think; everyone in the column was obsessed by one idea: to get back first.

Things were so lumped together, the sweet and the sour, that the prisoners saw the escort itself, now, as friend rather than foe. Now the enemy was the other column.

Their spirits rose, their anger passed.

"Get a move on, get a move on!" the rear shouted to the front.

Now our column had reached the street, while the other had passed out of sight behind the blocks of houses. They'd been racing blindly.

It was easier for us now, we were running down the middle of the street. And our escort had less to stumble over at the sides. This was where we ought to gain ground.

There was another reason why we simply had to reach the camp gates first:

the guards there were unusually slow in searching the column from the machine works. Ever since zeks had begun cutting one another's throats in the camp the authorities had arrived at one conclusion: that knives were being made at the machine works and smuggled in. So the zeks who worked there were gone over with special thoroughness on return to the camp. In late autumn, when the earth was already cold, the guards would shout at them: "Off with your boots, machineworks squad! Hold your boots in your hands."

And would frisk them barefoot.

Or, despite the frost, they'd pick men out at random, shouting: "You there, take off your right boot. And you, take off your left!"

A zek would pull off his boot and, hopping on one foot, turn it upside down and shake out the footrag. No knife, damn you!

Shukhov had heard—he didn't know whether it was true or not—that back in the summer the zeks from the machine works had brought back two poles for a volley-ball net and that there the knives were, there inside them. Ten long knives in each pole. And now knives would turn up occasionally, here and there.

So it was at a jog trot that they passed the new club and the residential block and the wood-processing plant, and reached the turning that led straight on to the gates.

"Hoooooo-ooo," shouted the whole column, in unison.

That was the turning we'd aimed at reaching before the others. The rival column was a hundred and fifty paces behind, on our right.

Now we could take things easy. Everyone was elated. As elated as a rabbit when it finds it can still terrify a frog.

There lay the camp, just as we'd left it in the morning: lights were on in the zone over the thick fence, specially powerful ones in front of the gatehouse. The entire area was flooded with light; it was as bright as day. They had to have it like that when they frisked us.

But we hadn't reached the gates yet.

"Halt!" shouted a guard and, handing his machine gun to a soldier, ran up close to the column (they weren't allowed to do that with their guns). "All those on the right carrying firewood dump it to their right."

He didn't have to guess about the firewood—the zeks were carrying it quite openly. A bundle fell, a second, a third. Some would have liked to conceal a stick or two inside the column, but their neighbors objected: "Throw it down as you're told! Do you want others to lose theirs because of you?"

Who's the zek's main enemy? Another zek. If only they weren't at odds with one another—ah, what a difference that'd make!

"Double time," shouted the head guard.

They advanced toward the gates.

Here five roads converged. An hour earlier all the other columns had met here. If they were paved, these roads, this would be just the place for the main square of a future city; and then processions would meet here, just as columns of zeks did now as they poured in from every direction, with sentries and guards all about.

The guards were already warming themselves indoors. They came out and formed a cordon across the road.

"Unbutton your coats. Unbutton your jackets."

They pulled the zeks' arms apart, the better to hug them and slap their sides. Same as in the morning, more or less.

It isn't so terrible to unbutton your coat now. We're going home.

That's what everyone used to say: "Going home."

We never had time to think of any other home.

While the head of the column was being frisked, Shukhov went over to Tsezar. "Tsezar Markovich, I'll run straight to the parcels office and keep a place in line for you."

Tsezar turned. The fringe of his dark mustache was tipped with frost.

"Why should you do that, Ivan Denisovich? Perhaps there won't be a parcel."

"Oh, well, it doesn't matter if there isn't. I'll wait ten minutes, anyway. If you don't turn up I'll go to the barracks."

(Shukhov reckoned like this: if Tsezar didn't come, maybe someone else would, then he could sell him his place in line.)

Obviously Tsezar was longing for his parcel.

"All right, Ivan Denisovich, run ahead and keep a place for me. Wait ten minutes, no longer."

And now Shukhov was on the point of being frisked. Today he had nothing to conceal. He would step forward fearlessly. He slowly unbuttoned his coat and undid the rope belt around his wadded jacket, and although he couldn't remember having anything forbidden, eight years in camp had given him the habit of caution: he thrust a hand into his pants pocket to make sure it was empty.

And there lay a small piece of broken hacksaw blade, the tiny length of steel that he'd picked up in his thriftiness at the building site without any intention of bringing it to camp.

He hadn't meant to bring it, but now, what a pity to throw it away! Why, he could make a little knife out of it, very handy for shoe repairing or tailoring!

If he'd intended to bring it with him he'd have thought hard of where to conceal it. But now the guards were only two rows ahead and the first of these rows was already stepping forward to be searched.

His choice had to be swift as the wind. Should he take cover behind the row in front of him and toss the bit of metal in the snow (it'd be noticed but they wouldn't know who the culprit was) or keep it on him?

For that strip of hacksaw he could get ten days in the cells, if they classed it as a knife.

But a cobbler's knife was money, it was bread.

A pity to throw it away.

He slipped it into his left mitten.

At that moment the next row was ordered to step forward and be searched.

Now the last three men stood in full view—Senka, Shukhov, and the man from the 32nd squad who had gone to look for the Moldavian.

Because they were three and the guards facing them were five, Shukhov could try a ruse. He could choose which of the two guards on the right to present himself to. He decided against a young pink-faced one and plumped for an older man with a gray mustache. The older one, of course, was experienced and could find the blade easily if he wanted to, but because of his age he would be fed up with the job. It must stink in his nose now like burning sulfur.

Meanwhile Shukhov had removed both mittens, the empty one and the one with the hacksaw, and held them in one hand (the empty one in front) together with the untied rope belt. He fully unbuttoned his jacket, lifted high the edges of his coat and jacket (never had he been so servile at the search but now he wanted to show he was innocent—Come on, frisk me!), and at the word of command stepped forward.

The guard slapped Shukhov's sides and back, and the outside of his pants pocket. Nothing there. He kneaded the edges of his coat and jacket. Nothing there either. He was about to pass him through when, for safety's sake, he crushed the mitten that Shukhov held out to him—the empty one.

The guard crushed it in his hand, and Shukhov felt as though pincers or iron were crushing everything inside him. One such squeeze on the other mitten and he'd be sunk—the cells on nine ounces of bread a day and hot stew one day in three. He imagined how weak he'd grow, how difficult he'd find it to get back to his present condition, neither fed nor starving.

And an urgent prayer rose in his heart: "Oh Lord, save me! Don't let them send me to the cells."

And while all this raced through his mind, the guard, after finishing with the right-hand mitten, stretched a hand out to deal with the other (he would have squeezed them at the same moment if Shukhov had held them in separate hands). Just then the guard heard his chief, who was in a hurry to get on, shout to the escort: "Come on, bring up the machine-works column."

And instead of examining the other mitten the old guard waved Shukhov on. He was through.

He ran off to catch up with the others. They had already formed fives in a sort of corridor between long beams, like horse stalls in a market, a sort of paddock for prisoners. He ran lightly, hardly feeling the ground. He didn't say a prayer of thanksgiving because he hadn't time, and anyway it would have been out of place.

The escort now drew aside. They were only waiting for their chief. They had gathered for their own use all the firewood the 104th had dumped before being frisked; what the guards had removed during the frisking itself was heaped near the gatehouse.

The moon had risen still higher; the cold grew keener in the pale bright night.

The head guard walked to the sentry house—he had to get a receipt for the four hundred and sixty-three prisoners. He spoke briefly to Priakhov, Volkovoi's deputy.

"K 460," shouted Priakhov.

The Moldavian, who had buried himself deep in the column, drew in his breath and went over to the right of the corridor. He was still hanging his head and his shoulders were hunched.

"Come here," Priakhov ordered, gesturing for him to walk around the column.

The Moldavian did so. He was ordered to stand there, his arms behind his back.

That meant they were going to charge him with attempting to escape. They'd put him in the cells.

Just in front of the gates, right and left of the "paddock," stood two guards. The gates, three times the height of a man, opened slowly. The command rang out:

"Form fives!" (No need here to order the zeks back from the gates; all the gates opened inwards, into the zone. Let the zeks mass as they wished and push against the gates from within, they wouldn't be able to break out.) "First. Second. Third . . ."

It was at the evening recount on their return through the gates that the prisoners, freezing and famished, found the icy wind hardest to bear. A bowl of thin cabbage soup, half burned, was as welcome to them as rain to parched earth. They'd swallowed it in one gulp. That bowl of soup—it was dearer than freedom, dearer than life itself, past, present, and future.

They passed through the gates, those zeks, like soldiers back from a campaign, brisk, taut, eager—clear the road for 'em.

For a trusty with a soft job at staff quarters, those prisoners on the march must have been something to think about.

[64]

After the recount a prisoner became a free man again—for the first time in the day since the guards had given them the morning signal for roll call. They passed through the big gates (of the zone), through the small gates (of the intermediate zone), through two more gates (on the parade ground)—and then they could scatter where they liked.

But not the squad leaders. They were caught by the officer who assigned them their work: "All squad leaders to the planning office."

Shukhov rushed past the prison, between the barracks, to the parcels office. Tsezar, meanwhile, went at a dignified, even pace in the opposite direction, to where people were swarming around a pole with a board nailed to it. On it was the name of anyone for whom a parcel was waiting, written in indelible pencil.

Most writing in the camp was done on plywood, not on paper. It was surer, somehow, more reliable. The guards and turnkeys used wood, too, for keeping tally of the zeks. You can scrape it clean for next day, and use it again. Economical.

Zeks who stay in camp all day can, among other odd jobs, read the names on the board, meet people who've got a parcel as they come in from work, and give them the number. Not much of a job, but it can earn you a cigarette.

Shukhov ran to the parcels office—a little annex to a barracks, to which in turn a small porch had been added. The porch had no door and was open to the weather. All the same, it was cozier that way; it had a roof, after all.

A line had formed along the walls of the porch. Shukhov joined it. There were some fifteen ahead of him. That meant over an hour's wait, to just before locking-up time. And there were others who'd be behind him in the line—the zeks of the powerhouse column who'd gone to look for their names on the board, and

the machine-works column too. Looked as though *they* would have to come again. Tomorrow morning.

People stood in the line with little bags and sacks. On the other side of the door (Shukhov himself hadn't ever received a parcel at this camp but he knew from gossip) guards opened the parcels, which came packed in wooden boxes, with hatchets. They took everything out and examined the contents. They cut, they broke, they fingered. They tipped things out from one container into another. If there was anything liquid, in glass jars or tins, they opened them and poured it out, though you had nothing but your hands or a cloth bag to hold it in. They didn't give you the jars; they were scared of something. If there was anything home-baked, or some tasty sweetmeats or sausage or smoked fish, the guard would take a bite of it himself. (And just you try to get high and mighty and complain, and they'll immediately say that this and that are forbidden and won't issue them to you at all.) Every zek who got a parcel had to give and give, starting with the guard who opened it. And when they'd finished their search they didn't give you the stuff in the box it had come in; they just swept everything into your bag, even into the skirt of your coat and . . . off you go. Sometimes they'd whisk you out so fast you'd be sure to leave something behind. No good going back for it. It wouldn't be there.

When he was in Ust-Izhma Shukhov had got parcels a couple of times. But he wrote to his wife that it was a waste—don't send them. Don't take the food out of the kids' mouths.

Although when he had been at liberty Shukhov had found it easier to feed his whole family than it ever was to feed himself now, he knew what those parcels cost. He knew too that his family wouldn't be able to keep it up for ten years. Better do without them.

But though he'd decided that way, every time someone in the squad, or close by in the barracks, received a parcel (which was almost every day) his heart ached because there wasn't one for him. And though he'd strictly forbidden his wife to send him anything even for Easter, and though he never thought of reading the list except for some rich squad member, every now and then he felt himself longing for someone to run up and say: "Shukhov! Why don't you go for your parcel? There's one for you."

But no one ran up.

He had less and less cause to remember Temgenovo and his home there. Life in camp wore him out from reveille to bedtime, with not a second for idle reflections.

Now as he stood among men who were buoying themselves up with the hope of soon digging their teeth into bits of salt pork, or spreading butter on their bread, or sweetening their mugs of tea with lumps of sugar, Shukhov had one wish only—to reach the mess hall in time and to eat his stew hot. It was only half as good when it was cold.

He figured that if Tsezar's name hadn't turned up on the list he would have gone back to the barracks long ago to wash. But if he'd found it there he would now be collecting bags, plastic mugs, and a basin. That would take him ten minutes. And Shukhov had promised to wait.

There in line Shukhov learned some news. Again there wasn't going to be a Sunday this week; again they were going to steal one of their Sundays. He, like everyone else, had expected it, for if there happened to be five Sundays in a month, they gave them three and made them work the other two. Shukhov had expected it, but when he heard it a spasm of pain caught his heart: who wouldn't begrudge the loss of that sweet day? Though what they were saying in the line

was right: they knew how to keep them jumping even on Sundays. They'd invent something—fixing up the baths, or building a wall somewhere, or cleaning up the yard. There were mattresses to be changed and shaken, bedbugs in the bunk frames to be exterminated. Or they'd have the idea of checking you with your photo. Or of carrying out an inventory—turning you with all your things into the yard and keeping you there half the day.

Nothing seems to make the authorities madder than zeks napping quietly after breakfast.

The line was moving, though slowly. People were coming in and shoving into the head of the line without even a pardon-me, just elbowing through to the front—a camp barber, a bookkeeper, a man who worked in the C.E.D. But they weren't rank-and-file, they were respectable trusties, pigs of the first order with soft jobs in the camps. The zeks who worked outside thought them lower than shit (a rating the trusties returned). But it was futile to protest—the trusties were a gang all their own, and were also in solid with the guards.

Now there were only ten ahead of Shukhov. Another seven had hurried in to line up behind him, when Tsezar, stooping, appearing in the doorway, wearing the new fur hat that had been sent him from outside.

Now take that hat. Tsezar must have tickled someone's palm to get permission for wearing a town hat so clean and new. They even robbed others of their bedraggled service hats. Here, wear the camp pig-fur model!

A strange-looking fellow with glasses was standing in line, his head buried in a newspaper. Tsezar at once made for him.

"Aha, Pyotr Mikhailych."

They bloomed like a couple of poppies. The strange-looking fellow said:

"Look what I've got! A fresh *Vechorka*.[1] They sent it by airmail."

"Really," said Tsezar, sticking his nose into the newspaper. How on earth could they make out such tiny print in the glimmer of that miserable lamp?

"There's a most fascinating review of a Zavadsky premiere."

Those Muscovites can smell one another at a distance, like dogs: they sniff and sniff when they meet in a way of their own. They talk so fast too, each trying to outtalk the other. When they're jabbering away like that you hear practically no Russian; they might be talking Latvian or Rumanian.

However, Tsezar had all his bags with him—everything in order.

"So I can . . . er . . . Tsezar Markovich," lisped Shukhov, "I'll take off now."

"Of course, of course," said Tsezar, raising his dark mustache above the top of the newspaper. "Tell me though, who's in front of me? And who's behind me?"

Shukhov told him his place in the line and then, with a gentle hint, asked: "Do you want me to bring you your supper?"

(That meant from the mess hall to the barracks, in a mess tin. This was strictly against the rules—there'd been many made about it. When they caught you they poured your food out of the mess tin onto the ground and put you in the guardhouse. All the same, food was carried and would go on being carried, because if a zek has anything to do he'll never find time to go to the mess hall with his squad.)

Shukhov asked: "Do you want me to bring you your supper?" but murmured to himself: "Surely he won't be stingy. Won't he give me his supper? After all, there's no kasha for supper, only thin stew."

---

[1] Vecheruyaya Moskva—an evening newspaper.

"No, no," said Tsezar with a smile. "Eat it yourself, Ivan Denisovich."

That was just what Shukhov was expecting. And now, like a bird on the wing, he darted from the porch and ran from one zone to the other.

The prisoners were scurrying in all directions. There was a time when the camp commandant had issued yet another order: on no account were prisoners to walk about the camp on their own. Wherever possible, a squad was to go intact. But when there could be no business for a whole squad to do at once—at the dispensary, say, or at the latrines—then groups of four or five were to be formed and a senior appointed to head them and take them there and back in a body.

The camp commandant took a very firm stand on that order. No one dared contradict him. The guards picked up solitary prisoners, took down their numbers, yanked them off to the cells—yet the order was a flop. It flopped quietly, like many much-touted orders. Someone, say, is sent for by the security boys—must you take another four or five with you? Or you have to get your food from the warehouse. Why the hell should I go with you? Someone has the strange idea of going to the C.E.D. to read newspapers. Who wants to go with him? And this fellow goes to have his boots mended, another to the drying shed, a third merely from one barracks to another (that's forbidden more strictly than anything else)—how can you hold them all back?

With that rule of his the commandant would have robbed them of their last shred of freedom, but it didn't work out, much as he tried, the fat pig.

Hurrying along the path, meeting a guard on the way and, to be on the safe side, taking off his hat to him, Shukhov ran into the barracks. The place was in an uproar: someone's bread ration had been swiped during the day and the poor fellow was shouting at the orderlies and the orderlies were shouting back. But the 104th's corner was empty.

Shukhov was always thankful if, on returning to camp, he found that his mattress hadn't been turned over and that the guards hadn't been snooping around. So that's all right.

He hurried to his bunk, taking off his coat as he ran. Up with the coat, up with the mittens and the nice bit of blade. He probed the depths of his mattress—the bread was there. Good that he'd sewn it in.

And out he ran. To the mess hall.

He reached it without meeting a guard —only a couple of zeks arguing over their bread ration.

Outside the moon shone brighter than ever. The lamps seemed to be paler now. The barracks cast deep shadows. The door to the mess hall lay beyond a broad porch with four steps. Now the porch too lay in shadow. But above it a small lamp was swaying, and creaking dismally in the cold. The light it cast was rainbow-hued, from the frost maybe, or the dirt on the glass.

The camp commandant had issued yet another strict order: the squads were to enter the mess hall in double file. To this he added: on reaching the steps they were to stay there and not climb onto the porch; they were to form up in fives and remain standing until the mess orderly gave them the go-ahead.

The post of mess orderly was firmly held by "the Limper." Because of his lameness he'd managed to get classed as disabled, but he was a hefty son-of-a-bitch. He'd got himself a birch club, and standing on the porch would hit anyone who came up the steps without his say-so. No, not anyone. He was smart, and could tell, even in the dark, when it was better to let a man alone—anyone who might give him as good as he got. He hit the down-and-outs. Once he hit Shukhov.

He was called an orderly. But, looking closer into it, he was a real prince—he palled around with the cooks.

Today all the squads may have turned up together or there may have been delay in getting things in order, but there was quite a crowd on the porch. Among them was the Limper, with his assistant. The mess chief himself was there too. They were handling the crowd without guards —the bruisers.

The mess chief was a fat pig with a head like a pumpkin and a broad pair of shoulders. He was bursting with energy and when he walked he seemed nothing but a lot of jerks, with springs for arms and legs. He wore a white lambskin hat without a number on it, finer than any civilian's. And his waistcoat was lamb-skin to match, with a number on it, true, but hardly bigger than a postage stamp— thanks to Volkovoi. He bore no number at all on his back. He respected no one and all the zeks were afraid of him. He held the lives of thousands in his hands. Once they'd tried to beat him up but all the cooks—a prize bunch of thugs they were—had leaped to his defense.

Shukhov would be in hot water if the 104th had already gone in. The Limper knew anyone by sight and, with his chief present, wouldn't think of letting a man in with the wrong squad; he'd make a point of putting the finger on him.

Prisoners had been known to slip in behind the Limper's back by climbing over the porch railings. Shukhov had done it too. But tonight, under the chief's very nose, that was out of the question— he'd bust you so bad that you'd only just manage to drag yourself off to the doctor.

Get along to the porch and see whether, among all those identical black coats, the 104th was still there.

He got there just as the men began shoving (what could they do? it would soon be time to turn in) as though they were storming a stronghold—the first step, the second, the third, the fourth. Got there! They poured onto the porch.

"Stop, you fuckers," the Limper shouted and raised his stick at the men in front. "Get back or I'll bash your heads in."

"What can we do about it?" they yelled back at him. "The men at the back are pushing us."

That was true, but those up in front were offering little resistance. They hoped to dash through into the mess hall.

The Limper put his club across his chest—it might have been a barricade in a street battle—and rushed headlong at the men in front. His assistant, the trusty, shared the stick with him, and so did the mess chief—who had apparently decided to soil his hands with it.

They pushed hard—they had plenty of strength, with all that meat in them. The zeks reeled back. The men in front toppled down onto the men behind them, bowled them over like wheat stalks.

"You fucking Limper, we'll fix you," cried a man in the crowd, hiding behind the others. As for the rest, they fell without a word, they got up without a word —as quick as they could, before being stepped on.

The steps were clear. The mess chief went back to the porch but the Limper stayed on the top.

"Form fives, blockheads," he shouted. "How many times have I told you I'll let you in when I'm ready?"

Shukhov imagined that he saw Senka's head right in front of the porch. He felt wildly elated, and using his elbows made an effort to push through to him. But, looking at those backs, he knew that it was beyond his strength. He wouldn't get through.

"Twenty-seventh," the Limper called, "go ahead."

The 27th bounded up and made a dash

for the door, and the rest surged after them. Shukhov, among them, was shoving with all his might. The porch quivered, and the lamp overhead protested shrilly.

"What again, you shits?" the Limper shouted in rage. Down came his stick, on a shoulder, on a back, pushing the men off, toppling one after another.

Again he cleared the steps.

From below Shukhov saw Pavlo at the Limper's side. It was he who led the squad to the mess hall—Tiurin wouldn't lower himself by joining in the hullabaloo.

"Form fives, hundred and fourth," Pavlo called from the porch. "Make way for them, friends."

Friends—just see them making way, fuck 'em.

"Let me through, you in front. That's my squad," Shukhov grunted, shoving against a back.

The man would gladly have done so but others were squeezing him from every side.

The crowd heaved, pushing away so that no one could breathe. To get its stew. Its lawful stew.

Shukhov tried something else. He grasped the porch rail on his left, got his arms around a pillar, and heaved himself up. He kicked someone's knee and caught a blow in the ribs; a few curses, but he was through. He planted a foot on the edge of the porch floor, close to the top step, and waited. Some of his pals who were already there gave him a hand.

The mess chief walked to the door and looked back.

"Come on, Limper, send in two more squads."

"One hundred and fourth," shouted the Limper. "Where d'you think you're crawling, shit?"

He slammed a man from another squad on the back of the neck with his stick.

"One hundred and fourth," shouted Pavlo, leading in his men.

"Whew!" gasped Shukhov in the mess hall. And, without waiting for Pavlo's instructions, he started looking for free trays.

The mess hall seemed as usual, with clouds of steam curling in through the door and the men sitting shoulder to shoulder—like seeds in a sunflower. Others pushed their way through the tables, and others were carrying loaded trays. Shukhov had grown used to it all over the years and his sharp eyes had noticed that S 280 had only five bowls on the tray he was carrying. This meant that it was the last tray-load for his squad. Otherwise the tray would have been full.

He went up to the man and whispered in his ear: "After you with that tray."

"Someone's waiting for it at the counter. I promised. . . ."

"Let him wait, the lazy bastard."

They came to an understanding.

S 280 carried his tray to the table and unloaded the bowls. Shukhov immediately grabbed it. At that moment the man it had been promised to ran up and tried to grab it. But he was punier than Shukhov. Shukhov shoved him off with the tray—what the hell are you pulling for? —and threw him against a post. Then putting the tray under his arm, he trotted off to the serving window.

Pavlo was standing in the line there, worried because there was no empty tray. He was delighted to see Shukhov. He pushed the man ahead of him out of the way: "Why are you standing here? Can't you see I've got a tray?"

Look, there was Gopchik—with another tray.

"They were arguing," he said with a laugh, "and I grabbed it."

Gopchik will do well. Give him another three years—he has still to grow up—and he'll become nothing less than a bread cutter. He's fated for it.

Pavlo told him to hand over the second of the trays to Yermolayev, a hefty Siberian who was serving a ten-year stretch, like Shukhov, for being caught by the Germans; then sent him to keep an eye on any table where the men might be finishing. Shukhov put his tray down and waited.

"One hundred and fourth," announced Pavlo at the counter.

In all there were five of these counters: three for serving regular food, one for zeks on special diets (ulcer victims, and bookkeeping personnel, as a favor), and one for the return of dirty dishes (that's where the dish-lickers gathered, sparring with one another). The counters were low—about waist level. The cooks themselves were out of sight; only their hands, and the ladles, could be seen.

The cook's hands were white and well cared for, but huge and hairy: a boxer's hands, not a cook's. He took a pencil and made a note on the wall—he kept his list there.

"One hundred and fourth—twenty-four portions."

Pantaleyev slopped into the mess hall. Nothing wrong with him, the son-of-a-bitch.

The cook took an enormous ladle and stirred, stirred, stirred. The soup kettle had just been refilled, almost up to the brim, and steam poured from it. Replacing the huge ladle with a smaller one he began serving the stew in twenty-ounce portions. He didn't go deep.

"One, two, three, four . . ."

Some of the bowls had been filled while the stuff from the bottom of the kettle hadn't yet settled after the stirring, and some were duds—nothing but soup. Shukhov made a mental note of which was which. He put ten bowls on his tray and carried them off. Gopchik waved from the second row of posts.

"Over here, Ivan Denisovich, over here."

No horsing around with bowls of stew. Shukhov was careful not to stumble. He kept his throat busy too.

"Hey you, H 920. Gently, uncle. Out of the way, my boy."

It was hard enough, in a crowd like this, to carry a single bowl without slopping it. He was carrying ten. Just the same, he put the tray down safely, on the end of the table that Gopchik had cleared. No splashes. He managed, too, to maneuver the tray so that the two bowls with the thickest stew were just opposite the place he was about to sit down in.

Yermolayev brought another ten bowls. Gopchik ran off and came back with Pavlo, the last four in their hands.

Kilgas brought the bread tray. Tonight they were being fed in accordance with the work they had done. Some got six ounces, some nine, and Shukhov twelve. He took a piece with a crust for himself, and six ounces from the middle of the loaf for Tsezar.

Now from all over the mess hall Shukhov's squad began streaming up, to collect their supper and eat it where they could. As he handed out the bowls, there were two things he had to take care of: he had to remember whom he'd served, and he had to watch out for the tray—and for his own corner of it. (He put his spoon into a bowl—one of the "thick" ones. Reserved, that meant.) Fetiukov was among the first to arrive. But he soon walked off, figuring there was nothing to be scrounged that particular evening; better to wander around the mess, hunting for leftovers (if someone doesn't finish his stew and pushes his bowl back, there are always people hustling to pounce on it, like vultures).

Shukhov counted the portions with Pavlo. Correct, apparently. He pushed across a bowl for Tiurin, one of the "thick" ones; and Pavlo poured his stew into a narrow German mess-tin, with a lid—you could carry it under your coat, close to your chest.

The empty trays were handed in. Pavlo sat there with his double helping, Shukhov with his two bowls. And now they had nothing more to say to one another—the sacred moments had come.

Shukhov took off his hat and laid it on his knees. He tasted one bowl, he tasted the other. Not bad—there was some fish in it. Generally, the evening stew was much thinner than at breakfast: if they're to work, prisoners must be fed in the morning; in the evening they'll go to sleep anyway.

He dug in. First he only drank the broth, drank and drank. As it went down, filling his whole body with warmth, all his guts began to flutter inside him at their meeting with that stew. Goo-ood! There It comes, that brief moment for which a zek lives.

And now Shukhov complained about nothing: neither about the length of his stretch, nor about the length of the day, nor about their swiping another Sunday. This was all he thought about now: we'll survive. We'll stick it out, God willing, till it's over.

He drained the hot soup from both bowls, and then tipped what was left in the second into the first, scraping it clean with his spoon. That set his mind at ease. Now he didn't have to think about the second and keep an eye or a hand on it.

Now that he could look freely he glanced at his neighbors' bowls. The one on his left was little more than water. The dirty snakes. The tricks they play! And on their fellow zeks.

He began to eat the cabbage with what was left of the soup. A potato had found its way into one of the bowls—Tsezar's. A medium-sized spud, frost-bitten, hard and sweetish. There wasn't much fish, just a few stray bits of bare backbone. But you must chew every bone, every fin, to suck the juice out of them, for the juice is healthy. It takes time, of course, but he was in no hurry to go anywhere. Today was a red-letter day for him: two helpings for dinner, two helpings for supper. Everything else could wait.

Except, maybe, that visit to the Lett for tobacco. None might be left in the morning.

He ate his supper without bread. A double helping *and* bread—that was going too far. The bread would do for tomorrow. The belly is a demon. It doesn't remember how well you treated it yesterday; it'll cry out for more to-morrow.

He ate up his stew without taking much interest in what was happening around him. No need for that: he wasn't on the lookout for extras, he was eating his own lawful portions. All the same, he noticed that when the fellow opposite got up a tall old man—U 81—sat down in his place. Shukhov knew he was in the 64th and had heard, while waiting in the parcels line, that the 64th had been sent to the Socialist Way of Life settlement that day instead of the 104th, and had spent the whole time without a chance of getting warm—putting up barbed wire, building their own zone.

He'd been told that this old man had spent years without number in camps and prisons, and that he hadn't benefited from a single amnesty. Whenever one ten-year stretch had run out they shoved another onto him right away.

Now Shukhov looked closely at the man. He held himself straight—the other zeks sat all hunched up—and looked as if he'd put something extra on the bench to sit on. There was nothing left to crop on his head: his hair had dropped out long since—the result of high living, no doubt. His eyes didn't dart after every-thing going on in the mess hall. He kept them fixed in an unseeing gaze at some spot over Shukhov's head. His worn

wooden spoon dipped rhythmically into the thin stew, but instead of lowering his head to the bowl like everybody else, he raised the spoon high to his lips. He'd lost all his teeth and chewed his bread with iron gums. All life had drained out of his face but it had been left, not sickly or feeble, but hard and dark like carved stone. And by his hands, big and cracked and blackened, you could see that he'd had little opportunity of doing soft jobs. But he wasn't going to give in, oh no! *He* wasn't going to put his nine ounces on the dirty, bespattered table—he put it on a well-washed bit of rag.

However, he couldn't go on watching the old man—he had other things to do. He finished his supper, licked his spoon clean, and put it in his boot. He pulled his hat over his eyes, got up, picked up his bread and Tsezar's, and went out. Another porch led from the mess hall. Two more orderlies stood there: they had nothing to do except unhook the door, let people through, and slip the hook on again.

Shukhov came out with a full belly. He felt pleased with himself and decided that, although it was close to curfew, he'd run over to the Lett all the same. Instead of taking the bread to his bar-racks, he strode to Barracks 7.

The moon was high—clean and white, as if chiseled out of the sky. It was clear up there and there were some stars out—the brightest of them. But he had even less time for stargazing than for watching people in the mess hall. One thing he realized—the frost was no milder. One of the civilians had said, and this had been passed on, that it was likely to drop to −25° in the night, and as low as −40° toward morning.

From far away in the settlement he heard the drone of a tractor. From the direction of the main thoroughfare an excavator squealed shrilly. And creak,

creak, went every pair of boots in which people walked or ran about the camp.

There was no wind.

He meant to buy the tobacco at the price he'd paid before—one ruble a glassful, though, outside, that amount would cost three times as much, and for some cuts even more. In forced-labor camps all the prices were local; it was quite different from anywhere else, because you couldn't save money and few had any at all, for it was very hard to come by. No one was paid by a kopeck for his work (at Ust-Izhma he'd received at least thirty rubles a month). If anyone's relatives sent money by mail he didn't get it in cash anyway; it was credited to his personal account. You could draw on a personal account once a month at the commissary to buy soap, moldy biscuits, and "Prima" cigarettes. Whether you liked the wares or not, you had to spend the amount the chief had given you a slip for. If you didn't, the money was lost—simply written off.

Shukhov did private jobs to get money, making slippers out of customers' rags—two rubles a pair—or patching torn jackets, price by agreement.

Barracks 7, unlike Barracks 9, wasn't in two big halves. It had a long passage, with ten doors opening off it. Each room housed a squad, packed into seven tiers of bunks. In addition, there was a little cubbyhole for the bucket and another for the senior orderly. The artists had a cubbyhole to themselves, too.

Shukhov headed for the Lett's room. He found him lying on a lower bunk, his feet propped on a ledge. He was talking to his neighbor in Latvian.

Shukhov sat down beside him. "Evening." "Evening," replied the Lett, without lowering his feet. The room was small, everyone was listening. Who was he? What did he want?

Both Shukhov and the Lett realized that people were curious, so Shukhov let the conversation drag on. Well, how are you doing? Oh, not so bad. Cold today. Yes.

Shukhov waited until everyone had started talking again. (They were arguing about the Korean war—now that the Chinese had joined in, would that mean a world war or not?) He leaned closer to the Lett.

"Any t'bacca?"

"Yes."

"Let's see it."

The Lett dropped his feet off the ledge, put them on the floor, sat up. He was a mean fellow, that Lett—filled a glass with tobacco as if he was afraid of putting in a single pinch too many.

He showed Shukhov his tobacco pouch and slid open the fastener.

Shukhov took a pinch and laid the leaf on his palm. He examined it. Same as last time, brownish, same rough cut. He held it to his nose and sniffed. That was the stuff. But to the Lett he said: "Not the same, somehow."

"The same, the same," the Lett said testily. "I never have any other kind. Always the same."

"All right," said Shukhov. "Stuff some into a glass for me. I'll have a smoke and perhaps take a second glassful."

He said "stuff" on purpose, because the Lett had the habit of dropping the tobacco in loosely.

The Lett brought out another pouch from under his pillow, fuller than the first. He took his glass out of a locker. It was really a plastic container, but Shukhov figured it held the same as an ordinary glass.

The Lett began to fray out the tobacco into the glass.

"Push it down, push it down," said Shukhov, laying his own thumb on it.

"I know how to do it," the Lett said sharply, jerking away the glass and press-

[73]

ing the tobacco, though lightly. He dropped in a little more.

Meanwhile, Shukhov had unbuttoned his jacket and was groping inside the cotton lining for a piece of paper that only he knew where to find. Using both hands he squeezed it along under the lining and forced it into a little hole in the cloth somewhere quite different, a small tear that he'd tacked with a couple of loose stitches. When the paper reached the hole he snapped the thread with a fingernail, folded the paper lengthwise (it had already been folded in a longish rectangle), and pulled it through the hole. Two rubles. Worn notes that didn't rustle.

In the room a prisoner shouted: "D'you mean to say you think Old Whiskers[1] will take pity on you? Why, he wouldn't trust his own brother. You haven't a chance, you ass."

One good thing about these "special" camps—you were free to let off steam. At Ust-Izhma you need only whisper that there was a shortage of matches outside, and they'd put you in the guardhouse and add another ten years to your stretch. But here you could bawl anything you liked from the top row of bunks—the squealers didn't pass it on, the security boys had stopped caring.

The trouble was, you didn't have much time to talk in.

"Ugh, you're making it lie too loose," Shukhov complained.

"Oh well, there you are," said the Lett, adding a pinch on top.

Shukhov took his pouch out of an inside pocket and poured in the tobacco from the glass.

"All right," he said, deciding not to waste the first precious cigarette by smoking it hurriedly. "Stuff it full again."

Wrangling a bit more, he poured the second glassful into his pouch, handed

_____
[1] Stalin.

over the two rubles, and left with a nod.

As soon as he was outside again he doubled back to Barracks 9. He didn't want to miss Tsezar when he came back with that package.

But Tsezar was already there, sitting on his bunk and gloating over the parcel. Its contents were laid out on his bunk and on top of the locker, but as there was no direct light there—Shukhov's bunk was in the way—it wasn't very easy to see.

Shukhov stooped, passed between Tsezar's bunk and the captain's, and handed Tsezar his bread ration.

"Your bread, Tsezar Markovich."

He didn't say, "Well, did you get it?" That would have been to hint, "I kept that place in the line and now have a right to my share." The right was his, that he knew, but even eight years as a convict hadn't turned him into a jackal—and the longer he spent at the camp the stronger he made himself.

But his eyes were another matter. Those eyes, the hawklike eyes of a zek, darted to one side and slid swiftly over what was laid out there; and although the food hadn't been unpacked and some of the bags were still unopened, that quick look and the evidence of his nose told him that Tsezar had got sausage, condensed milk, a plump smoked fish, salt pork, crackers, biscuits, four pounds of lump sugar and what looked like butter, as well as cigarettes and pipe tobacco— and that wasn't all.

He learned all this during the brief moment it took him to say: "Your bread, Tsezar Markovich."

Tsezar, all excited and looking a bit tipsy (and who wouldn't, after getting a parcel like that!) waved the bread away: "Keep it, Ivan Denisovich."

His bowl of stew, and now this six ounces of bread—that was a full supper, and of course Shukhov's fair share of the parcel.

And he put out of his mind any idea of getting something tasty from what Tsezar had laid out. There's nothing worse than working your belly to no purpose.

Well, he had his twelve ounces and now this extra six, besides the piece in his mattress, at least another six ounces. Not bad. He'd eat six now and some more later, and still have next day's ration for work. Living high, eh! As for the hunk in the mattress, let it stay there! A good thing he'd found time to sew it in! Someone in the 75th had had a hunk pinched from his locker. That was a dead loss; nothing could be done about it.

People imagine that the package a man gets is a sort of nice, tight sack he has only to slit open and be happy. But if you work it out it's a matter of easy come, easy go. Shukhov had known cases when before his parcel arrived a fellow would be doing odd jobs to earn a bit of extra kasha, or cadging cigarette butts—just like anybody else. He has to share with the guard and the squad leader—and how can he help giving a little something to the trusty in the parcels office? Why, next time the fellow may mislay your parcel and a week may go by before your name appears again on the list! And that other fellow at the place where you hand in your food to be kept for you, safe from friskers and pilferers—Tsezar will be there before the morning roll call, with everything in a sack—he must have his cut too, and a good one, if you don't want him little by little swiping more than you gave him. Sitting there all day, the rat, shut up with other people's food —try to keep an eye on him! And there must be something for services like Shukhov's. And something to the bath attendant for issuing you decent underwear—not much but something. And for the barber who shaves you "with paper" (for wiping the razor on—he usually does it on your knee). Not much to him either

but, still, three or four butts. And at the C.E.D., for your letters to be kept separate and not get lost. And if you want to goof off a day or two and lie in bed, instead of going to work, you have to slip the doctor something. And what about the neighbor you share a locker with (the captain, in Tsezar's case)? He must have his cut. After all, he sees every blessed ounce you take. Who'd be nervy enough not to give him his share?

So leave envy to those who always think the radish in the other fellow's hand is bigger than yours. Shukhov knows life and never opens his belly to what doesn't belong to him.

Meanwhile he pulled off his boots, climbed up to his bunk, took the strip of hacksaw out of his mitten, and decided that tomorrow he'd look around for a good pebble and start whetting down the blade to make a cobbler's knife. Four days' work, he figured, if he sat over it mornings and evenings, and he'd have a fine little knife with a sharp, curved blade.

But now he had to conceal that find of his, if only till morning. He'd slip it into the edge of the partition under the crossbeam. And as the captain hadn't returned yet to his bunk down below and the sawdust wouldn't fall on his face, Shukhov turned back the head of his mattress and set about hiding the thing.

His top-bunk neighbors could see what he was doing: Alyosha the Baptist and—across the aisle, in the next tier—the two Estonians. But he didn't worry about them.

Fetiukov walked through the barracks. He was sobbing, all hunched up, his mouth smeared with blood. So he'd been beaten up again—over the bowls! With no attempt to hide his tears, and looking at no one, he passed the whole squad, crawled into his bunk, and buried his face in his mattress.

When you thought about it, you

couldn't help feeling sorry for him. He wouldn't live to see the end of his stretch. His attitude was all wrong.

Just then the captain turned up. He looked cheerful as he carried a pot of tea, special tea, you can bet! Two tea barrels stood in the barracks, but what sort of tea could you call it? Sewage: warm water with a touch of coloring, dishwater smelling of the barrel—of steamed wood and rot. That was tea for the workers. But the captain must have taken a pinch of real tea from Tsezar, put it in his pot, and hurried to the hot-water faucet. And now, well satisfied, he settled down beside his locker.

"Nearly scalded my fingers at the faucet," he boasted. Down there Tsezar spread a sheet of paper, and began laying this and that on it. Shukhov turned the head of his mattress back. He didn't want to see what was going on; he didn't want to upset himself. But even now they couldn't get along without him; Tsezar rose to his full height, his eyes level with Shukhov's, and winked.

"Ivan Denisovich! Er . . . lend me your 'ten days.' "

That meant a small penknife. Yes, Shukhov had one—he kept it concealed in the partition. A bit shorter than half a finger but it cut salt pork five fingers thick. He'd made the blade himself, mounted it and whetted it sharp.

He crawled to the beam. He fished the knife out. He handed it over. Tsezar nodded and ducked below.

That knife's a breadwinner too. After all, you can be put in the cells for keeping it, and only a man without a conscience would say: lend us your knife, we're going to slice some sausage, and you can go fuck off.

Now Tsezar was again in his debt.

Having settled the bread and knife business, Shukhov opened his tobacco pouch. First he took a pinch of tobacco out of it, equal to what he'd borrowed, and stretched a hand across the aisle to Eino the Estonian. Thanks.

The Estonian's lips stretched in a sort of smile. He muttered something to his "brother," and together they rolled the pinch of tobacco into a cigarette. Let's try Shukhov's tobacco.

No worse than yours. Try it, if you please. He'd like to try it himself, but some timekeeper in his brain told him that the evening count would very soon be starting. This was just the time the guards poked around the barracks. If he was going to smoke now he'd have to go into the corridor, but up there in his bunk he somehow felt warmer. The barracks was, as a matter of fact, far from warm—that film of frost was still on the ceiling. He'd shiver in the night, but now it was bearable.

Shukhov stayed in his bunk and began crumbling little bits off his bread. He listened unwillingly to Tsezar and Buinovsky, talking below over their tea.

"Help yourself, captain. Help yourself, don't hold back. Take some of this smoked fish. Have a slice of sausage."

"Thanks, I will."

"Spread some butter on that bread. It's real Moscow bread."

"D'you know, I simply can't believe they're still baking pure white bread anywhere. Such luxury reminds me of a time when I happened to be in Archangel. . . ."

The two hundred voices in Shukhov's half of the barracks were making a terrific din, but he fancied he heard the rail being struck. No one else seemed to have heard it. He also noticed that "Snubnose," the guard, had come into the barracks. He was no more than a boy, small and rosy-cheeked. He was holding a sheet of paper, and it was clear from this and his manner that he'd come, not to turn them all out for the evening count or catch smokers, but to get someone.

"Snubnose" checked something on his

list and said: "Where's the hundred and fourth?"

"Here," they answered. The Estonians hid their cigarettes and waved away the smoke.

"Where's the squad leader?"

"Well?" said Tiurin from his bunk, lowering his feet reluctantly.

"Your people signed those forms—about the extra stuff they were wearing?"

"They'll sign them," said Tiurin with assurance.

"They're overdue."

"My men haven't had much education. It's not an easy job. (This about Tsezar and the captain! What a squad leader! Never at a loss for an answer.) No pens. No ink."

"Ought to have them."

"They take them away from us."

"Well, look out, squad leader. If you go on talking like that I'll put you in the guardhouse with the rest," "Snubnose" promised Tiurin, but mildly. "Now about those forms—see they're handed in to the guardroom before roll call tomorrow morning. And give orders that all prohibited garments are to be surrendered to personal property. Get that?"

"I get it."

(The captain was in luck, thought Shukhov. He hadn't heard a word, he was having such a fine time with his sausage.)

"Let's see now," said the guard. "S 311. He one of yours?"

"Have to look at my list," said Tiurin vaguely. "Expect me to keep all those damned numbers in my head?"

(He was playing for time. He wanted to save Buinovsky one night at least, by dragging things out till the count.)

"Buinovsky. He here?"

"Eh? Here I am," called the captain from his haven under Shukhov's bunk.

There you are; the quickest louse is always the first to be caught in the comb.

"You? Yes, that's right. S 311. Get ready."

"Where am I to go?"

"You know where."

The captain sighed. He grunted. Nothing more. It must have been easier for him to take out a squadron of destroyers into the dark, stormy night than to tear himself away from this friendly chat and set out for the icy cells.

"How many days?" he asked, his voice falling.

"Ten. Come on, come on. Get going."

At that moment the barracks orderlies shouted: "Evening count. All out for evening count."

This meant that the guard who was to count them had already entered the barracks.

The captain looked around. Should he take his coat? Anyway, they'd strip it off him when he got there, leaving him only his jacket. Better go as he was. He'd hoped that Volkovoi would forget (but Volkovoi never forgot anyone) and he had made no preparations, hadn't even hidden a pinch of tobacco in his jacket. And to carry it in his hands—that would be useless; they'd take it from him the minute they frisked him.

All the same . . . Tsezar slipped him a couple of cigarettes as he put on his hat.

"Well, brothers, good-by," said the captain with an embarrassed nod to his fellow prisoners, and followed the guard out.

A few voices shouted: Keep your chin up. But what could you really say to him? They knew the cells, the 104th did; they'd built them. Brick walls, cement floor, no windows, a stove they lit only to melt the ice on the walls and make pools on the floor. You slept on bare boards, and if you'd any teeth left to eat with after all the chattering they'd be doing, they gave you nine ounces of bread day after day and hot stew only on the third, sixth, and ninth.

Ten days. Ten days "hard" in the cells —if you sat them out to the end, your health would be ruined for the rest of your life. T.B. and nothing but hospital for you till you kicked the bucket.

As for those who got fifteen days "hard" and sat them out—they went straight into a hole in the cold earth.

As long as you're in the barracks— praise the Lord and sit tight.

"Come on now, out you get, before I count three," shouted the barracks commander. "Anyone who isn't out will have his number taken. I'll give it to the guard."

The barracks commander was one of the biggest bastards. After all, just think, he's locked in with us all night, but the way he acts, not afraid of anyone! On the contrary, everyone's afraid of him. Some of us he betrays to the guards, others he wallops himself. He lost a thumb in a scrap and is classed as an invalid, but his face is the face of a thug. Actually he *is* a thug with a criminal record, but among the charges against him was one under Article 58, 14, and that's how he landed in with us.

He wouldn't think twice about taking your number and passing it to the guard —and that means two days in the guardhouse, with work. So instead of just trailing to the door one by one they all rushed out in a crowd, tumbling down from the bunks as if they were bears and pressing to the narrow exit.

Shukhov, the cigarette in his palm— he'd craved it so long and had already rolled it—sprang nimbly down, and slipped his feet into the valenki. He was on the point of leaving when he felt a twinge of pity for Tsezar. It wasn't that he wanted to make anything more out of the man; he felt genuinely sorry for him. For all his high opinion of himself, Tsezar didn't know a thing about life—

after collecting his parcel he shouldn't have gloated over it; he should have taken it to the storeroom right away before the evening count. Eating's something that can wait. But now what was Tsezar going to do with all that stuff? He couldn't carry his sack with him to the count. What a horselaugh that would bring! Four hundred zeks roaring their heads off. But to leave it in the barracks no matter how briefly meant that the first to run back from the count would swipe it. (At Ust-Izhma it was even crueler: there, when we came back from work, the crooks got in first and cleaned out all our lockers.)

Shukhov saw that Tsezar realized the danger. He was bustling here and there, but too late. He was stuffing the sausage and salt pork under his jacket. That at least he could save by taking it to the count.

Pityingly, Shukhov gave him some advice: "Sit here till the last moment, Tsezar Markovich. Hide here in the shadow and stay till everyone has left. And when the guard comes by the bunks with the orderlies and pokes into everything, come out and say you're feeling bad. I'll go out first and I'll be back first. That's the way. . . ."

And he ran off.

At first he elbowed his way through the crowd mercilessly (protecting his cigarette in his fist, however). In the corridor, which served both halves of the barracks, and near the door, the men in front were hanging back, the cagy beasts, clinging to two rows to the walls on each side, leaving just enough room for any fool who liked the cold to squeeze through. They were going to stay here; they've been out all day. Why should they freeze needlessly for another ten minutes? No fools here! You croak today but *I* mean to live till tomorrow.

At any other time Shukhov too would

have clung to the wall. But now he strode to the door and even grinned.

"What are you scared of, you idiots? Never seen Siberian frost before? Come outside and warm yourselves by the wolf's sun. Give us a light, uncle."

He lit his cigarette at the door and moved out onto the porch. "Wolf's sun," that's what they'd called the moon in Shukhov's village.

The moon rode high now. As high again, and it would be at its zenith. The sky was greenish-white; the rare stars shone brilliantly. The snow gleamed white, the barracks walls gleamed white. The lamps had little effect.

There was a dense black crowd outside one of the barracks. The zeks had come out for the count. They were coming out over there too. But it wasn't the sound of voices you heard from the barracks—it was the creaking of boots on the snow.

Some prisoners were coming down the steps and lining up, opposite the barracks. Five in front, then three behind. Shukhov joined the three. After an extra bit of bread, and with a cigarette between your lips, it wasn't so bad standing there. Good tobacco—the Lett hadn't gypped him. Strong, and smelled good.

Gradually, other prisoners trailed through the door. Two or three more lines of five were forming behind him. They came out angry now. Why were those rats jostling in the corridor? Why weren't they coming out? Why should we have to freeze for them?

No zek ever saw a clock or a watch. What use were they to him anyway? All he needs to know is: will reveille sound soon? How long to roll call? How long to dinner? To the last clanging of the rail?

The evening count, everyone said, was at nine. But it never finished at nine— they would sometimes recount two or even three times. You never got away before ten. And at five o'clock next morning they hounded you out of your bunk with the first clanging of the rail. No wonder that Moldavian had dozed off down at the shop before work was over today. Wherever a zek gets a bit of warmth into him he falls asleep on the spot. You lose so much sleep during the week that on a Sunday—provided they don't send you to work—whole barrack-fuls of zeks sleep the day through.

Now they're streaming forward. At last! The barracks commander and the guard were dragging them out, kicking them in the ass. Serve 'em right, the tricky bastards.

"What?" the zeks in front shouted at the late comers. "Pretty smart, huh? Want to lick the cream off the shit, you rats? If you'd come out earlier we'd be through now."

The whole barracks had been emptied. Four hundred men—eighty ranks of five. They lined up in a column, the ones in front strictly in fives, the others any old way.

"Get into line there, you at the back," the barracks commander shouted from the steps.

They didn't move, fuck 'em.

Tsezar came out shivering, pretending he was sick. At his heels were four orderlies, two from each half of the barracks, and a prisoner who limped. They stood in front so that Shukhov was now a row farther back. Tsezar was sent to the rear of the column.

The guard came out too.

"Form fives!" he shouted to the rear of the column, furiously.

"Form fives!" shouted the barracks commander even more furiously.

The men didn't budge, fuck 'em.

The barracks commander rushed from the porch to the rear of the column, swearing and hitting out.

But he was careful whom he hit. Only the meek ones.

The ranks formed. He came back. He shouted:

"First. Second. Third . . ."

As soon as they'd been counted the men broke away and rushed into the barracks. All square for today with the authorities.

All square, unless there's a recount. Those parasites were such morons, they counted worse than any herdsman. For all that he may be unable to read or write, a herdsman knows if there's a calf missing when he's driving the herd. And these parasites had been trained—whatever good it'd done them.

The previous winter there'd been no drying sheds at all for the boots, and the zeks had had to leave their valenki in the barracks night after night. So if the count was repeated, everyone had to be driven outside again, a second, a third, a fourth time—already undressed, just as they were, wrapped in blankets. Since then a drying shed had been built; it wasn't big enough for all the boots at one time, but at least each of the squads could get the benefit of it once every two or three days. So now any recount was held inside. They merely shifted the zeks from one half of the barracks to the other, counting them as they filed through.

Shukhov wasn't the first to be back, but he kept an eye on anyone ahead of him. He ran up to Tsezar's bunk and sat on it. He took off his boots, and climbed onto the top of a tier of bunks close by the stove. He put his boots on the stove —first-comer's prerogative—then back to Tsezar's bunk. He sat there cross-legged, one eye on guard for Tsezar (they might swipe his packages from under the head of his bunk), the other for himself (they might push his boots off the stove).

"Hey," he shouted, "hey you, Red. Want to get that boot in your teeth? Put your own up but don't touch other peoples'."

The prisoners poured in like a stream.

The men in the 20th shouted: "Give us your boots."

As soon as they'd left the barracks with the boots the door was locked after them. When they ran back they shouted: "Citizen chief. Let us in."

And the guards gathered in their quarters with their boards and did the bookkeeping: had anyone escaped, or was everything in order?

Well, Shukhov needn't think about such things that evening. Here came Tsezar, diving between the tiers of bunks on his way back.

"Thank you, Ivan Denisovich."

Shukhov nodded, and shot up to his bunk like a squirrel. Now he could finish his bread, smoke a second cigarette, go to sleep.

But he'd had such a good day, he felt in such good spirits, that somehow he wasn't in the mood for sleep yet.

He must make his bed now—there wasn't much to it. Strip his mattress of the grubby blanket and lie on it (it must have been '41 when he last slept in sheets —that was at home; it even seemed odd for women to bother about sheets, all that extra laundering). Head on the pillow, stuffed with shavings of wood; feet in jacket sleeve; coat on top of blanket and—Glory be to Thee, O Lord. Another day over. Thank You I'm not spending tonight in the cells. Here it's still bearable.

He lay with his head near the window, but Alyosha, who slept next to him on the same level, across a low wooden railing, lay the opposite way, to catch the light. He was reading his Bible again.

The electric light was quite near. You could read and even sew by it.

Alyosha heard Shukhov's whispered prayer, and, turning to him: "There you are, Ivan Denisovich, your soul is begging to pray. Why don't you give it its freedom?"

Shukhov stole a look at him. Alyosha's eyes glowed like two candles.

"Well, Alyosha," he said with a sigh,

"it's this way. Prayers are like those appeals of ours. Either they don't get through or they're returned with 'rejected' scrawled across 'em.' "

Outside the staff quarters were four sealed boxes—they were cleared by a security officer once a month. Many were the appeals that were dropped into them. The writers waited, counting the weeks: there'll be a reply in two months, in one month. . . .

But the reply doesn't come. Or if it does it's only "rejected."

"But, Ivan Denisovich, it's because you pray too rarely, and badly at that. Without really trying. That's why your prayers stay unanswered. One must never stop praying. If you have real faith you tell a mountain to move and it will move. . . ."

Shukhov grinned and rolled another cigarette. He took a light from the Estonian.

"Don't talk nonsense, Alyosha. I've never seen a mountain move. Well, to tell the truth, I've never seen a mountain at all. But you, now, you prayed in the Caucasus with all that Baptist society of yours—did you make a single mountain move?"

They were an unlucky group too. What harm did they do anyone by praying to God? Every damn one of them had been given twenty-five years. Nowadays they cut all cloth to the same measure—twenty-five years.

"Oh, we didn't pray for that, Ivan Denisovich," Alyosha said earnestly. Bible in hand, he drew nearer to Shukhov till they lay face to face. "Of all earthly and mortal things Our Lord commanded us to pray only for our daily bread. 'Give us this day our daily bread.' "

"Our ration, you mean?" asked Shukhov.

But Alyosha didn't give up. Arguing more with his eyes than his tongue, he plucked at Shukhov's sleeve, stroked his arm, and said: "Ivan Denisovich, you shouldn't pray to get parcels or for extra stew, not for that. Things that man puts a high price on are vile in the eyes of Our Lord. We must pray about things of the spirit—that the Lord Jesus should remove the scum of anger from our hearts. . . ."

"Listen to me. At our church in Polomnya we had a priest . . ."

"Don't talk to me about your priest," Alyosha said imploringly, his brow furrowed with distress.

"No, listen." Shukhov propped himself up on an elbow. "In Polomnya, our parish, there isn't a man richer than the priest. Take roofing, for instance. We charge thirty-five rubles a day to ordinary people for mending a roof, but the priest a hundred. And he forks up without a whimper. He pays alimony to three women in three different towns, and he's living with a fourth. And he keeps that bishop of his on a hook, I can tell you. Oh yes, he gives his fat hand to the bishop, all right. And he's thrown out every other priest they've sent there. Wouldn't share a thing with 'em."

"Why are you talking to me about priests? The Orthodox Church has departed from Scripture. It's because their faith is unstable that they're not in prison."

Shukhov went on calmly smoking and watching his excited companion.

"Alyosha," he said, withdrawing his arm and blowing smoke into his face. "I'm not against God, understand that. I do believe in God. But I don't believe in paradise or in hell. Why do you take us for fools and stuff us with your paradise and hell stories? That's what I don't like."

He lay back, dropping his cigarette ash with care between the bunk frame and the window, so as to singe nothing of the captain's below. He sank into his own thoughts. He didn't hear Alyosha's mumbling.

"Well," he said conclusively, "however much you pray it doesn't shorten your stretch. You'll sit it out from beginning to end anyhow."

"Oh, you mustn't pray for that either," said Alyosha, horrified. "Why do you want freedom? In freedom your last grain of faith will be choked with weeds. You should rejoice that you're in prison. Here you have time to think about your soul. As the Apostle Paul wrote: 'Why all these tears? Why are you trying to weaken my resolution? For my part I am ready not merely to be bound but even to die for the name of the Lord Jesus.' "

Shukhov gazed at the ceiling in silence. Now he didn't know either whether he wanted freedom or not. At first he'd longed for it. Every night he'd counted the days of his stretch—how many had passed, how many were coming. And then he'd grown bored with counting. And then it became clear that men like him wouldn't ever be allowed to return home, that they'd be exiled. And whether his life would be any better there than here—who could tell?

Freedom meant one thing to him— home.

But they wouldn't let him go home.

Alyosha was speaking the truth. His voice and his eyes left no doubt that he was happy in prison.

"You see, Alyosha," Shukhov explained to him, "somehow it works out all right for you: Jesus Christ wanted you to sit in prison and so you are—sitting there for His sake. But for whose sake am *I* here? Because we weren't ready for war in forty-one? For that? But was that *my* fault?"

"Seems like there's not going to be a recount," Kilgas murmured from his bunk.

"Yeah," said Shukhov. "We ought to write it up in coal inside the chimney. No second count." He yawned. "Might as well get to sleep."

And at that very moment the door bolt rattled to break the calm that now reigned in the barracks. From the corridor ran two of the prisoners who'd taken boots to the drying shed.

"Second count," they shouted.

On their heels came a guard.

"All out to the other half."

Some were already alseep. They began to grumble and move about, they put their boots on (no one ever took his wadded trousers off at night—you'd grow numb with cold unless you wore them under your blanket).

"Damn them," said Shukhov. Mildly, because he hadn't gone to sleep yet.

Tsezar raised a hand and gave him two biscuits, two lumps of sugar, and a slice of sausage.

"Thank you, Tsezar Markovich," said Shukhov, leaning over the edge of his bunk. "Come on now, hand up that sack of yours. I'll put it under my mattress." (It's not so easy to swipe things from the top bunks as you go by. Anyway, who'd look for anything in Shukhov's bunk?)

Tsezar handed up his sack and Shukhov hid it under the mattress. Then he waited a little till more men had been sent out—he wouldn't have to stand barefoot so long in the corridor. But the guard scowled at him and shouted: "Come on, you there in the corner."

Shukhov sprang lightly to the floor (his boots and footrags were so well placed on the stove it would be a pity to move them). Though he'd made so many slippers for others he hadn't a pair of his own. But he was used to this—and the count didn't take long.

They confiscate slippers too if they find them in daytime.

As for the squads who'd sent their boots to be dried, it wasn't so bad for them, now the recount was held indoors. Some wore slippers, some just their foot-rags, some went barefoot.

"Come on, come on," growled the guard.

"Do you want to be carried out, you shits?" the barracks commander shouted.

They shoved them all into the other half of the barracks, and loiterers into the corridor. Shukhov stood against the wall near the bucket. The floor was moist underfoot. An icy draft crept in from the porch.

They had them all out now and once again the guard and the orderly did their round, looking for any who might be dozing in dark corners. There'd be trouble if they counted short. It would mean still another recount. Round they went, round they went, and came back to the door.

"One, two, three, four. . . ." Now they released you faster, for they were counting one by one. Shukhov managed to squeeze in eighteenth. He ran back to his bunk, put his foot on the support—a heave, and he was up.

All right. Feet back into the sleeve of his jacket. Blanket on top. Then the coat. And to sleep. Now they'd be letting everybody from the other half of the barracks into our half. But that's not our worry.

Tsezar returned. Shukhov lowered his sack to him.

Alyosha returned. Impractical, that's his trouble. Makes himself nice to every-one but doesn't know how to do favors that get paid back.

"Here you are, Alyosha," said Shu-khov, and handed him a biscuit.

Alyosha smiled. "Thank you. But you've got nothing yourself."

"Eat it."

(We've nothing but we always find a way to make something extra.)

Now for that slice of sausage. Into the mouth. Getting your teeth into it. Your teeth. The meaty taste. And the meaty juice, the real stuff. Down it goes, into your belly. Gone.

The rest, Shukhov decided, for the morning. Before the roll call.

And he buried his head in the thin, unwashed blanket, deaf now to the crowd of zeks from the other half as they jostled between the bunk frames, waiting to be counted.

Shukhov went to sleep fully content. He'd had many strokes of luck that day: they hadn't put him in the cells; they hadn't sent his squad to the settlement; he'd swiped a bowl of kasha at dinner; the squad leader had fixed the rates well; he'd built a wall and enjoyed doing it; he'd smuggled that bit of hacksaw blade through; he'd earned a favor from Tsezar that evening; he'd bought that tobacco. And he hadn't fallen ill. He'd got over it.

A day without a dark cloud. Almost a happy day.

There were three thousand six hundred and fifty-three days like that in his stretch. From the first clang of the rail to the last clang of the rail.

Three thousand six hundred and fifty-three days.

The three extra days were for leap years.

THE LIFE AND WORKS OF
ALEKSANDR SOLZHENITSYN

By GEORGES NIVAT

NOVEMBER 1962. The news spread through Moscow, and then throughout the West: the latest issue of the Moscow literary magazine *Novy Mir* contained a factual story describing life in the forced labor camps. This story, *Odin den Ivana Denisovicha* (*One Day in the Life of Ivan Denisovich*), was written by someone whose name had never been heard of before. It ran to sixty-five closely printed pages and—a most unusual circumstance —was accompanied by a preface by Aleksandr Tvardovsky, the editor of *Novy Mir:* "The subject matter of Aleksandr Solzhenitsyn's novel is unusual in Soviet literature. It echoes the unhealthy phenomena in our life associated with the period of the personality cult, now exposed and rejected by the Party. Although these events are so recent in point of time, they seem very remote to us. But whatever the past was like, we in the present must not be indifferent to it."

Nearly a decade has now elapsed since Solzhenitsyn's sudden appearance in the forefront of contemporary Russian literature. Since then Tvardovsky has been dismissed from the editorship of *Novy Mir,* and Solzhenitsyn himself has been excluded from the Soviet Writers' Union. In his own country he has become an "unperson"; but outside the U.S.S.R. his two great novels quickly brought him worldwide fame. The Nobel Prize for Literature for 1970 was awarded to him, a writer with a reputation only eight years old, to crown the efforts of one whose work is banned in his own country. This rapid ascension is easily explained. It is the recognition accorded a writer who has squarely faced a question over which men everywhere are brooding today more anxiously than ever: What meaning can human action still have in this age of cruel and apparently incorrigible absurdity? For Solzhenitsyn speaks not only for Russia, the theater of his own experience and of his own fight for life, but for the whole of our racked planet. He shuts us up in a cruel, absurd, closed world, much as Kafka and Beckett do; but while for them there is no escape, for him there is. He knows, at first hand, the utter bleakness of the human condition in the century of the concentration camp. But however hopeless things may seem, he never loses hope. Hence his universal appeal.

Solzhenitsyn aims, first and foremost, at breaking down the walls that divide and isolate men. The thickest of all these walls is the one erected by the perversion of human speech. The world is sick, dreadfully sick; men have failed to communicate, they are forfeiting the gifts of dialogue, of pity and charity. The hero of *Pravaya Rouka* (*The Right Hand*), a short story that reads like a marginal addition to *Rakovi Korpus* (*Cancer Ward*), muses as he watches some girls going and coming in the hospital grounds: "I felt myself in the grip of an agonizing pity, without quite knowing whom I pitied . . . Was it my contemporaries, those who had frozen to death in the Demyansk district, those consumed in the ovens of Auschwitz, those exterminated at Dzezkazgan, those finished off in the *taiga,* because not one of them would ever have one of these girls—or was it the latter I pitied, these girls whom I could never tell and who would never know . . ."

Solzhenitsyn has thought about human history, particularly that of Russia, and history seems to him like a mighty river of living waters flowing more often underground than in the open. The river's course is underground in periods when falsehood prevails, when human society breaks down, when "justice," which is to mankind what conscience is to the individual, is eclipsed and denied to the majority of men. At such times, in such waters, Solzhenitsyn likens justice to a frail ark manned by a small number of the just and the righteous. His prime concern as a novelist is to reestablish communication between the men of the society which he describes, and to reveal the subterranean flow of justice.

The first object of his attack and accusation is falsehood. That Russian literature, so enamored of justice and truth, should ever have deviated from them seems to him monstrous, and he is never more scathing than when he turns on the writers who have purveyed lies, who have deflected literature from the depiction of truth, who rather than face the reality of nature and man's unending uphill struggle have glossed them over with what Lukács has called "a boundless artificiality of story and characters"—referring to the literature of the Stalin era, subjected to constant "manipulation." Solzhenitsyn's writings are an intrinsic part of his public attitude, of his struggle for a return to truth, on all subjects and at all costs. In this fight for truth lies the strength of his position as the central figure of what is now a public debate. His masterpiece as a publicist will doubtless remain his open letter to the Fourth Soviet Writers' Congress, dated May 16, 1967. In this letter he attacks censorship, the root of the evil. In his literary work he carries on the fight unceasingly, speaking out again and again—with the artlessness of Ivan Denisovich, with the inexhaustible good nature of Matryona, with the courageous stubbornness of the Communist Grachikov in *For the Good of the Cause,* in the great discussions of *V Krouge Pervon* (*The First Circle*) and *Cancer Ward.*

Solzhenitsyn was born on December 11, 1918, at Kislovodsk in the Caucasus. He spent his childhood in Rostov-on-Don, with a mother who adored him and made great sacrifices for him. His father, a student at Moscow University, was killed in action on the German front in 1918, six months before Solzhenitsyn was born. His mother worked as a secretary. Delicate in constitution, she died in 1944 while her only son was at the German front in World War II.

Solzhenitsyn has stated that he felt the desire to write very early, "long before understanding what a writer is and why he writes." He went to school at Rostov-on-Don, then studied mathematics and physics at Rostov University, while also taking the correspondence courses of the Moscow Institute of Philosophy, Literature, and History. His training as a mathematician was to have a strong influence on his work as a writer; earlier it influenced his life when he was transferred in 1942 to an artillery school after he had enlisted in the army as a private. He went through the war as an artillery officer, becoming a battery commander. In February 1945, while serving in East Prussia, he was arrested by the security police for some caustic remarks on Stalin's leadership noted by the censor in a private letter he had written to a friend. In July 1945, he was sentenced to eight years' imprisonment in corrective labor camps. Thanks to his proficiency in mathematics, he spent the latter half of his sentence in privileged conditions, in a prison research institute similar to the one described in *The First Circle*.

In March 1953, he was released from prison, and, without being brought to trial, was sentenced to "perpetual exile" in Kazakhstan. That same year he underwent a long course of treatment in a Tashkent hospital for a cancer of the throat that was successfully cured. He then worked as a mathematics teacher in a secondary school. He was finally released from exile in 1956, and was "rehabilitated" in 1957. As his sole defense he read his story *One Day* to the judges of the military court before which he appeared. Now a free man, he settled some hundred miles southeast of Moscow, at Ryazan in Central Russia, a region of vast horizons, long-lingering autumns, and multicolored church domes signaling to each other from hill to hill.

This region, noted for its pure, melodious Russian, is the setting of his story *Matrioni Dvor* (*Matryona's House*); it is the Russia of which the patients in his book *Cancer Ward* talk and dream. Without it Solzhenitsyn would not be what he is. He has made no secret of what he owes to this softly blurred landscape. He has described it lovingly in his short prose poems, in his *Malinkie Istoriya* (*Tiny Stories*): "When you travel the by-roads of Central Russia you begin to understand the secret of the

pacifying Russian countryside. It is in the churches. They trip up the slopes, ascend the high hills, come down to the broad rivers like princesses in white and red, they lift their bell-towers—graceful, shapely, all different—high over mundane timber and thatch, they nod to each other from afar, from villages that are cut off and invisible to each other they soar to the same heaven."

At Ryazan he finished *The First Circle* and wrote *Matryona's House*, his play *Ogon na Vetrou* (*A Flame in the Wind*), and his prose poems. In 1963 he relinquished his teaching post to devote himself to writing, for by then, thanks to Tvardovsky and also to Khrushchev, who allowed *One Day* to be published and praised, he was a celebrity.

It was only after Khrushchev's fall from power (in October 1964) that Solzhenitsyn began to come under serious attack. As soon as *One Day* appeared some critics insinuated that its denunciation of the concentration camps was excessive and misguided. On November 17, 1966, the first part of *Cancer Ward* was discussed at length at a meeting of the prose section of the Moscow writers' organization (a branch of the Writers' Union). The report of this memorable meeting (published in Russian in Munich in 1970) shows that at that time the majority of the Moscow writers were in favor of publishing the novel. But by then numerous typewritten copies of the original text of both *Cancer Ward* and *The First Circle* had reached the West, and the two novels were soon published there in several countries.

This multiplication of texts was the work of *Samizdat*, the "self-publishing" of underground writings in typewritten or mimeographed form, a system of publishing that is now widely practiced in the Soviet Union. Inevitably some copies are smuggled out of the country. It had happened before, as early as 1929, when the

Soviet writer Boris Pilnyak was accused of publishing his novel *Mahogany* abroad; it happened again with Pasternak's *Doctor Zhivago,* and again with Sinyavsky and Daniel. Pilnyak underwent "self-criticism." Pasternak wrote a letter to the head of the government in an attempt to clear himself. Sinyavsky and Daniel pleaded not guilty before the judges who sentenced them to five and seven years' detention respectively.

Solzhenitsyn reacted characteristically by rounding on his accusers and attacking the root of the evil: the Soviet system of censorship. Inevitably the censors muzzle the living and approve only of the dead. As he put it in his moving and courageous letter to the Fourth Soviet Writers' Congress (May 16, 1967): "Pushkin's words are really coming true: 'They are capable of loving only the dead.' " The smear campaign against him intensified. It was said that he had collaborated with the Germans; it was not for nothing he had been arrested in 1945. His literary archives were confiscated by the security police. The statements and denials he sent to the press went unacknowledged and unpublished. Outstanding Soviet writers like Aleksandr Tvardovsky and Veniamin Kaverin spoke out in Solzhenitsyn's defense, but to no effect, for the literary bureaucrats were systematically denouncing him as a nihilist and a schizophrenic. Mikhail Sholokhov, a Nobel Prize laureate, sided against Solzhenitsyn, declaring that he should be sent back to prison.

In November 1969, he was excluded from the Soviet Writers' Union. All means of subsistence were denied him, and he withdrew to the country house of Mstislav Rostropovich, the world-famous cellist, who is himself now discredited in the eyes of the Soviet authorities for publicly protesting against official censorship. Solzhenitsyn's books have been withdrawn from public libraries and are no longer available in the Soviet Union. Official disapproval has consigned him to oblivion. But he refuses to give up the fight and continues to speak out in defense of those who have been imprisoned or interned in mental hospitals. His open letter of June 15, 1970, protesting against the internment of the geneticist Jaures Medvedev is worthy of Zola's *J'accuse.* In the long history of discord between writers and rulers, Solzhenitsyn's conflict with the leaders of his country is one of the sharpest and most stirring.

Meanwhile he goes on writing; his work is far from finished. When he received the Nobel Prize for 1970, at fifty-two, his literary powers were at their highest and strongest. And though he may well go on from strength to strength, it seems likely that the award will mark a turning point in his work. Until now he has set himself the task of speaking the truth as he sees it about the concentration-camp world that looms so large in the life of twentieth-century man. His subsequent work may be expected to explore the historical and philosophical implications of this theme with deepening insight. He may now be said to have achieved his initial purpose, which was to make us hear what he himself has called "the mute tocsin of history."

The writings of Solzhenitsyn have a peculiar fascination for the western reader. The world he describes is immense and hostile, yet it is a part of ourselves; its destiny is at once opposed to us and shared by us. Here, in his books, is the whole of Stalin's opaque, incomprehensible Russia which had hitherto cast its shadow over us without our being able to spell out the riddle. Solzhenitsyn takes us to the heart of this world; he makes us understand it from the inside. He would have his place in literature if only for having dispelled this darkness and let in the light—which neither the confessions of defectors nor the "secret memoirs" of Khrushchev have been able to do.

Stalin's Russia showed the world a smooth surface, without a crack or rift; here we are taken beneath the surface and the cracks are visible. It is the great strength of Solzhenitsyn's art that he brings so sharply into focus not only the camps and the prisoners, which officially did not exist, but also the inter-relationship which, under Stalin, connected each individual with the ruling power. At every moment of his life the Soviet citizen, caught in the web of Stalinist logic, had no option but to respond to the unrelenting pressure from above. He was engaged in a continual, inescapable dialogue with State power, a dialogue limited, needless to say, to the simple alternative of repeating his perpetual act of allegiance or rebelling against it. The tentacles of State power reached into every home and heart: that is the main theme of *The First Circle*. The relentless logic of the potentate cloistered in the Kremlin was imposed on all, and felt by all, from the top to the bottom of the scale. Everybody was continually filling in questionnaires, and these, running to millions, formed a vast network connecting everybody with the secret files at the center of the system.

"As every man goes through life he fills in a number of forms for the record, each containing a number of questions. A man's answer to one question on one form becomes a little thread, permanently connecting him to the local center of personnel records administration. There are thus hundreds of little threads radiating from every man, millions of threads in all. If these threads were suddenly to become visible, the whole sky would look like a spider's web, and if they materialized as rubber bands, buses, trams, and even people would all lose the ability to move, and the wind would be unable to carry torn-up newspapers or autumn leaves along the streets of the city."

The system enslaves the individual, and the individual acquiesces in an enslavement which Solzhenitsyn reads into the whole of nature. For him it seems to be an obsessive metaphor applicable to all the phenomena of life. He reads it into the landscape; into the mysterious behavior of ants who return instinctively to their home in a burning log, there to perish; into the animals in the Tashkent zoo, which Oleg Kostoglotov, on his release from hospital, had been asked by Dyomka to visit. Solzhenitsyn is saying that once a man has reached a certain degree of destitution and bondage, he is marked forever. He can never again be free. Thus the characters in his works, like Kostoglotov, who have borne the yoke of absolute deprivation, cannot see the world otherwise than through the lens of their own camp and prison experience.

Moreover, all history must be reconsidered in the bleak light of this destitution experienced by the inmate of the concentration camp. Everything heroic or moving bequeathed to us by history must be remeasured by the yardstick of the twentieth century. And after this confrontation nothing remains. The courage displayed in Czarist times by the wives of the exiled Decembrists, who followed their husbands to Siberia in their own carriages, cannot be compared to the ordeal of the wives of today's deported prisoners. The sufferings of Anna Karenina pale beside those of Elizaveta Anatolyevna, reduced to being an attendant in the Tashkent hospital. All the bulwarks formerly erected by man against adversity have been overthrown. What so sharply distinguishes today's victims from yesterday's is that they cannot choose, cannot say a word: the absurd machine of oppression swallows them up. And yet the history of their sufferings will be written.

Each work by Solzhenitsyn is always presented as a simple fragment of reality or, if you like, a "slice of life." Now it is twenty-four hours in the life of a political prisoner called Ivan Denisovich Shukhov; now it is three long days in the special prison of Mavrino. The first part of *Cancer Ward* records three days in the collective life of a group of hospital patients; the second part deals with the same roomful of people, except for some new arrivals and a few departures. One may say, then, that Solzhenitsyn foregoes storytelling, the contrivings and make-believe of plot and subplot, in the name of a higher truth.

Narrative fiction, with plot and denouement, arose and flourished in the leisure civilization of yesterday's elite. Solzhenitsynian man is too much absorbed in the simple process of his own survival, whether he is contending with the antiworld of the labor camps, the harshness of *kolkhoz* life, or the fearful inroads of cancer. His characters are never shown in their native place, in the bosom of their family; they are always uprooted and transplanted into a cruel and alien setting to which they must adjust themselves if they are to survive. Only Matryona is seen in her own home, but the whole point of the story lies in showing how little she is attached to her meager belongings and how eager those around her are to snatch them from her even before she is dead. Solzhenitsynian man has no possessions, no inheritance. This means that he is continually confronted with essentials, indeed with the very biological facts of life—hunger, tumors, fear.

This utter reduction to essentials explains Solzhenitsyn's partiality for the short novel or novella; its pointedness and symbolic concentration enable him to display human behavior in face of a hostile, alienating reality, and to do so without any dramatization. Indeed, Solzhenitsyn's two full-length novels may be described as polyphonic novellas in which the talk and the inner thoughts of many characters are confronted. His novels show no fundamental change of technique, and plot remains equally absent; only now the expanded confrontation of speech and action provides a more complete description of man's conflict with reality. He has practiced simultaneously the two techniques of the novella and the novel, but neither took precedence over the other in his literary apprenticeship.

Four very fine novellas by Solzhenitsyn were published in the Soviet Union before he fell out of favor with the authorities. All four are centered on an ordinary character who is in fact a just and honest person. The closing words of *Matryona's House* apply equally well to all of them: "We all lived beside her and did not understand that she was that just person without whom, according to the proverb, the village could not endure. Nor the city. Nor all our land." The seemingly incidental proverb referring to village life is an example of that poetic enlargement of the context to which Solzhenitsyn's novellas seem to lead quite naturally: the more condensed the human material of the story, the more sharply the symbol is thrown into relief.

The detailed realism of *One Day in the Life of Ivan Denisovich* tells on the reader. From the hammering on the iron rail at reveille to the last search before lights out, Solzhenitsyn describes the daily routine, the preoccupations, even the mental view of the world of a prisoner who seems to have little to distinguish him from the others. Most striking of all is the spareness of the story and the scope it achieves by the most modest of means. There is not a hint of pathos. A camera eye follows Shukhov through the day, catching him as he filches two extra bowls of mush from the cook dishing it out at the hatch, and then anxiously awaits his share, for it is the privilege of the brigade leader to dole out the extra helpings; or as he stands in suspense next to Tsezar, hoping to get the butt of the latter's cigarette, which at that moment he covets more than his freedom. The microcosm of the work camp, with its rows of wooden barracks, its stone punishment block, its compound lit up at night by crisscrossing searchlights, the construction site of the unfinished power plant deep in snow, all the wiles Shukhov has had to learn in order to survive, his relations with his fellow prisoners of Work Brigade 104—it is all described in a spare, incisive, straightforward style. If anything, the truth is understated. Shukhov has never understood why he was arrested after escaping from a German POW camp and making his way back to his own lines. How could he, when the interrogator who sentenced him did not understand it? And anyhow the interrogator himself had turned up in one of the camps through which Shukhov passed.

A Russian peasant, forty years old, bald, toothless, shabby, prematurely aged, Shukhov has become inured to camp life, he has drawn himself in and shrunk—the indispensable condition for survival. And by now freedom has less attraction for him than the butt of Tsezar's cigarette—Tsezar Markovich, an intellectual who receives packages from home and so has bribed his way into a soft job in the camp administration. Yet Shukhov has retained his integrity, he has not been turned into a brute or a "jackal." He has even retained the peasant's religious respect for food: he never eats without first taking off his cap. It would never occur to him to inform on his mates. He is a man who takes pride in his work; out of a set task he makes a personal creation; thus he saves himself from dehumanization. The scene on the construction site as Shukhov builds his wall, always laying his bricks neatly in line, is perhaps the finest in the book. Likewise, in his dealings with the brigade, he maintains a basically free and unselfish relationship with others.

The Austrian critic Ernst Fischer has compared *One Day* with Beckett's *Endgame,* but mistakenly in one respect, for Beckett shows the breakdown of communication between men utterly alienated, while Solzhenitsyn's characters, for all their enforced degradation, keep open a human line of communication.

Solzhenitsyn's other two novellas have the same telling minuteness of description. *Stantsiya Krechetovka (An Incident at Krechetovka Station)* describes the demoralization in the rear during the great Russian retreat of 1941; *For the Good of the Cause,* the Communist bureaucracy of a Russian town. At the center of both stories is the same type of disinterested character, to whom covetousness is unknown. Lieutenant Zotov is a guileless young man unattracted by the vulgar pleasures that amuse others. He welcomes hardship, tormented as he is by the inexplicable defeat of the Russian armies. But, for all his good nature, Zotov does wrong in denouncing a transient artist whom the shifting chaos of war has stranded at Krechetovka and whom he mistakes for a spy. His mistake results from the corrupting influence of Stalinist education based on militancy and suspicion.

Grachikov too, the hero of *For the Good of the Cause,* is one of those unsophisticated, truth-seeking Russians whom Solzhenitsyn is fond of depicting. "It is not with stones but with men that Communism must be built, Victor Vavilovich! That takes longer and is more difficult. Stones! Why, even if we put the finishing touches to them tomorrow, there would still be nothing like Communism in that!"

However much they may have in common, Solzhenitsyn's heroes are diverse and highly individualized, and it is this diversity that brings home to us the essential point: that man's nature is too rich, too inventive, and too many-sided to conform to a single ideology. These four short novels describe the conflict between an omnipotent power seeking to impose its stereotype, and an individual guided by conscience alone, whose acts show up the artificiality of the official patterns of behavior.

The style of these novellas ranges from the seeming coldness of objectivity to the most vibrant lyricism. The latter is marked by the reduction of sentences to short, clear-cut units often graduated in an almost metrical sequence. The use of jargons peculiar to the camp, the army, the bureaucracy, tersely conveys something of the background and habits of different characters. But Solzhenitsyn's marvelous command of language extends also, and above all, to the vivid colloquialisms and proverbial lore of popular speech. Only popular speech can reflect the Russian soul at its purest. In Solzhenitsyn's eyes, the use of a single unneeded word is the first step toward the distortion and perversion of truth.

But how is one to overcome the opacity which such perversion creates, to regain the transparency, the freedom, the sanctity of human speech? This question, one of the central concerns of Solzhenitsyn's work, comes most movingly to the fore in *The First Circle*. This vast epic novel gives him room in which to display a broad spectrum of Russian speech, from the rambling thoughts of the senile despot, as fierce as ever though his mind and memory are giving way, to the peasant talk of the last of his subjects, the humble handyman Spiridon, toothless, bald, nearly blind, and semi-literate.

The very theme of this polyphonic work is concerned with human speech, or rather with a monstrous scientific perversion of it which the author's talent alone makes credible. Will the spoken word, with its nuances of kindness or revolt, become a mere voice-print as easily decipherable and classifiable as a finger print, at the behest of the tyrant and thanks to the ability of the engineers and scientists whom he has caged together at Mavrino?

A Kafkaesque network of top secret laboratories, research groups engaged in acoustic experiments, the whole life of a special prison for highly qualified political prisoners—all this is set in motion by a few words pronounced out of compassion by the young diplomat Innokenty Volodin. Prompted by an irrepressible sense of generosity and pity, Innokenty hurries out of his ministry, slips into a callbox in a crowded metro station, and in a muffled voice tries to warn his old family doctor of the trap being set for him by the security police. A few words of sympathy, called forth by the utter innocence of the doctor, whose "crime" is his desire to share a medical discovery with foreign colleagues. A few words of compassion, awkwardly blurted out. From that moment Innokenty is doomed. From the peak of success he will soon be cast down and engulfed in the Dantesque inferno of the GULAG. Later chapters show him taken into custody at the Lubyanka, dazed and subjected to the humiliating body searches, to imperturbable questioning, to the inexorable workings of a prison routine designed to reduce a man to a nameless number. But Volodin's fall is also an achievement; though almost involuntary, and no sooner done than regretted, it makes of Volodin a veritable saint and contributes powerfully to the underlying dynamism of this immense fresco of *The First Circle* and its inmates.

Volodin's telephone call to the old doctor sets in motion the whole establishment at Mavrino, a technological research institute staffed by prisoners, all of them former professors and academicians who have been through the inferno of the camps. On Stalin's orders, they have been assembled in this "special prison"—the first circle of hell, where Dante, to spare them the torments of the damned, had placed the sages of antiquity, who had known nothing of the Christian verities. Materially speaking, the Mavrino prisoners are treated well enough, but they are plagued by informers and foolish, over-zealous guardians; they are cut off indefinitely from wife and family, from real life, from the sources of love and affection. Their reactions vary: some consent to increase their chances of freedom by putting their talents at the service of the tyrant; others refuse and so are listed for transfer back to the labor camps, to the more terrible circles of hell. Thus at the end of the book Gleb Nerzhin and a few others are driven off in a Black Maria disguised as a meat delivery truck, on the first lap of their journey to the place of lingering death where they will doubtless rejoin Ivan Denisovich, an old hand, and Innokenty Volodin, a novice.

The special prison for scientists and technicians is a world of hope pitted against despair, of intelligence pitted against uncomprehending intolerance and oppression. Solzhenitsyn brings that world to life with arresting vividness—an amazing compound of scrupulous realism, scathing irony, and lively, humorous, often profound talk. The prison is a ship bearing its cargo of human beings, helpless but brilliant men, stripped of all their belongings but inalienably endowed with the highest degree of intellectual lucidity; a ship whose lights seem all the brighter in the surrounding darkness of Stalinist society, where any misstep may plunge a man into the abyss.

If Volodin is the unheralded saint of *The First Circle,* Gleb Nerzhin is its explicit hero. Among all the prisoners at Mavrino, he stands out as the unflinching truth-seeker. His two closest friends, the Communist Rubin and the chivalrous Sologdin, have unshakable convictions; one believes in the laws of dialectics, the other believes only in people; one is a Westernist, the other a Slavophile. In them continues the age-old duel between two hostile Russias. As for Gleb, he is still seeking his way. He looks for enlightenment from two very different men: the mystical painter Kondrashov and the peasant handyman Spiridon. The latter represents the Russian people, with its rooted distrust, its abrupt outspokenness, its sibylline aphorisms, but also its incredible powers of endurance and its blind fidelity to family and land through all the hallucinating zigzags of contemporary history. Nearly blind, stripped of everything, stoic and long-suffering, Spiridon incarnates the same moral strength as Ivan Denisovich. But there is another source of strength, more secret, more mystical, symbolized by the Holy Grail. The landing of a disused back staircase at Mavrino has been converted into a studio; there the artist-prisoner Kondrashov paints pictures for the officials who patronize him. And unknown to them he paints for himself what he intends to be the greatest picture of his life, the moment when Parsifal first sees the castle of the Holy Grail: "It is what a man might experience when he suddenly glimpses the image of perfection."

Here, in the center of the book, we come to what might be called its mystical core. To overlook these few chapters where there wells up, from the densely compacted matter of realistic descriptions, the clear living water of the Spirit

[93]

would be to misjudge the book and mistake its meaning. The Grail is but one symbol among others, all referring back to deeper things than those that meet the eye. Transfigured, the ship of the research prison becomes a veritable Ark. "From this ark, serenely plowing its way through the darkness, it was easy for them to survey, as from a great height, the whole tortuous, errant flow of history; yet at the same time, like people completely immersed in it, they could see every pebble in its depths." Indeed, it may be said of the whole book that it has a double focus, affording both a comprehensive view of things, "as from a great height," and a concentrated perception of the smallest details. The scope of his realism here is probably unmatched, covering every walk of Russian life, recording every variety of speech, probing into the mind of the solitary tyrant, in the dead silence of his nighttime office, and into that of the toothless handyman at Mavrino. But it is all an organic part of a poetic and prophetic vision: poetic because of the luminous resurgence of the symbol, prophetic because of the promise of redemption thus held out.

This poetic aspect of *The First Circle* is underlined by its structure. It is an immense fresco, broken up into eighty-seven chapters, but covering a period of only three days. This division into short chapters is not a device for recording simultaneous or overlapping actions, but a means of connecting the sequence of events in depth. The narrative hinges on two banquets, one for the privileged, the other for the prisoners; at one, Fear is the uninvited guest, while at the other we find Renunciation, the greatest freedom of all.

Each chapter is more a poetic unit than a chronological one. Each has a mood of its own; and nearly always, at least at the end of the chapter, the sentences tend to fall into poetic rhythm. By the same secret process a human act, at first simply a response to the stimulus of circumstances, is turned into a creative act, into an "achievement." Epic in its sweep, mystical in the underlying message it conveys, but also entertainingly satirical and humorous, *The First Circle* is one of those great works of Russian literature which, as Tolstoy said, never fit the pattern of any definite literary form. *The First Circle* was written between 1955 and 1958. Immediately afterward, Solzhenitsyn wrote the novellas mentioned above.

He turned next to the theater, for which he had already written two satirical pieces: he now wrote the play *Flame in the Wind*, or, *The Light That Is in You*. There are some fine things in his plays, but they do not always come to life. In 1961 he completed his series of *Tiny Stories,* which are prose poems of philosophical meditations, in the tradition of Turgenev.

With his latest work, *Cancer Ward* (1963–1967), he arrived at the zenith of his powers and worked out to perfection the form in which he had already cast *The First Circle,* that of the polyphonic novel. *Cancer Ward* not only deals with the perversion of communication between men and the reopening of the channels of speech, but also shows that the antiworld against which men fight is not the GULAG, the death camp, but death itself. Faced with the "Great Leveler," men rediscover the means of communicating.

In *Cancer Ward* Solzhenitsyn sets out to open our eyes afresh to the scandal of death. There it is, lying under the patients' bedclothes, coiling around the neck of Yefrem Podduyev, lurking in the vitals of Dr. Dontsova, burrowing into the neck of Federau and Rusanov. Its approach reconciles the ward's most irreconcilable antagonists; its passage is recorded in five columns in the hospital statistics. It shakes Vadim out of his deepest convictions; it creates a fellowship between prisoner and jailer, Party militant and profiteer, a superstitious old woman and a young Communist. Of all ways of dying, Solzhenitsyn has chosen the one he himself has faced: by cancer, whose workings remain so baffling and terrifying. Of all its different forms, he has chosen cancer of the tongue and throat. Rusanov, the very embodiment of petty, stultifying officialdom, the stickler for having forms properly filled out, the heartless denouncer of innocent men, finds himself from one day to the next in crowded intimacy with Yefrem Podduyev, the tough, uncouth vagrant who has roughed it from one end of the country to the other, and with the quiet, unassuming Federau, whose German blood dooms him to deportation in accordance with the Stalinist logic of "racial solidarity."

Solzhenitsyn draws a graphic picture of hospital life, the slow passing of time, the events of the day, the qualms and terrors of the sick. His portraits of the doctors, mostly women, are admirable. Diagnostics are strictly scientific; nothing is inexact or vague in the medical terminology. Above all, he makes us enter into the personal outlook of each patient in turn. Nine beds with nine cancer patients: we share the fears and feelings and innermost thoughts of each, listen to their talk, and witness their clashes, outbursts, and intense moments of common hope.

Cancer Ward takes us into the stronghold where a random, disparate group of men are beset by death. Over them hangs a threat whose terrible reality and nearness leave no room for illusions. Whatever the conditioning a man has undergone, it now counts for nothing and he must reckon only with his own conscience. Hence the agonizing remorse of Rusanov during his long nightmare, as he

painfully crawls through a concrete tunnel and meets the victims of years before whose lives he wrecked.

This process also occurs with Yefrem Podduyev, as he comes to terms with his imminent death and begins to review his past. He is not much of a reader, but Oleg Kostoglotov puts a book into his hands, a volume of tales by Tolstoy called *What Men Live By*. He reads it and he finds that the stories speak "softly and simply to the heart." Yefrem and all the others are confronted by the riddle: what do men live by? Even Shulubin, the old Bolshevik, humiliated by the betrayal of his ideals and metamorphosed now into a haggard, owlish creature, as the mad miller in Pushkin's *Russalka* was metamorphosed into a raven, sees his disease as the outcome of his unresisting acceptance of that betrayal. Solzhenitsyn has something in common with the Tolstoy of *Three Deaths,* the Tolstoy who looked to animals and even plants for the secret of serenity and communion with nature. Yefrem remembers how the old peasants used to die back home on the river Kama: "They prepared themselves quietly . . . And they departed easily, as if they were just moving into a new house."

In the chapter entitled "The First Day of Creation," the symbol of the apricot tree appears, linking together all the "elect" of Solzhenitsyn's "ark": the Kadmins, Oleg, Vega. One of the wonders of the Russian East, this tree, when in bloom, forms a huge pink ball fifteen or twenty feet in diameter. The vision of this "pink miracle" meets Oleg's eyes as he sits on the teahouse balcony, in the Old Town, on the morning of his release from hospital. The apricot tree symbolizes moral beauty, the gift in store for the man who renounces the mirage of material prosperity and even the simple happiness of human love. For in their frustration, their eagerness, their enforced and purposeless chastity, these men and women all yearn for or grope toward a love transcending mere sexual relations, like the naïve Asya or the pragmatic Zoya. The theme is treated on two levels, that of the children and that of the grown-ups, with an astonishing mixture of straightforwardness and restraint.

Certainly these lives described by Solzhenitsyn are far removed from the radiant world of childhood conjured up in *War and Peace,* for example; and even Solzhenitsyn's adolescents are already well on their way to adulthood, and to its perversions. The "children" in *Cancer Ward,* Asya and Dyomka, still have one foot in the mysterious land of childhood. Under all the accumulated sediments of adult life, and all its alienations, Solzhenitsyn invites us to recognize the living waters of the initial baptism. In the very center of *Cancer Ward,* but far from the hospital room where Rusanov is sleeping off his injection, is the wilderness paradise of Ush-Terek, made doubly dear to Oleg by the goodness of those full-grown children, the exiled Kadmins, an old doctor and his wife. Let a man "unburden himself" and he will discover the intoxication of a return to life, symbolized by the feverish first movement of Tchaikovsky's Fourth Symphony, by the miracle of the flowering apricot tree

hidden away in the maze of narrow streets in an Uzbek town, by all that beauty of which, like Oleg, he may "make a present to himself in honor of the day of creation."

Solzhenitsyn's work has only begun to be studied and thought about, arousing a wide and varied response in the West. Not surprisingly, for he is very much a writer of the twentieth century: he deals with twentieth-century man's most harrowing experience, life and death in the concentration camp. His pen has the power, as none other has had, of telling what deportation and the resulting degradation do to men. And the men he describes are not aloof or unattached: he shows them in their togetherness and interdependence. There is nothing outside themselves which they can call their own; they have lost everything, and that, as some of them discover, is the precondition of salvation.

There may be things in *Cancer Ward* or *The First Circle* which smack of old-fashioned idealism, and seem mawkish or nebulous, yet we find that we too can identify with his characters and recognize them all too well. Their destitution resembles that of our mimetic and conditioned society; and the dazzled bewilderment we are sometimes made to share is the bewilderment of harrowed survivors.

Georges Nivat is head of the Department of Russian Languages and Literature at the Sorbonne in Paris.
Translated by James Emmons.

THE 1970 PRIZE

By KJELL STRÖMBERG

THE STORY of the award of the Nobel Prize to Aleksandr Solzhenitsyn bears some similarities to what happened twelve years earlier, when another great Russian writer, Boris Pasternak, was so honored. Under pressure from his conformist colleagues and, later, from the Russian authorities, Pasternak was forced to renounce the Prize he had first accepted. Later the Swedish Academy, to the anonymous applause of Soviet officials, crowned Mikhail Sholokhov, the poet-laureate of the regime.

Solzhenitsyn, spurned by his "right-thinking" colleagues, who, moreover, had already drummed him out of their professional society, accepted the Prize but canceled his visit to Stockholm to receive it personally on December 10, the very eve of his birthday). He apparently feared that he would have been refused re-entry to his country. Solzhenitsyn, like Pasternak, wished to live and die in the fatherland.

Solzhenitsyn had not always been considered by his peers to be the black sheep of the flock. Indeed, he was even proposed for the Lenin Prize—a windfall that would have been most welcome to a man who had just served a long sentence in Stalin's prisons, with loss of his civil rights. Then, unexpectedly, the two great novels of Solzhenitsyn, which had been banned in the Soviet Union, crossed the borders by mysterious means and found thousands of readers. Translated into a score of languages, they were finally published (and in a few countries in Russian) in spite of the formal protestations of the author. Everywhere—in France, England, Western Germany, the United States—he was hailed as the greatest living Russian writer. The Swedish P.E.N. Club, which had successfully proposed Samuel Beckett in 1969, the following year officially proposed Solzhenitsyn for the honor.

In Soviet Russia the press kept bleakly silent, but perhaps an attempt at intimidating the Nobel jury can be found in the decision of the Union of Soviet Writers to oust Solzhenitsyn in December of 1969. The pretext was not hard to find— he had taken a clearly anti-Soviet position, not only in his writings but also in an open letter which denied the accusation and, what is worse, he dared to publish in several "bourgeois" newspapers. On the evidence of a news story published in a leading English daily he was also accused of depositing the profits from his foreign publications with the International Committee for Health, a foundation whose "principal mission was to organize hostile actions against the U.S.S.R. and the other Socialist nations."

The Academy reached its decision on October 8, 1970, to award the Nobel

Prize for Literature to Aleksandr Solzhenitsyn "for the ethical power with which he has pursued the indispensable traditions of Russian literature."

The choice had been made—and this is probably unique in the chronicles of the Nobel Committee for Literature—without the Committee deeming it necessary to proceed to a deep analysis of the laureate's work by some expert, in this case an authority on Russian language and literature, whose written critique might be of value to the judges in reaching a decision. We must conclude, then, that they had formed a firm opinion by themselves, on the basis only of the many translations published in recent years in the principal European languages, including Scandinavian.

At the time Solzhenitsyn was vacationing at the dacha of his friend Mstislav Rostropovich, the celebrated cellist. He informed a Swedish journalist who had succeeded in reaching him by telephone that he was accepting the Prize and that he intended to go to Stockholm "insofar as it depends on me." To a few foreign newsmen who had come to congratulate and interview him the following day he found it necessary to close his door, sending his regrets that he was unable to make any further statement.

Solzhenitsyn replied to the Swedish Academy with a brief telegram in which he said that in their decision to award him the Nobel Prize he found an homage to Russian literature and to the tormented history of his country. He also announced once again that he intended to go to Stockholm to receive the award in person.

The hostile attitude of Soviet literary circles soon developed into an intensive press campaign against him, intensifying gradually as the day of the awards drew nearer. As he became fully aware of the humiliations to which he would have to submit in order to get permission to go abroad, Solzhenitsyn was obliged to abandon his travel plans. He explained his situation in a long letter to the Swedish Academy, dated November 27, and transmitted through diplomatic channels. This is the gist of his message, which he asked to have published in its entirety:

> In the last few weeks the hostile attitude towards my Prize, as expressed in my country's press, and the renewed banning of my books (people have been fired from their jobs or ousted from institutions for having read them), have convinced me that my trip to Stockholm would be used to cut me off from the land of my birth, that is, to keep me from re-entering my country.

He also feared, he said, "the fatigue of the solemn ceremonies" which would accompany the awarding of the Prize, together with "the spectacular reactions which my traveling to Stockholm might provoke." At the same time he was prepared to deliver the address required by the statutes of the Nobel Foundation within the six years following December 10, 1970, or to forward the text. He would, therefore, accept the diploma and medal in Moscow "from the hands of your representatives at such time as may be mutually convenient."

There is no word in the document about the disposition of the 400,000 Swedish crowns which went with the award for 1970.

Translated by Dale McAdoo.

Rabindranath Tagore

1913

"Because of his profoundly sensitive,

fresh, and beautiful verse, by which,

with consummate skill, he has made

his poetic thought, expressed in his

own English words, a part of the

literature of the West"

Illustrated by AMBROGIANI

PRESENTATION ADDRESS

By *HARALD HJÄRNE*

CHAIRMAN OF THE NOBEL COMMITTEE
OF THE SWEDISH ACADEMY

———

In AWARDING the Nobel Prize for Literature to the Anglo-Indian poet, Rabindranath Tagore, the Academy has found itself in the happy position of being able to accord this recognition to an author who, in conformity with the express wording of Alfred Nobel's last will and testament, had "during the current year" written the finest poems "of an idealistic tendency." Moreover, after exhaustive and conscientious deliberation, having concluded that these poems of his most nearly approach the prescribed standard, the Academy thought that there was no reason to hesitate because the poet's name was still comparatively unknown in Europe, due to the distant location of his home. There was even less reason since the founder of the Prize laid it down in set terms as his "express wish and desire that, in the awarding of the Prize, no consideration should be paid to the nationality to which any proposed candidate might belong."

Tagore's *Gitanjali: Song Offerings* (1912), a collection of religious poems, was the one of his works that especially arrested the attention of the selecting critics. Since last year the book, in a real and full sense, has belonged to English literature, for the author himself, who by education and practice is a poet in his native Indian tongue, has bestowed upon the poems a new dress, alike perfect in form and personally original in inspiration. This has made them accessible to all in England, America, and the entire Western world for whom noble literature is of interest and moment. Quite independently of any knowledge of his Bengali poetry, irrespective, too, of differences of religious faiths, literary schools, or party aims, Tagore has been hailed from various quarters as a new and admirable master of that poetic art which has been a never-failing concomitant of the expansion of British civilization ever since the days of Queen Elizabeth. The features of this poetry that won immediate and enthusiatic admiration are the perfection with which the poet's own ideas and those he has absorbed have been harmonized into a complete whole; his rhythmically balanced style, that, to quote an English critic's opinion, "combines at once the feminine grace of poetry with the virile power of prose"; his austere, by some termed classic, taste in the choice of words and his use of the other elements of expression in a borrowed tongue—those features, in short, that stamp an original work as such, but which at the same time render more difficult its reproduction in another language.

The same estimate is true of the second cycle of poems that came before us, *The Gardener, Lyrics of Love and Life* (1913). In this work, however, as the author himself points out, he has recast rather than interpreted his earlier inspirations. Here we see another phase of his personality, now subject to the alternately blissful and torturing experiences of youthful love, now prey to the feelings of longing and joy that the vicissitudes of life give rise to, the whole interspersed nevertheless with glimpses of a higher world.

English translations of Tagore's prose stories have been published under the title *Indian Journals* (1913). Though the form of these tales does not bear his own stamp—the rendering being by another hand— their content gives evidence of his versatility and wide range of observation, of his heartfelt sympathy with the fates and experiences of differing types of men, and of his talent for plot construction and development.

Tagore has since published both a collection of poems, poetic pictures of childhood and home life, symbolically entitled *The Crescent Moon* (1913), and a number of lectures given before American and English university audiences, which in book form he calls *Sādhanā: The Realization of Life* (1913). They embody his views of the ways in which man can arrive at a faith in the light of which it may be possible to live. This very seeking of his to discover the true relation between faith and thought makes Tagore stand out as a poet of rich endowment, characterized by his great profundity of thought, but most of all by his warmth of feeling and by the moving power of his figurative language. Seldom indeed in the realm of imaginative literature are attained so great a range and diversity of note and of color, capable of expressing with equal harmony and grace the emotions of every mood from the longing of the soul after eternity to the joyous merriment prompted by the innocent child at play.

Concerning our understanding of this poetry, by no means exotic but truly universally human in character, the future will probably add to what we know now. We do know, however, that the poet's motivation extends to the effort of reconciling two spheres of civilization widely separated, which above all is the characteristic mark of our present epoch and constitutes its most important task and problem. The true inwardness of this work is most clearly and purely revealed in the efforts exerted in the Christian mission-field throughout the world. In times to come, historical inquirers will know better how to appraise its importance and influence, even in what is at present hidden from our gaze and where no or only grudging recognition is accorded. They will undoubtedly form a higher estimate of it than the one now deemed fitting in many quarters. Thanks to this movement, fresh, bubbling springs of living water have been tapped, from which poetry in particular may draw inspiration, even though those springs are perhaps intermingled with alien streams, and whether or not they be traced to their right source or their origin be attributed to the depths of the dream world. More especially, the influence of Western culture and religion has provided in many places the first definite impulse toward a revival and regeneration of the vernacular language, i.e., its liberation from the bondage of an artificial tradition, and consequently also toward a development of its capacity for nurturing and sustaining a vein of living and natural poetry.

The Christian mission has exercised its influence as a rejuvenating force in India, too, where in conjunction with religious revivals many of the vernaculars were early put to literary use, thereby acquiring status and stability. However, with only too regular frequency, they fossilized again under pressure from the new tradition that gradually established itself. But the influence of the Christian faith has extended far beyond the range of the actually registered proselytizing work. The struggle that the last century witnessed between the living vernaculars and the sacred language of ancient times for control over the new literatures springing into life would have had a very different course and outcome, had not the former found able support in the fostering care bestowed upon them by some self-sacrificing missionaries.

It was in Bengal, the oldest Anglo-Indian province and the scene many years before of the indefatigable labors of that missionary pioneer, Carey, to promote his own religion and to improve the vernacular language, that Rabindranath Tagore was born in 1861. He was a scion of a respected family that had already given evidence of intellectual ability in many areas. The surroundings in which the boy and young man grew up were in no sense primitive or calculated to hem in his conceptions of the world and of life. On the contrary, in his home there prevailed, along with a highly cultivated appreciation of art, a profound reverence for the inquiring spirit and wisdom of the forefathers of the race, whose texts were used for family devotional worship. Around him, too, there was then coming into being a new literary spirit that consciously sought to reach forth to the people and to make itself acquainted with their life needs. This new spirit gained in force as reforms were at last introduced by the Government, after the agonizing conflict and confusion of the Indian Mutiny.

Rabindranath's father was one of the leading and most zealous members of a religious community to which his son still belongs. That body, known by the name of *"Brahmo Samaj,"* did not arise as a sect of the ancient Hindu type, with the purpose of spreading the worship of some particular godhead as superior to all others. Rather, it was founded early in the nineteenth century by an enlightened and influential man who had been much impressed by the doctrines of Christianity, Judaism, and Islam, which he had studied. He endeavored to give to the native Hindu traditions, handed down from the past, an interpretation in agreement with what he conceived to be the spirit and import of the Christian faith. Doctrinal controversy has since been rife regarding the interpretation of truth that he and his successors were thus led to give, whereby the community has been subdivided into a number of independent sects. The character, too, of the community, appealing essentially to highly trained intellectual minds, has from its inception always precluded any large growth of the numbers of its avowed adherents. Nevertheless, the indirect influence exercised by the body, even upon the development of popular education and literature, is held to be very considerable indeed. Among those community members who have grown up in recent years, Rabindranath Tagore has labored to a pre-eminent degree. To them he has stood as a revered master and prophet. That intimate interplay of teacher and pupil so earnestly sought after has attained a deep, hearty, and simple manifestation both in religious life and in literary training.

To carry out his life's work Tagore equipped himself with a many-sided culture, European as well as Indian, extended and matured by travels abroad and by advanced study in London. In his youth he traveled widely in his own land, accompanying his father as far as the Himalayas. He was still quite young when he began to write in Bengali, and he has tried his hand in prose and poetry, lyrics, and dramas. In addition to his descriptions of the life of the common people of his own country, he has dealt in separate works with questions in literary criticism, philosophy, and sociology. At one period, some time ago, there occurred a break in the busy round of his activities, for he then felt obliged, in accord with immemorial practice among his race, to pursue for a time a contemplative hermit life in a boat floating on the waters of a tributary of the sacred Ganges River. After he returned to ordinary life, his reputation among his own people as a man of refined wisdom and chastened piety grew greater from day to day. The open-air school which he established in western Bengal, beneath the sheltering branches of the mango tree, has brought up numbers of youths who as devoted disciples have spread his teaching throughout the land. To this place he has now retired, after spending nearly a year as an honored guest in the literary circles of England and America and attending the Religious History Congress held in Paris last summer (1913).

Wherever Tagore has encountered minds open to receive his high teaching, the reception accorded him has been that suited to a bearer of good tidings which are delivered, in language intelligible to all, from that treasure house of the East whose existence had long been conjectured. His own attitude, moreover, is that he is but the intermediary, giving freely of that to which by birth he has access. He is not at all anxious to shine before men as a genius or as an inventor of some new thing. In contrast to the cult of work, which is the product of life in the fenced-in cities of the Western world, with its fostering of a restless, contentious spirit; in contrast to its struggle to conquer nature for the love of gain and profit, "as if we are living," Tagore says, "in a hostile world where we have to wrest everything we want from an unwilling and alien arrangement of things"; in contrast to all that enervating hurry and scurry, he places before us the culture that in the vast, peaceful, and enshrining forests of India attains its perfection, a culture that seeks primarily the quiet peace of the soul in ever-increasing harmony with the life of nature herself. It is a poetical, not a historical, picture that Tagore here reveals to us to confirm his promise that a peace awaits us, too. By virtue of the right associated with the gift of prophecy, he freely depicts the scenes that have loomed before his creative vision at a period contemporary with the beginning of time.

He is, however, as far removed as anyone in our midst from all that we are accustomed to hear dispensed and purveyed in the market places as Oriental philosophy, from painful dreams about the transmigration of souls and the impersonal *karma,* from the pantheistic, and in reality abstract, belief that is usually regarded as peculiarly characteristic of the higher civilization in India. Tagore himself is not even prepared to admit that a belief of that description can claim any authority from the profoundest utterances of the wise men of the past. He peruses his Vedic hymns, his *Upanishads,* and indeed the theses of Buddha himself, in such a manner that he discovers in them what is for him an irrefutable truth. If he seeks the divinity in nature, he finds there a living personality with the features of omnipotence, the all-embracing lord of nature, whose preternatural spiritual power nevertheless likewise reveals its presence in all temporal life, small as well as great, but especially in the soul of man predestined for eternity. Praise, prayer, and fervent devotion pervade the song offerings that he lays at the feet of this nameless divinity of his. Ascetic and even ethic austerity would appear to be alien to his type of divinity worship, which may be characterized as a species of esthetic theism. Piety of that description is in full concord with the whole of his poetry, and it has bestowed peace upon him. He proclaims the coming of that peace for weary and careworn souls even within the bounds of Christendom.

This is mysticism, if we like to call it so, but not a mysticism that, relinquishing personality, seeks to become absorbed in an All that approaches a Nothingness, but one that, with all the talents and faculties of the soul trained to their highest pitch, eagerly sets forth to meet the living Father of all creation. This more strenuous type of mysticism was not wholly unknown even in India before the days of Tagore, hardly indeed among the ascetics and philosophers of ancient times but rather in the many forms of *bhakti,* a piety whose very essence is the profound love of and reliance upon God. Ever since the Middle Ages, influenced in some measure by other religious cultures and religions, *bhakti* has sought the ideals of its faith in the different phases of Hinduism, varied in character but each to all intents monotheistic in conception. All those higher forms of faith have disappeared or have been depraved past recognition, choked by the superabundant growth of that mixture of cults that has attracted to its banner all those Indian peoples who lacked an adequate power of resistance to its blandishments. Even though Tagore may have borrowed one or another note from the orchestral symphonies of his native predecessors, yet he treads upon firmer ground in this age that draws the peoples of the earth closer together along paths of peace, and of strife too, to joint and collective responsibilities, and that spends its own energies in dispatching greetings and good wishes far over land and sea. Tagore, though, in thought-impelling pictures, has shown us how all things temporal are swallowed up in the eternal:

> *Time is endless in thy hands, my lord. There is none to count thy minutes.*
>
> *Days and nights pass and ages bloom and fade like flowers. Thou knowest how to wait.*
>
> *Thy centuries follow each other perfecting a small wild flower.*
>
> *We have no time to lose, and having no time, we must scramble for our chances. We are too poor to be late.*
>
> *And thus it is that time goes by, while I give it to every querulous man who claims it, and thine altar is empty of all offerings to the last.*
>
> *At the end of the day I hasten in fear lest thy gate be shut; but I find that yet there is time.*

Rabindranath Tagore sent this message by telegram: "I beg to convey to the Swedish Academy my grateful appreciation of the breadth of understanding which has brought the distant near, and has made a stranger a brother."

GITANJALI
SONG OFFERINGS

By RABINDRANATH TAGORE

Translated from the Bengali by the author

INTRODUCTION
By W. B. YEATS

A few days ago I said to a distinguished Bengali doctor of medicine, "I know no German, yet if a translation of a German poet had moved me, I would go to the British Museum and find books in English that would tell me something of his life, and of the history of his thought. But though these prose translations from Rabindranath Tagore have stirred my blood as nothing has for years, I shall not know anything of his life, and of the movements of thought that have made them possible, if some Indian traveler will not tell me." It seemed to him natural that I should be moved, for he said, "I read Rabindranath every day, to read one line of his is to forget all the troubles of the world." I said, "An Englishman living in London in the reign of Richard the Second had he been shown translations from Petrarch or from Dante, would have found no books to answer his questions, but would have questioned some Florentine banker or Lombard merchant as I question you. For all I know, so abundant and simple is this poetry, the new Renaissance has been born in your country and I shall never know of it except by hearsay." He answered, "We have other poets, but none that are his equal; we call this the epoch of Rabindranath. No poet seems to me as famous in Europe as he is among us. He is as great in music as in poetry, and his songs are sung from the west of India into Burmah wherever Bengali is spoken. He was already famous at nineteen when he wrote his first novel; and plays, written when he was but little older, are still played in Calcutta. I so much admire the completeness of his life; when he was very young he wrote much of natural objects, he would sit all day in his garden; from his twenty-fifth year or so to his thirty-fifth perhaps, when he had a great sorrow, he wrote the most beautiful love poetry in our language"; and then he said with deep emotion, "Words can never express what I owed at seventeen to his love poetry. After that his art grew deeper, it became religious and philosophical; all the aspirations of mankind are in his hymns. He is the first among our saints who has not refused to live, but has spoken out of Life itself, and that is why we give him our love." I may have changed his well-chosen words in my memory but not his thought. "A little while ago he was to read divine service in one of our churches—we of the Brahma

Samaj use your word 'church' in English
—it was the largest in Calcutta and not
only was it crowded, people even standing in the windows, but the streets were
all but impassable because of the
people."

Other Indians came to see me and
their reverence for this man sounded
strange in our world, where we hide great
and little things under the same veil of
obvious comedy and half-serious de-
preciation. When we were making the
cathedrals had we a like reverence for
our great men? "Every morning at three
—I know, for I have seen it," one said to
me, "he sits immovable in contemplation,
and for two hours does not awake from
his reverie upon the nature of God. His
father, the Maha Rishi, would sometimes
sit there all through the next day; once,
upon a river, he fell into contemplation
because of the beauty of the landscape,
and the rowers waited for eight hours before they could continue their journey."
He then told me of Mr. Tagore's family
and how for generations great men have
come out of its cradles. "Today," he said,
"there are Gogonendranath and Abanin-
dranath Tagore, who are artists; and
Dwijendranath, Rabindranath's brother,
who is a great philosopher. The squirrels
come from the boughs and climb on to
his knees and the birds alight upon his
hands." I notice in these men's thought a
sense of visible beauty and meaning as
though they held that doctrine of
Nietzsche that we must not believe in the
moral or intellectual beauty which does
not sooner or later impress itself upon
physical things. I said, "In the East you
know how to keep a family illustrious.
The other day the curator of a Museum
pointed out to me a little dark-skinned
man who was arranging their Chinese
prints and said, 'That is the hereditary
connoisseur of the Mikado, he is the
fourteenth of his family to hold the
post.' " He answered. "When Rabin-

dranath was a boy he had all round him
in his home literature and music." I
thought of the abundance, of the simplicity of the poems, and said, "In your
country is there much propagandist writing, much criticism? We have to do so
much, especially in my own country, that
our minds gradually cease to be creative,
and yet we cannot help it. If our life was
not a continual warfare, we would not
have taste, we would not know what is
good, we would not find hearers and
readers. Four-fifths of our energy is spent
in the quarrel with bad taste, whether in
our own minds or in the minds of
others." "I understand," he replied, "we
too have our propagandist writing. In the
villages they recite long mythological
poems adapted from the Sanscrit in the
Middle Ages, and they often insert passages telling the people that they must do
their duties."

II

I have carried the manuscript of these
translations about with me for days,
reading it in railway trains, or on the top
of omnibuses and in restaurants, and I
have often had to close it lest some
stranger would see how much it moved
me. These lyrics—which are in the original, my Indians tell me, full of subtlety
of rhythm, of untranslatable delicacies of
color, of metrical invention—display in
their thought a world I have dreamed of
all my life long. The work of a supreme
culture, they yet appear as much the
growth of the common soil as the grass
and the rushes. A tradition, where poetry
and religion are the same thing, has
passed through the centuries, gathering
from learned and unlearned metaphor
and emotion, and carried back again to
the multitude the thought of the scholar
and of the noble. If the civilization of
Bengal remains unbroken, if that common mind which—as one divines—runs

through all, is not, as with us, broken into a dozen minds that know nothing of each other, something even of what is most subtle in these verses will have come, in a few generations, to the beggar on the roads. When there was but one mind in England Chaucer wrote his *Troilus and Cressida,* and though he had written to be read, or to be read out—for our time was coming on apace—he was sung by minstrels for a while. Rabindranath Tagore, like Chaucer's forerunners, writes music for his words, and one understands at every moment that he is so abundant, so spontaneous, so daring in his passion, so full of surprise, because he is doing something which has never seemed strange, unnatural, or in need of defense. These verses will not lie in little well-printed books upon ladies' tables, who turn the pages with indolent hands that they may sigh over a life without meaning, which is yet all they can know of life, or be carried about by students at the university to be laid aside when the work of life begins, but as the generations pass, travelers will hum them on the highway and men rowing upon rivers. Lovers, while they await one another, shall find, in murmuring them, this love of God a magic gulf wherein their own more bitter passion may bathe and renew its youth. At every moment the heart of this poet flows outward to these without derogation or condescension, for it has known that they will understand; and it has filled itself with the circumstance of their lives. The traveler in the red-brown clothes that he wears that dust may not show upon him, the girl searching in her bed for the petals fallen from the wreath of her royal lover, the servant or the bride awaiting the master's home-coming in the empty house, are images of the heart turning to God. Flowers and rivers, the blowing of conch shells, the heavy rain of the Indian July, or the parching heat, are images of the moods of that heart in union or in separation; and a man sitting in a boat upon a river playing upon a lute, like one of those figures full of mysterious meaning in a Chinese picture, is God Himself. A whole people, a whole civilization, immeasurably strange to us, seems to have been taken up into this imagination; and yet we are not moved because of its strangeness, but because we have met our own image, as though we had walked in Rossetti's willow wood, or heard, perhaps for the first time in literature, our voice as in a dream.

Since the Renaissance the writing of European saints—however familiar their metaphor and the general structure of their thought—has ceased to hold our attention. We know that we must at last forsake the world, and we are accustomed in moments of weariness or exaltation to consider a voluntary forsaking; but how can we, who have read so much poetry, seen so many paintings, listened to so much music, where the cry of the flesh and the cry of the soul seem one, forsake it harshly and rudely? What have we in common with St. Bernard covering his eyes that they may not dwell upon the beauty of the lakes of Switzerland, or with the violent rhetoric of the Book of Revelation? We would, if we might, find, as in this book, words full of courtesy. "I have got my leave. Bid me farewell, my brothers! I bow to you all and take my departure. Here I give back the keys of my door—and I give up all claims to my house. I only ask for last kind words from you. We were neighbors for long, but I received more than I could give. Now the day has dawned and the lamp that lit my dark corner is out. A summons has come and I am ready for my journey." And it is our own mood, when it is furthest from à Kempis or John of the Cross, that cries, "And because I love this life, I know I shall love death as well." Yet it is not only in our thoughts of the parting that this book fathoms all. We had not known that we loved God, hardly it may be that we believed in Him; yet looking backward upon our life we discover, in our exploration of the pathways of woods, in our delight in the lonely places of hills, in that mysterious claim that we have made, unavailingly, on the women that we have loved, the emotion that created this insidious sweetness. "Entering my heart unbidden even as one of the common crowd unknown to me, my king, thou didst press the signet of eternity upon many a fleeting moment." This is no longer the sanctity of the cell and of the scourge; being but a lifting up, as it were, into a greater intensity of the mood of the painter, painting the dust and the sunlight, and we go for a like voice to St. Francis and to William Blake who have seemed so alien in our violent history.

III

We write long books where no page perhaps has any quality to make writing a pleasure, being confident in some general design, just as we fight and make money and fill our heads with politics— all dull things in the doing—while Mr. Tagore, like the Indian civilization itself, has been content to discover the soul and surrender himself to its spontaneity. He often seems to contrast his life with that of those who have lived more after our fashion, and have more seeming weight in the world, and always humbly as though he were only sure his way is best for him: "Men going home glance at me and smile and fill me with shame. I sit like a beggar maid, drawing my skirt over my face, and when they ask me, what it is I want, I drop my eyes and answer them not." At another time, remembering how his life had once a different shape, he will say, "Many an hour have I spent in the strife of the good and the evil, but now it is the pleasure of my playmate of the empty days to draw my heart on to him; and I know not why is this sudden call to what useless inconsequence." An innocence, a simplicity that one does not find elsewhere in literature makes the birds and the leaves seem as near to him as they are near to children, and the changes of the seasons great events as before our thoughts had arisen between them and us. At times I wonder if he has it from the literature of Bengal or from religion, and at other times, remembering the birds alighting on his brother's hands, I find pleasure in thinking it hereditary, a mystery that was growing through the centuries like the courtesy of a Tristan or a Pelanore. Indeed, when he is speaking of children, so much a part of himself this quality seems, one is not certain that he is not also speaking of the saints, "They build their houses with sand and they play with empty shells. With withered leaves they weave their boats and smilingly float them on the vast deep. Children have their play on the seashore of worlds. They know not how to swim, they know not how to cast nets. Pearl fishers dive for pearls, merchants sail in their ships, while children gather pebbles and scatter them again. They seek not for hidden treasures, they know not how to cast nets."

W. B. YEATS

September 1912

GITANJALI

1

Thou hast made me endless, such is thy pleasure. This frail vessel thou emptiest again and again, and fillest it ever with fresh life.

This little flute of a reed thou hast carried over hills and dales, and hast breathed through it melodies eternally new.

At the immortal touch of thy hands my little heart loses its limits in joy and gives birth to utterance ineffable.

Thy infinite gifts come to me only on these very small hands of mine. Ages pass, and still thou pourest, and still there is room to fill.

2

When thou commandest me to sing it seems that my heart would break with pride; and I look to thy face, and tears come to my eyes.

All that is harsh and dissonant in my life melts into one sweet harmony—and my adoration spreads wings like a glad bird on its flight across the sea.

I know thou takest pleasure in my singing. I know that only as a singer I come before thy presence.

I touch by the edge of the far spreading wing of my song thy feet which I could never aspire to reach.

Drunk with the joy of singing I forget myself and call thee friend who art my lord.

3

I know not how thou singest, my master! I ever listen in silent amazement.

The light of thy music illumines the world. The life breath of thy music runs from sky to sky. The holy stream of thy music breaks through all stony obstacles and rushes on.

My heart longs to join in thy song, but vainly struggles for a voice. I would speak, but speech breaks not into song, and I cry out baffled. Ah, thou hast made my heart captive in the endless meshes of thy music, my master!

4

Life of my life, I shall ever try to keep my body pure, knowing that thy living touch is upon all my limbs.

I shall ever try to keep all untruths out from my thoughts, knowing that thou art that truth which has kindled the light of reason in my mind.

I shall ever try to drive all evils away from my heart and keep my love in flower, knowing that thou hast thy seat in the inmost shrine of my heart.

And it shall be my endeavor to reveal thee in my actions, knowing it is thy power gives me strength to act.

5

I ask for a moment's indulgence to sit by thy side. The works that I have in hand I will finish afterwards.

Away from the sight of thy face my heart knows no rest nor respite, and my work becomes an endless toil in a shoreless sea of toil.

Today the summer has come at my window with its sighs and murmurs; and the bees are plying their minstrelsy at the court of the flowering grove.

Now it is time to sit quiet, face to face
with thee, and to sing dedication of life
in this silent and overflowing leisure.

6

Pluck this little flower and take it, delay
not! I fear lest it droop and drop into the
dust.

It may not find a place in thy garland,
but honor it with a touch of pain from
thy hand and pluck it. I fear lest the day
end before I am aware, and the time of
offering go by.

Though its color be not deep and its
smell be faint, use this flower in thy service and pluck it while there is time.

7

My song has put off her adornments. She
has no pride of dress and decoration.
Ornaments would mar our union; they
would come between thee and me; their
jingling would drown thy whispers.

My poet's vanity dies in shame before
thy sight. O master poet, I have sat down
at thy feet. Only let me make my life
simple and straight, like a flute of reed
for thee to fill with music.

8

The child who is decked with prince's
robes and who has jeweled chains round
his neck loses all pleasure in his play; his
dress hampers him at every step.

In fear that it may be frayed, or
stained with dust he keeps himself from
the world, and is afraid even to move.

Mother, it is no gain, thy bondage of
finery, if it keep one shut off from the
healthful dust of the earth, if it rob one
of the right of entrance to the great fair
of common human life.

9

O fool, to try to carry thyself upon thy
own shoulders! O beggar, to come to beg
at thy own door!

Leave all thy burdens on his hands
who can bear all, and never look behind
in regret.

Thy desire at once puts out the light
from the lamp it touches with its breath.
It is unholy—take not thy gifts through
its unclean hands. Accept only what is
offered by sacred love.

10

Here is thy footstool and there rest thy
feet where live the poorest, and lowliest,
and lost.

When I try to bow to thee, my obei-
sance cannot reach down to the depth
where thy feet rest among the poorest,
lowliest, and lost.

Pride can never approach to where
thou walkest in the clothes of the humble
among the poorest, and lowliest, and lost.

My heart can never find its way to
where thou keepest company with the
companionless among the poorest, the
lowliest, and the lost.

11

Leave this chanting and singing and telling of beads! Whom dost thou worship in
this lonely dark corner of a temple with
doors all shut? Open thine eyes and see
thy God is not before thee!

He is there where the tiller is tilling the
hard ground and where the pathmaker is
breaking stones. He is with them in sun
and in shower, and his garment is
covered with dust. Put off thy holy
mantle and even like him come down on
the dusty soil!

Deliverance? Where is this deliverance to be found? Our master himself has joyfully taken upon him the bonds of creation; he is bound with us all for ever.

Come out of thy meditations and leave aside thy flowers and incense! What harm is there if thy clothes become tattered and stained? Meet him and stand by him in toil and in sweat of thy brow.

12

The time that my journey takes is long and the way of it long.

I came out on the chariot of the first gleam of light, and pursued my voyage through the wildernesses of worlds leaving my track on many a star and planet.

It is the most distant course that comes nearest to thyself, and that training is the most intricate which leads to the utter simplicity of a tune.

The traveler has to knock at every alien door to come to his own, and one has to wander through all the outer worlds to reach the innermost shrine at the end.

My eyes strayed far and wide before I shut them and said "Here art thou!"

The question and the cry "Oh, where?" melt into tears of a thousand streams and deluge the world with the flood of the assurance "I am!"

13

The song that I came to sing remains unsung to this day.

I have spent my days in stringing and in unstringing my instrument.

The time has not come true, the words have not been rightly set; only there is the agony of wishing in my heart.

The blossom has not opened; only the wind is sighing by.

I have not seen his face, nor have I listened to his voice; only I have heard his gentle footsteps from the road before my house.

The livelong day has passed in spreading his seat on the floor; but the lamp has not been lit and I cannot ask him into my house.

I live in the hope of meeting with him; but this meeting is not yet.

14

My desires are many and my cry is pitiful, but ever didst thou save me by hard refusals; and this strong mercy has been wrought into my life through and through.

Day by day thou art making me worthy of the simple, great gifts that thou gavest to me unasked—this sky and the light, this body and the life and the mind—saving me from perils of overmuch desire.

There are times when I languidly linger and times when I awaken and hurry in search of my goal; but cruelly thou hidest thyself from before me.

Day by day thou art making me worthy of thy full acceptance by refusing me ever and anon, saving me from perils of weak, uncertain desire.

15

I am here to sing thee songs. In this hall of thine I have a corner seat.

In thy world I have no work to do; my useless life can only break out in tunes without a purpose.

When the hour strikes for thy silent worship at the dark temple of midnight, command me, my master, to stand before thee to sing.

When in the morning air the golden harp is tuned, honor me, commanding my presence.

16

I have had my invitation to this world's festival, and thus my life has been blessed. My eyes have seen and my ears have heard.

It was my part at this feast to play upon my instrument, and I have done all I could.

Now, I ask, has the time come at last when I may go in and see thy face and offer thee my silent salutation?

17

I am only waiting for love to give myself up at last into his hands. That is why it is so late and why I have been guilty of such omissions.

They come with their laws and their codes to bind me fast; but I evade them ever, for I am only waiting for love to give myself up at last into his hands.

People blame me and call me heedless; I doubt not they are right in their blame.

The market day is over and work is all done for the busy. Those who come to call me in vain have gone back in anger. I am only waiting for love to give myself up at last into his hands.

18

Clouds heap upon clouds and it darkens. Ah, love, why dost thou let me wait outside at the door all alone?

In the busy moments of the noontide work I am with the crowd, but on this dark lonely day it is only for thee that I hope.

If thou showest me not thy face, if thou leavest me wholly aside, I know not how I am to pass these long, rainy hours.

I keep gazing on the far away gloom of the sky, and my heart wanders wailing with the restless wind.

19

If thou speakest not I will fill my heart with thy silence and endure it. I will keep still and wait like the night with starry vigil and its head bent low with patience.

The morning will surely come, the darkness will vanish, and thy voice pour down in golden streams breaking through the sky.

Then thy word will take wing in songs from every one of my birds' nests, and thy melodies will break forth in flowers in all my forest groves.

20

On the day when the lotus bloomed, alas, my mind was straying, and I knew it not. My basket was empty and the flower remained unheeded.

Only now and again a sadness fell upon me, and I started up from my dream and felt a sweet trace of a strange fragrance in the south wind.

That vague sweetness made my heart ache with longing and it seemed to me that it was the eager breath of the summer seeking for its completion.

I knew not then that it was so near, that it was mine, and that this perfect sweetness had blossomed in the depth of my own heart.

21

I must launch out my boat. The languid hours pass by on the shore—Alas for me!

The spring has done its flowering and taken leave. And now with the burden of faded futile flowers I wait and linger.

The waves have become clamorous, and upon the bank in the shady lane the yellow leaves flutter and fall.

What emptiness do you gaze upon! Do you need feel a thrill passing through the air with the notes of the far away song floating from the other shore?

22

In the deep shadows of the rainy July, with secret steps, thou walkest, silent as night, eluding all watchers.

Today the morning has closed its eyes, heedless of the insistent calls of the loud east wind, and a thick veil has been drawn over the ever-wakeful blue sky.

The woodlands have hushed their songs, and doors are all shut at every house. Thou art the solitary wayfarer in this deserted street. Oh my only friend, my best beloved, the gates are open in my house—do not pass by like a dream.

23

Art thou abroad on this stormy night on the journey of love, my friend? The sky groans like one in despair.

I have no sleep tonight. Ever and again I open my door and look out on the darkness, my friend!

I can see nothing before me. I wonder where lies thy path!

By what dim shore of the ink-black river, by what far edge of the frowning forest, through what mazy depth of gloom art thou threading thy course to come to me, my friend?

24

If the day is done, if birds sing no more, if the wind had flagged tired, then draw the veil of darkness thick upon me, even as thou hast wrapt the earth with the coverlet of sleep and tenderly closed the petals of the drooping lotus at dusk.

From the traveler, whose sack of provisions is empty before the voyage is ended, whose garment is torn and dust-laden, whose strength is exhausted, remove shame and poverty, and renew his life like a flower under the cover of thy kindly night.

25

In the night of weariness let me give myself up to sleep without struggle, resting my trust upon thee.

Let me not force my flagging spirit into a poor preparation for thy worship.

It is thou who drawest the veil of night upon the tired eyes of the day to renew its sight in a fresher gladness of awakening.

26

He came and sat by my side but I woke not. What a cursed sleep it was, O miserable me!

He came when the night was still; he had his harp in his hands, and my dreams became resonant with its melodies.

Alas, why are my nights all thus lost? Ah, why do I ever miss his sight whose breath touches my sleep?

27

Light, oh where is the light? Kindle it with the burning fire of desire!

There is the lamp but never a flicker of a flame—is such thy fate, my heart! Ah, death were better by far for thee!

Misery knocks at thy door, and her message is that thy lord is wakeful, and he calls thee to the love-tryst through the darkness of night.

The sky is overcast with clouds and the rain is ceaseless. I know not what this is that stirs in me—I know not its meaning.

A moment's flash of lightning drags down a deeper gloom on my sight, and my heart gropes for the path to where the music of the night calls me.

Light, oh where is the light! Kindle it with the burning fire of desire! It thunders and the wind rushes screaming through the void. The night is black as a black stone. Let not the hours pass by in the dark. Kindle the lamp of love with thy life.

28

Obstinate are the trammels, but my heart aches when I try to break them.

Freedom is all I want, but to hope for it I feel ashamed.

I am certain that priceless wealth is in thee, and that thou art my best friend, but I have not the heart to sweep away the tinsel that fills my room.

The shroud that covers me is a shroud of dust and death; I hate it, yet hug it in love.

My debts are large, my failures great, my shame secret and heavy; yet when I come to ask for my good, I quake in fear lest my prayer be granted.

29

He whom I enclose with my name is weeping in this dungeon. I am ever busy building this wall all around; and as this wall goes up into the sky day by day I lose sight of my true being in its dark shadow.

I take pride in this great wall, and I plaster it with dust and sand lest a least hole should be left in this name; and for all the care I take I lose sight of my true being.

30

I came out alone on my way to my tryst. But who is this that follows me in the silent dark?

I move aside to avoid his presence but I escape him not.

He makes the dust rise from the earth with his swagger; he adds his loud voice to every word that I utter.

He is my own little self, my lord, he knows no shame; but I am ashamed to come to thy door in his company.

31

"Prisoner, tell me, who was it that bound you?"

"It was my master," said the prisoner. "I thought I could outdo everybody in the world in wealth and power, and I amassed in my own treasure-house the money due to my king. When sleep overcame me I lay upon the bed that was for my lord, and on waking up I found I was a prisoner in my own treasure-house."

"Prisoner, tell me who was it that wrought this unbreakable chain?"

"It was I," said the prisoner, "who forged this chain very carefully. I thought my invincible power would hold the world captive leaving me in a freedom undisturbed. Thus night and day I worked at the chain with huge fires and cruel hard strokes. When at last the work was done and the links were complete and unbreakable, I found that it held me in its grip."

32

By all means they try to hold me secure who love me in this world. But it is otherwise with thy love which is greater than theirs, and thou keepest me free.

Lest I forget them they never venture to leave me alone. But day passes by after day and thou art not seen.

If I call not thee in my prayers, if I keep not thee in my heart, thy love for me still waits for my love.

33

When it was day they came into my house and said, "We shall only take the smallest room here."

They said, "We shall help you in the worship of your God and humbly accept only our own share of his grace"; and then they took their seat in a corner and they sat quiet and meek.

But in the darkness of night I find they break into my sacred shrine, strong and turbulent, and snatch with unholy greed the offerings from God's altar.

34

Let only that little be left of me whereby I may name thee my all.

Let only that little be left of my will

whereby I may feel thee on every side, and come to thee in everything, and offer to thee my love every moment.

Let only that little be left of me whereby I may never hide thee.

Let only that little of my fetters be left whereby I am bound with thy will, and thy purpose is carried out in my life—and that is the fetter of thy love.

35

Where the mind is without fear and the head is held high;

Where knowledge is free;

Where the world has not been broken up into fragments by narrow domestic walls;

Where words come out from the depth of truth;

Where tireless striving stretches its arms towards perfection:

Where the clear stream of reason has not lost its way into the dreary desert sand of dead habit;

Where the mind is led forward by thee into ever-widening thought and action—

Into that heaven of freedom, my Father, let my country awake.

36

This is my prayer to thee, my lord—strike, strike at the root of penury in my heart.

Give me the strength lightly to bear my joys and sorrows.

Give me the strength to make my love fruitful in service.

Give me the strength never to disown the poor or bend my knees before insolent might.

Give me the strength to raise my mind high above daily trifles.

And give me the strength to surrender my strength to thy will with love.

37

I thought that my voyage had come to its end at the last limit of my power—that the path before me was closed, that provisions were exhausted and the time come to take shelter in a silent obscurity.

But I find that thy will knows no end in me. And when old words die out on the tongue, new melodies break forth from the heart; and where the old tracks are lost, new country is revealed with its wonders.

38

That I want thee, only thee—let my heart repeat without end. All desires that distract me, day and night, are false and empty to the core.

As the night keeps hidden in its gloom the petition for light, even thus in the depth of my unconsciousness rings the cry—I want thee, only thee.

As the storm still seeks its end in peace when it strikes against peace with all its might, even thus my rebellion strikes against thy love and still its cry is—I want thee, only thee.

39

When the heart is hard and parched up, come upon me with a shower of mercy.

When grace is lost from life, come with a burst of song.

When tumultuous work raises its din on all sides shutting me out from beyond, come to me, my lord of silence, with thy peace and rest.

When my beggarly heart sits crouched, shut up in a corner, break open the door, my king, and come with the ceremony of a king.

When desire blinds the mind with delusion and dust, O thou holy one, thou wakeful, come with thy light and thy thunder.

40

The rain has held back for days and days, my God, in my arid heart. The horizon is fiercely naked—not the thinnest cover of a soft cloud, not the vaguest hint of a distant cool shower.

Send thy angry storm, dark with death, if it is thy wish, and with lashes of lightning startle the sky from end to end.

But call back, my lord, call back this pervading silent heat, still and keen and cruel, burning the heart with dire despair.

Let the cloud of grace bend low from above like the tearful look of the mother on the day of the father's wrath.

41

Where dost thou stand behind them all, my lover, hiding thyself in the shadows? They push thee and pass thee by on the dusty road, taking thee for naught. I wait here weary hours spreading my offerings for thee, while passers-by come and take my flowers, one by one, and my basket is nearly empty.

The morning time is past, and the noon. In the shade of evening my eyes are drowsy with sleep. Men going home glance at me and smile and fill me with shame. I sit like a beggar maid, drawing my skirt over my face, and when they ask me, what it is I want, I drop my eyes and answer them not.

Oh, how, indeed, could I tell them that for thee I wait, and that thou hast promised to come. How could I utter for shame that I keep for my dowry this poverty. Ah, I hug this pride in the secret of my heart.

I sit on the grass and gaze upon the sky and dream of the sudden splendor of thy coming—all the lights ablaze, golden pennons flying over thy car, and they at the roadside standing agape, when they see thee come down from thy seat to raise me from the dust, and set at thy side this ragged beggar girl a-tremble with shame and pride, like a creeper in a summer breeze.

But time glides on and still no sound of the wheels of thy chariot. Many a procession passes by with noise and shouts and glamour of glory. Is it only thou who wouldst stand in the shadow silent and behind them all? And only I who would wait and weep and wear out my heart in vain longing?

42

Early in the day it was whispered that we should sail in a boat, only thou and I, and never a soul in the world would know of this our pilgrimage to no country and to no end.

In that shoreless ocean, at thy silently listening smile my songs would swell in melodies, free as waves, free from all bondage of words.

Is the time not come yet? Are there works still to do? Lo, the evening has come down upon the shore and in the fading light the seabirds come flying to their nests.

Who knows when the chains will be off, and the boat, like the last glimmer of sunset, vanish into the night?

43

The day was when I did not keep myself in readiness for thee; and entering my heart unbidden even as one of the common crowd, unknown to me, my king, thou didst press the signet of eternity upon many a fleeting moment of my life.

And today when by chance I light upon them and see thy signature, I find they have lain scattered in the dust mixed with the memory of joys and sorrows of my trivial days forgotten.

Thou didst not turn in contempt from my childish play among dust, and the steps that I heard in my playroom are the same that are echoing from star to star.

44

This is my delight, thus to wait and watch at the wayside where shadow chases light and the rain comes in the wake of the summer.

Messengers, with tidings from unknown skies, greet me and speed along the road. My heart is glad within, and the breath of the passing breeze is sweet.

From dawn till dusk I sit here before my door, and I know that of a sudden the happy moment will arrive when I shall see.

In the meanwhile I smile and I sing all alone. In the meanwhile the air is filling with the perfume of promise.

45

Have you not heard his silent steps? He comes, comes, ever comes.

Every moment and every age, every day and every night he comes, comes, ever comes.

Many a song have I sung in many a mood of mind, but all their notes have always proclaimed, "He comes, comes, ever comes."

In the fragrant days of sunny April through the forest path he comes, comes, ever comes.

In the rainy gloom of July nights on the thundering chariot of clouds he comes, comes, ever comes.

In sorrow after sorrow it is his steps that press upon my heart, and it is the golden touch of his feet that makes my joy to shine.

wind at the festival of morning light. Let me sleep undisturbed even if my lord comes of a sudden to my door.

Ah, my sleep, precious sleep, which only waits for his touch to vanish. Ah, my closed eyes that would open their lids only to the light of his smile when he stands before me like a dream emerging from darkness of sleep.

Let him appear before my sight as the first of all lights and all forms. The first thrill of joy to my awakened soul let it come from his glance. And let my return to myself be immediate return to him.

46

I know not from what distant time thou art ever coming nearer to meet me. Thy sun and stars can never keep thee hidden from me for aye.

In many a morning and eve thy footsteps have been heard and thy messenger has come within my heart and called me in secret.

I know not why today my life is all astir, and a feeling of tremulous joy is passing through my heart.

It is as if the time were come to wind up my work, and I feel in the air a faint smell of thy sweet presence.

47

The night is nearly spent waiting for him in vain. I fear lest in the morning he suddenly come to my door when I have fallen asleep wearied out. Oh friends, leave the way open to him—forbid him not.

If the sound of his steps does not wake me, do not try to rouse me, I pray. I wish not to be called from my sleep by the clamorous choir of birds, by the riot of

48

The morning sea of silence broke into ripples of bird songs; and the flowers were all merry by the roadside; and the wealth of gold was scattered through the rift of the clouds while we busily went on our way and paid no heed.

We sang no glad songs nor played; we went not to the village for barter; we spoke not a word nor smiled; we lingered not on the way. We quickened our pace more and more as the time sped by.

The sun rose to the mid sky and doves cooed in the shade. Withered leaves danced and whirled in the hot air of noon. The shepherd boy drowsed and dreamed in the shadow of the banyan tree, and I laid myself down by the water and stretched my tired limbs on the grass.

My companions laughed at me in scorn; they held their heads high and hurried on; they never looked back nor rested; they vanished in the distant blue haze. They crossed many meadows and hills, and passed through strange, faraway countries. All honor to you, heroic host of the interminable path! Mockery and reproach pricked me to rise, but found no response in me. I gave myself up for lost in the depth of a glad humiliation—in the shadow of a dim delight.

The repose of the sun-embroidered green gloom slowly spread over my heart. I forgot for what I had traveled, and I surrendered my mind without struggle to the maze of shadows and songs.

At last, when I woke from my slumber and opened my eyes, I saw thee standing by me, flooding my sleep with thy smile. How I had feared that the path was long and wearisome, and the struggle to reach thee was hard!

49

You came down from your throne and stood at my cottage door.

I was singing all alone in a corner, and the melody caught your ear. You came down and stood at my cottage door.

Masters are many in your hall, and songs are sung there at all hours. But the simple carol of this novice struck at your love. One plaintive little strain mingled with the great music of the world, and with a flower for a prize you came down and stopped at my cottage door.

50

I had gone a-begging from door to door in the village path, when thy golden chariot appeared in the distance like a gorgeous dream and I wondered who was this King of all kings!

My hopes rose high and methought my evil days were at an end, and I stood waiting for alms to be given unasked and for wealth scattered on all sides in the dust.

The chariot stopped where I stood. Thy glance fell on me and thou camest down with a smile. I felt that the luck of my life had come at last. Then of a sudden thou didst hold out thy right hand and say "What hast thou to give to me?"

Ah, what a kingly jest was it to open thy palm to a beggar to beg! I was confused and stood undecided, and then from my wallet I slowly took out the least little grain of corn and gave it to thee.

But how great my surprise when at the day's end I emptied my bag on the floor to find a least little grain of gold among the poor heap. I bitterly wept and wished that I had had the heart to give thee my all.

51

The night darkened. Our day's works had been done. We thought that the last guest had arrived for the night and the doors in the village were all shut. Only some said, The king was to come. We laughed and said "No, it cannot be!"

It seemed there were knocks at the door and we said it was nothing but the wind. We put out the lamps and lay down to sleep. Only some said, "It is the messenger!" We laughed and said "No, it must be the wind!"

There came a sound in the dead of the night. We sleepily thought it was the distant thunder. The earth shook, the walls rocked, and it troubled us in our sleep. Only some said, It was the sound of wheels. We said in a drowsy murmur, "No, it must be the rumbling of clouds!"

The night was still dark when the drum sounded. The voice came "Wake up! delay not!" We pressed our hands on our hearts and shuddered with fear. Some said, "Lo, there is the king's flag!" We stood up on our feet and cried "There is no time for delay!"

The king has come—but where are lights, where are wreaths? Where is the throne to seat him? Oh, shame, oh utter shame! Where is the hall, the decorations? Some one has said, "Vain is this cry! Greet him with empty hands, lead him into thy rooms all bare!"

Open the doors, let the conch-shells be sounded! In the depth of the night has come the king of our dark, dreary house. The thunder roars in the sky. The darkness shudders with lightning. Bring out thy tattered piece of mat and spread it in the courtyard. With the storm has come of a sudden our king of the fearful night.

52

I thought I should ask of thee—but I dared not—the rose wreath thou hadst on thy neck. Thus I waited for the morning, when thou didst depart, to find a few fragments on the bed. And like a beggar I searched in the dawn only for a stray petal or two.

Ah me, what is it I find? What token left of thy love? It is no flower, no spices, no vase of perfumed water. It is thy mighty sword, flashing as a flame, heavy as a bolt of thunder. The young light of morning comes through the window and spreads itself upon thy bed. The morning bird twitters and asks, "Woman, what hast thou got?" No, it is no flower, no spices, nor vase of perfumed water—it is thy dreadful sword.

I sit and muse in wonder, what gift is this of thine. I can find no place where to hide it. I am ashamed to wear it, frail as I am, and it hurts me when I press it to my bosom. Yet shall I bear in my heart this honor of the burden of pain, this gift of thine.

From now there shall be no fear left for me in this world, and thou shalt be victorious in all my strife. Thou hast left death for my companion and I shall crown him with my life. Thy sword is with me to cut asunder my bonds, and there shall be no fear left for me in the world.

From now I leave off all petty decorations. Lord of my heart, no more shall there be for me waiting and weeping in corners, no more coyness and sweetness of demeanor. Thou hast given me thy sword for adornment. No more doll's decorations for me!

53

Beautiful is thy wristlet, decked with stars and cunningly wrought in myriad-colored jewels. But more beautiful to me thy sword with its curve of lightning like the outspread wings of the divine bird of Vishnu, perfectly poised in the angry red light of the sunset.

It quivers like the one last response of life in ecstasy of pain at the final stroke of death; it shines like the pure flame of being burning up earthly sense with one fierce flash.

Beautiful is thy wristlet, decked with starry gems; but thy sword, O lord of thunder, is wrought with uttermost beauty, terrible to behold or to think of.

54

I asked nothing from thee; I uttered not my name to thine ear. When thou took'st thy leave I stood silent. I was alone by the well where the shadow of the tree fell aslant, and the women had gone home with their brown earthen pitchers full to the brim. They called me and shouted,

"Come with us, the morning is wearing on to noon." But I languidly lingered awhile lost in the midst of vague musings.

I heard not thy steps as thou camest. Thine eyes were sad when they fell on me; thy voice was tired as thou spokest low—"Ah, I am a thirsty traveler." I started up from my day-dreams and poured water from my jar on thy joined palms. The leaves rustled overhead; the cuckoo sang from the unseen dark, and perfume of *babla* flowers came from the bend of the road.

I stood speechless with shame when my name thou didst ask. Indeed, what had I done for thee to keep me in remembrance? But the memory that I could give water to thee to allay thy thirst will cling to my heart and enfold it in sweetness. The morning hour is late, the bird sings in weary notes, *neem* leaves rustle overhead and I sit and think and think.

55

Languor is upon your heart and the slumber is still on your eyes.

Has not the word come to you that the flower is reigning in splendor among thorns? Wake, oh awaken! Let not the time pass in vain!

At the end of the stony path, in the country of virgin solitude my friend is sitting all alone. Deceive him not. Wake, oh awaken!

What if the sky pants and trembles with the heat of the midday sun—what if the burning sand spreads its mantle of thirst—

Is there no joy in the deep of your heart? At every footfall of yours, will not the harp of the road break out in sweet music of pain?

56

Thus it is that thy joy in me is so full. Thus it is that thou hast come down to me. O thou lord of all heavens, where would be thy love if I were not?

Thou hast taken me as thy partner of all this wealth. In my heart is the endless play of thy delight. In my life thy will is ever taking shape.

And for this, thou who art the King of kings hast decked thyself in beauty to captivate my heart. And for this thy love loses itself in the love of thy lover, and there art thou seen in the perfect union of two.

57

Light, my light, the world-filling light, the eye-kissing light, heart-sweetening light!

Ah, the light dances, my darling, at the center of my life; the light strikes, my darling, the chords of my love; the sky opens, the wind runs wild, laughter passes over the earth.

The butterflies spread their sails on the sea of light. Lilies and jasmines surge up on the crest of the waves of light.

The light is shattered into gold on every cloud, my darling, and it scatters gems in profusion.

Mirth spreads from leaf to leaf, my darling, and gladness without measure. The heaven's river has drowned its banks and the flood of joy is abroad.

58

Let all the strains of joy mingle in my last song—the joy that makes the earth flow over in the riotous excess of the grass, the joy that sets the twin brothers, life and death, dancing over the wide world, the joy that sweeps in with the tempest, shaking and waking all life with laughter, the joy that sits still with its tears on the open red lotus of pain, and the joy that throws everything it has upon the dust, and knows not a word.

59

Yes, I know, this is nothing but thy love, O beloved of my heart—this golden light that dances upon the leaves, these idle clouds sailing across the sky, this passing breeze leaving its coolness upon my forehead.

The morning light has flooded my eyes —this is thy message to my heart. Thy face is bent from above, thy eyes look down on my eyes, and my heart has touched thy feet.

60

On the seashore of endless worlds children meet. The infinite sky is motionless overhead and the restless water is boisterous. On the seashore of endless worlds the children meet with shouts and dances.

They build their houses with sand and they play with empty shells. With withered leaves they weave their boats and smilingly float them on the vast deep. Children have their play on the seashore of worlds.

They know not how to swim, they know not how to cast nets. Pearl fishers dive for pearls, merchants sail in their ships, while children gather pebbles and scatter them again. They seek not for hidden treasures, they know not how to cast nets.

The sea surges up with laughter and pale gleams the smile of the sea beach. Death-dealing waves sing meaningless ballads to the children, even like a mother while rocking her baby's cradle. The sea plays with children, and pale gleams the smile of the sea beach.

On the seashore of endless worlds children meet. Tempest roams in the pathless sky, ships get wrecked in the trackless water, death is abroad and children play. On the seashore of endless worlds is the great meeting of children.

61

The sleep that flits on baby's eyes—does anybody know from where it comes? Yes, there is a rumor that it has its dwelling where, in the fairy village among shadows of the forest dimly lit with glow-worms, there hang two timid buds of enchantment. From there it comes to kiss baby's eyes.

The smile that flickers on baby's lips when he sleeps—does anybody know where it was born? Yes, there is a rumor that a young pale beam of a crescent moon touched the edge of a vanishing autumn cloud, and there the smile was first born in the dream of a dew-washed morning—the smile that flickers on baby's lips when he sleeps.

The sweet, soft freshness that blooms on baby's limbs—does anybody know where it was hidden so long? Yes, when the mother was a young girl it lay pervading her heart in tender and silent mystery of love—the sweet, soft freshness that has bloomed on baby's limbs.

62

When I bring to you colored toys, my child, I understand why there is such a play of colors on clouds, on water, and why flowers are painted in tints—when I give colored toys to you, my child.

When I sing to make you dance I truly know why there is music in leaves, and why waves send their chorus of voices to the heart of the listening earth—when I sing to make you dance.

When I bring sweet things to your greedy hands, I know why there is honey in the cup of the flower and why fruits are secretly filled with sweet juice—when I bring sweet things to your greedy hands.

When I kiss your face to make you smile, my darling, I surely understand what the pleasure is that streams from the sky in morning light, and what delight that is which the summer breeze brings to my body—when I kiss you to make you smile.

63

Thou hast made me known to friends whom I knew not. Thou hast given me seats in homes not my own. Thou hast brought the distant near and made a brother of the stranger.

I am uneasy at heart when I have to leave my accustomed shelter; I forget that there abides the old in the new, and that there also thou abidest.

Through birth and death, in this world or in others, wherever thou leadest me it is thou, the same, the one companion of my endless life who ever linkest my heart with bonds of joy to the unfamiliar.

When one knows thee, then alien there is none, then no door is shut. Oh, grant me my prayer that I may never lose the bliss of the touch of the one in the play of the many.

64

On the slope of the desolate river among tall grasses I asked her, "Maiden, where do you go shading your lamp with your mantle? My house is all dark and lonesome—lend me your light!" She raised her dark eyes for a moment and looked at my face through the dusk. "I have come to the river," she said, "to float my lamp on the stream when the daylight wanes in the west." I stood alone among tall grasses and watched the timid flame of her lamp uselessly drifting in the tide.

In the silence of gathering night I asked her, "Maiden, your lights are all lit—then where do you go with your lamp? My house is all dark and lonesome,—lend me your light." She raised her dark eyes on my face and stood for a moment doubtful. "I have come," she said at last, "to dedicate my lamp to the sky." I stood and watched her light uselessly burning in the void.

In the moonless gloom of midnight I asked her, "Maiden, what is your quest holding the lamp near your heart? My house is all dark and lonesome—lend me your light." She stopped for a minute and thought and gazed at my face in the dark. "I have brought my light," she said, "to join the carnival of lamps." I stood and watched her little lamp uselessly lost among lights.

65

What divine drink wouldst thou have, my God, from this overflowing cup of my life?

My poet, is it thy delight to see thy creation through my eyes and to stand at the portals of my ears silently to listen to thine own eternal harmony?

Thy world is weaving words in my mind and thy joy is adding music to them. Thou givest thyself to me in love and then feelest thine own entire sweetness in me.

66

She who ever had remained in the depth of my being, in the twilight of gleams and of glimpses; she who never opened her veils in the morning light, will be my last gift to thee, my God, folded in my final song.

Words have wooed yet failed to win her; persuasion has stretched to her its eager arms in vain.

I have roamed from country to country keeping her in the core of my heart, and around her have risen and fallen the growth and decay of my life.

Over my thoughts and actions, my slumbers and dreams, she reigned yet dwelled alone and apart.

Many a man knocked at my door and asked for her and turned away in despair.

There was none in the world who ever saw her face to face, and she remained in her loneliness waiting for thy recognition.

67

Thou art the sky and thou art the nest as well.

O thou beautiful, there in the nest it is thy love that encloses the soul with colors and sounds and odors.

There comes the morning with the golden basket in her right hand bearing the wreath of beauty, silently to crown the earth.

And there comes the evening over the lonely meadows deserted by herds, through trackless paths, carrying cool drafts of peace in her golden pitcher from the western ocean of rest.

But there, where spreads the infinite sky for the soul to take her flight in, reigns the stainless white radiance. There is no day nor night, nor form nor color, and never, never a word.

68

Thy sunbeam comes upon this earth of mine with arm outstretched and stands at my door the livelong day to carry back to thy feet clouds made of my tears and sighs and songs.

With fond delight thou wrappest about thy starry breast that mantle of misty cloud, turning it into numberless shapes and folds and coloring it with hues ever-changing.

It is so light and so fleeting, tender and tearful and dark, that is why thou lovest it, O thou spotless and serene. And that is why it may cover thy awful white light with its pathetic shadows.

69

The same stream of life that runs through my veins night and day runs through the world and dances in rhythmic measures.

It is the same life that shoots in joy through the dust of the earth in numberless blades of grass and breaks into tumultuous waves of leaves and flowers.

It is the same life that is rocked in the ocean-cradle of birth and of death, in ebb and in flow.

I feel my limbs are made glorious by the touch of this world of life. And my pride is from the life-throb of ages dancing in my blood this moment.

70

Is it beyond thee to be glad with the gladness of this rhythm? to be tossed and lost and broken in the whirl of this fearful joy?

All things rush on, they stop not, they

look not behind, no power can hold them back, they rush on.

Keeping steps with that restless, rapid music, seasons come dancing and pass away—colors, tunes, and perfumes pour in endless cascades in the abounding joy that scatters and gives up and dies every moment.

71

That I should make much of myself and turn it on all sides, thus casting colored shadows on thy radiance—such is thy *maya*.

Thou settest a barrier in thine own being and then callest thy severed self in myriad notes. This thy self-separation has taken body in me.

The poignant song is echoed through all the sky in many-colored tears and smiles, alarms and hopes; waves rise up and sink again, dreams break and form. In me is thy own defeat of self.

This screen that thou hast raised is painted with innumerable figures with the brush of the night and the day. Behind it thy seat is woven in wondrous mysteries of curves, casting away all barren lines of straightness.

The great pageant of thee and me has overspread the sky. With the tune of thee and me all the air is vibrant, and all ages pass with the hiding and seeking of thee and me.

72

He it is, the innermost one, who awakens my being with his deep hidden touches.

He it is who puts his enchantment upon these eyes and joyfully plays on the chords of my heart in varied cadence of pleasure and pain.

He it is who weaves the web of this *maya* in evanescent hues of gold and silver, blue and green, and lets peep out through the folds his feet, at whose touch I forget myself.

Days come and ages pass, and it is ever he who moves my heart in many a name, in many a guise, in many a rapture of joy and of sorrow.

73

Deliverance is not for me in renunciation. I feel the embrace of freedom in a thousand bonds of delight.

Thou ever pourest for me the fresh draft of thy wine of various colors and fragrance, filling this earthen vessel to the brim.

My world will light its hundred different lamps with thy flame and place them before the altar of thy temple.

No, I will never shut the doors of my senses. The delights of sight and hearing and touch will bear thy delight.

Yes, all my illusions will burn into illumination of joy, and all my desires ripen into fruits of love.

74

The day is no more, the shadow is upon the earth. It is time that I go to the stream to fill my pitcher.

The evening air is eager with the sad music of the water. Ah, it calls me out into the dusk. In the lonely lane there is no passer by, the wind is up, the ripples are rampant in the river.

I know not if I shall come back home. I know not whom I shall chance to meet. There at the fording in the little boat the unknown man plays upon his lute.

75

Thy gifts to us mortals fulfill all our needs and yet run back to thee undiminished.

The river has its everyday work to do and hastens through fields and hamlets; yet its incessant stream winds towards the washing of thy feet.

The flower sweetens the air with its perfume; yet its last service is to offer itself to thee.

Thy worship does not impoverish the world.

From the words of the poet men take what meanings please them; yet their last meaning points to thee.

76

Day after day, O lord of my life, shall I stand before thee face to face? With folded hands, O lord of all worlds, shall I stand before thee face to face?

Under thy great sky in solitude and silence, with humble heart shall I stand before thee face to face?

In this laborious world of thine, tumultuous with toil and with struggle, among hurrying crowds shall I stand before thee face to face?

And when my work shall be done in this world, O King of kings, alone and speechless shall I stand before thee face to face?

77

I know thee as my God and stand apart—I do not know thee as my own and come closer. I know thee as my father and bow before thy feet—I do not grasp thy hand as my friend's.

I stand not where thou comest down

and ownest thyself as mine, there to clasp thee to my heart and take thee as my comrade.

Thou art the Brother amongst my brothers, but I heed them not, I divide not my earnings with them, thus sharing my all with thee.

In pleasure and in pain I stand not by the side of men, and thus stand by thee. I shrink to give up my life, and thus do not plunge into the great waters of life.

78

When the creation was new and all the stars shone in their first splendor, the gods held their assembly in the sky and sang "Oh, the picture of perfection! the joy unalloyed!"

But one cried of a sudden—"It seems that somewhere there is a break in the chain of light and one of the stars has been lost."

The golden string of their harp snapped, their song stopped, and they cried in dismay—"Yes, that lost star was the best, she was the glory of all heavens!"

From that day the search is unceasing for her, and the cry goes on from one to the other that in her the world has lost its one joy!

Only in the deepest silence of night the stars smile and whisper among themselves—"Vain is this seeking! Unbroken perfection is over all!"

79

If it is not my portion to meet thee in this my life then let me ever feel that I have missed thy sight—let me not forget for a moment, let me carry the pangs of this sorrow in my dreams and in my wakeful hours.

As my days pass in the crowded market of this world and my hands grow full with the daily profits, let me ever feel that I have gained nothing—let me not forget for a moment, let me carry the pangs of this sorrow in my dreams and in my wakeful hours.

When I sit by the roadside, tired and panting, when I spread my bed low in the dust, let me ever feel that the long journey is still before me—let me not forget for a moment, let me carry the pangs of this sorrow in my dreams and in my wakeful hours.

When my rooms have been decked out and the flutes sound and the laughter there is loud, let me ever feel that I have not invited thee to my house—let me not forget for a moment, let me carry the pangs of this sorrow in my dreams and in my wakeful hours.

80

I am like a remnant of a cloud of autumn uselessly roaming in the sky, O my sun ever-glorious! Thy touch has not yet melted my vapor, making me one with thy light, and thus I count months and years separated from thee.

If this be thy wish and if this be thy play, then take this fleeting emptiness of mine, paint it with colors, gild it with gold, float it on the wanton wind and spread it in varied wonders.

And again when it shall be thy wish to end this play at night, I shall melt and vanish away in the dark, or it may be in a smile of the white morning, in a coolness of purity transparent.

81

On many an idle day have I grieved over lost time. But it is never lost, my lord.

Thou hast taken every moment of my life in thine own hands.

Hidden in the heart of things thou art nourishing seeds into sprouts, buds into blossoms, and ripening flowers into fruitfulness.

I was tired and sleeping on my idle bed and imagined all work had ceased. In the morning I woke up and found my garden full with wonders of flowers.

82

Time is endless in thy hands, my lord. There is none to count thy minutes.

Days and nights pass and ages bloom and fade like flowers. Thou knowest how to wait.

Thy centuries follow each other perfecting a small wild flower.

We have no time to lose, and having no time we must scramble for our chances. We are too poor to be late.

And thus it is that time goes by while I give it to every querulous man who claims it, and thine altar is empty of all offerings to the last.

At the end of the day I hasten in fear lest thy gate be shut; but I find that yet there is time.

83

Mother, I shall weave a chain of pearls for thy neck with my tears of sorrow.

The stars have wrought their anklets of light to deck thy feet, but mine will hang upon thy breast.

Wealth and fame come from thee and it is for thee to give or to withhold them. But this my sorrow is absolutely mine own, and when I bring it to thee as my offering thou rewardest me with thy grace.

84

It is the pang of separation that spreads throughout the world and gives birth to shapes innumerable in the infinite sky.

It is this sorrow of separation that gazes in silence all night from star to star and becomes lyric among rustling leaves in rainy darkness of July.

It is this overspreading pain that deepens into loves and desires, into sufferings and joys in human homes; and this it is that ever melts and flows in songs through my poet's heart.

85

When the warriors came out first from their master's hall, where had they hid their power? Where were their armor and their arms?

They looked poor and helpless, and the arrows were showered upon them on the day they came out from their master's hall.

When the warriors marched back again to their master's hall where did they hide their power?

They had dropped the sword and dropped the bow and the arrow; peace was on their foreheads, and they had left the fruits of their life behind them on the day they marched back again to their master's hall.

86

Death, thy servant, is at my door. He has crossed the unknown sea and brought thy call to my home.

The night is dark and my heart is fearful—yet I will take up the lamp, open my gates and bow to him my welcome. It is thy messenger who stands at my door.

I will worship him with folded hands, and with tears. I will worship him placing at his feet the treasure of my heart.

He will go back with his errand done, leaving a dark shadow on my morning; and in my desolate home only my forlorn self will remain as my last offering to thee.

87

In desperate hope I go and search for her in all the corners of my room; I find her not.

My house is small and what once has gone from it can never be regained.

But infinite is thy mansion, my lord, and seeking her I have come to thy door.

I stand under the golden canopy of thine evening sky and lift my eager eyes to thy face.

I have come to the brink of eternity from which nothing can vanish—no hope, no happiness, no vision of a face seen through tears.

Oh, dip my emptied life into that ocean, plunge it into the deepest fullness. Let me for once feel that lost sweet touch in the allness of the universe.

88

Deity of the ruined temple! The broken strings of *Vina* sing no more your praise. The bells in the evening proclaim not your time of worship. The air is still and silent about you.

In your desolate dwelling comes the vagrant spring breeze. It brings the tidings of flowers—the flowers that for your worship are offered no more.

Your worshiper of old wanders ever longing for favor still refused. In the eventide, when fires and shadows mingle with the gloom of dust, he wearily comes back to the ruined temple with hunger in his heart.

Many a festival day comes to you in silence, deity of the ruined temple. Many a night of worship goes away with lamp unlit.

Many new images are built by masters of cunning art and carried to the holy stream of oblivion when their time is come.

Only the deity of the ruined temple remains unworshiped in deathless neglect.

89

No more noisy, loud words from me— such is my master's will. Henceforth I deal in whispers. The speech of my heart will be carried on in murmurings of a song.

Men hasten to the King's market. All the buyers and sellers are there. But I have my untimely leave in the middle of the day, in the thick of work.

Let then the flowers come out in my garden, though it is not their time; and let the midday bees strike up their lazy hum.

Full many an hour have I spent in the strife of the good and the evil, but now it is the pleasure of my playmate of the empty days to draw my heart on to him; and I know not why is this sudden call to what useless inconsequence!

90

On the day when death will knock at thy door what wilt thou offer to him?

Oh, I will set before my guest the full vessel of my life—I will never let him go with empty hands.

All the sweet vintage of all my autumn days and summer nights, all the earnings and gleanings of my busy life will I place before him at the close of my days when death will knock at my door.

91

O thou the last fulfilment of life, Death, my death, come and whisper to me!

Day after day have I kept watch for thee; for thee have I borne the joys and pangs of life.

All that I am, that I have, that I hope and all my love have ever flowed towards thee in depth of secrecy. One final glance from thine eyes and my life will be ever thine own.

The flowers have been woven and the garland is ready for the bridegroom. After the wedding the bride shall leave her home and meet her lord alone in the solitude of night.

92

I know that the day will come when my sight of this earth shall be lost, and life will take its leave in silence, drawing the last curtain over my eyes.

Yet stars will watch at night, and morning rise as before, and hours heave like sea waves casting up pleasures and pains.

When I think of this end of my moments, the barrier of the moments breaks and I see by the light of death thy world with its careless treasures. Rare is its lowliest seat, rare is its meanest of lives.

Things that I longed for in vain and things that I got—let them pass. Let me but truly possess the things that I ever spurned and overlooked.

93

I have got my leave. Bid me farewell, my brothers! I bow to you all and take my departure.

Here I give back the keys of my door —and I give up all claims to my house. I only ask for last kind words from you.

We were neighbors for long, but I received more than I could give. Now the day has dawned and the lamp that lit my dark corner is out. A summons has come and I am ready for my journey.

94

At this time of my parting, wish me good luck, my friends! The sky is flushed with the dawn and my path lies beautiful.

Ask not what I have with me to take there. I start on my journey with empty hands and expectant heart.

I shall put on my wedding garland. Mine is not the red-brown dress of the traveler, and though there are dangers on the way I have no fear in my mind.

The evening star will come out when my voyage is done and the plaintive notes of the twilight melodies be struck up from the King's gateway.

95

I was not aware of the moment when I first crossed the threshold of this life.

What was the power that made me open out into this vast mystery like a bud in the forest at midnight!

When in the morning I looked upon the light I felt in a moment that I was no stranger in this world, that the inscrutable without name and form had taken me in its arms in the form of my own mother.

Even so, in death the same unknown will appear as ever known to me. And because I love this life, I know I shall love death as well.

The child cries out when from the right breast the mother takes it away, in the very next moment to find in the left one its consolation.

96

When I go from hence let this be my parting word, that what I have seen is unsurpassable.

I have tasted of the hidden honey of this lotus that expands on the ocean of light, and thus am I blessed—let this be my parting word.

In this playhouse of infinite forms I have had my play and here have I caught sight of him that is formless.

My whole body and my limbs have thrilled with his touch who is beyond touch; and if the end comes here, let it come—let this be my parting word.

97

When my play was with thee I never questioned who thou wert. I knew nor shyness nor fear, my life was boisterous.

In the early morning thou wouldst call me from my sleep like my own comrade and lead me running from glade to glade.

On those days I never cared to know the meaning of songs thou sangest to me. Only my voice took up the tunes, and my heart danced in their cadence.

Now, when the playtime is over, what is this sudden sight that is come upon me? The world with eyes bent upon thy feet stands in awe with all its silent stars.

98

I will deck thee with trophies, garlands of my defeat. It is never in my power to escape unconquered.

I surely know my pride will go to the wall, my life will burst its bonds in exceeding pain, and my empty heart will sob out in music like a hollow reed, and the stone will melt in tears.

I surely know the hundred petals of a lotus will not remain closed for ever and the secret recess of its honey will be bared.

From the blue sky an eye shall gaze upon me and summon me in silence. Nothing will be left for me, nothing whatever, and utter death shall I receive at thy feet.

99

When I give up the helm I know that the time has come for thee to take it. What there is to do will be instantly done. Vain is this struggle.

Then take away your hands and silently put up with your defeat, my heart, and think it your good fortune to sit perfectly still where you are placed.

These my lamps are blown out at every little puff of wind, and trying to light them I forget all else again and again.

But I shall be wise this time and wait in the dark, spreading my mat on the floor; and whenever it is thy pleasure, my lord, come silently and take thy seat here.

100

I dive down into the depth of the ocean of forms, hoping to gain the perfect pearl of the formless.

No more sailing from harbor to harbor with this my weather-beaten boat. The days are long passed when my sport was to be tossed on waves.

And now I am eager to die into the deathless.

Into the audience hall by the fathomless abyss where swells up the music of toneless strings I shall take this harp of my life.

I shall tune it to the notes of for ever, and, when it has sobbed out its last utterance, lay down my silent harp at the feet of the silent.

101

Ever in my life have I sought thee with my songs. It was they who led me from door to door, and with them have I felt about me, searching and touching my world.

It was my songs that taught me all the lessons I ever learnt; they showed me secret paths, they brought before my sight many a star on the horizon of my heart.

They guided me all the day long to the mysteries of the country of pleasure and pain, and, at last, to what palace gate have they brought me in the evening at the end of my journey?

102

I boasted among men that I had known you. They see your pictures in all works of mind. They come and ask me, "Who is he?" I know not how to answer them. I say, "Indeed, I cannot tell." They blame me and they go away in scorn. And you sit there smiling.

I put my tales of you into lasting songs. The secret gushes out from my heart. They come and ask me, "Tell me all your meanings." I know not how to answer them. I say, "Ah, who knows what they mean!" They smile and go away in utter scorn. And you sit there smiling.

103

In one salutation to thee, my God, let all my senses spread out and touch this world at thy feet.

Like a rain-cloud of July hung low with its burden of unshed showers let all my mind bend down at thy door in one salutation to thee.

Let all my songs gather together their diverse strains into a single current and flow to a sea of silence in one salutation to thee.

Like a flock of homesick cranes flying night and day back to their mountain nests let all my life take its voyage to its eternal home in one salutation to thee.

THE POST OFFICE

By RABINDRANATH TAGORE

DRAMATIS PERSONÆ

MADHAV

AMAL, *his adopted child*

SUDHA, *a little flower girl*

THE DOCTOR

DAIRYMAN

WATCHMAN

GAFFER

VILLAGE HEADMAN, *a bully*

KING'S HERALD

ROYAL PHYSICIAN

ACT I

(MADHAV's *House*)

MADHAV. What a state I am in! Before he came, nothing mattered; I felt so free. But now that he has come, goodness knows from where, my heart is filled with his dear self, and my home will be no home to me when he leaves. Doctor, do you think he——

PHYSICIAN. If there's life in his fate, then he will live long. But what the medical scriptures say, it seems——

MADHAV. Great heavens, what?

PHYSICIAN. The scriptures have it: "Bile or palsey, cold or gout spring all alike."

MADHAV. Oh, get along, don't fling your scriptures at me; you only make me more anxious; tell me what I can do.

PHYSICIAN (*taking snuff*). The patient needs the most scrupulous care.

MADHAV. That's true; but tell me how.

PHYSICIAN. I have already mentioned, on no account must he be let out of doors.

MADHAV. Poor child, it is very hard to keep him indoors all day long.

PHYSICIAN. What else can you do? The autumn sun and the damp are both very bad for the little fellow—for the scriptures have it:

"In wheezing, swoon or in nervous fret,
In jaundice or leaden eyes——"

MADHAV. Never mind the scriptures, please. Eh, then we must shut the poor thing up. Is there no other method?

PHYSICIAN. None at all: for, "In the wind and in the sun——"

MADHAV. What will your "in this and in that" do for me now? Why don't you let them alone and come straight to the point? What's to be done then? Your system is very, very hard for the poor boy; and he is so quiet too with all his pain and sickness. It tears my heart to see him wince, as he takes your medicine.

PHYSICIAN. The more he winces, the surer is the effect. That's why the sage Chyabana observes: "In medicine as in good advices, the least palatable ones are the truest." Ah, well! I must be trotting now. (*Exit*)

(GAFFER *enters.*)

MADHAV. Well, I'm jiggered, there's Gaffer now.

GAFFER. Why, why, I won't bite you.

MADHAV. No, but you are a devil to send children off their heads.

GAFFER. But you aren't a child, and you've no child in the house; why worry then?

MADHAV. Oh, but I have brought a child into the house.

GAFFER. Indeed, how so?

MADHAV. You remember how my wife was dying to adopt a child?

GAFFER. Yes, but that's an old story; you didn't like the idea.

MADHAV. You know, brother, how hard all this getting money in has been. That somebody else's child would sail in and waste all this money earned with so much trouble— Oh, I hated the idea. But this boy clings to my heart in such a queer sort of way——

GAFFER. So that's the trouble! and your money goes all for him and feels jolly lucky it does go at all.

MADHAV. Formerly, earning was a sort of passion with me; I simply couldn't help working for money. Now, I make money and as I know it is all for this dear boy, earning becomes a joy to me.

GAFFER. Ah, well, and where did you pick him up?

MADHAV. He is the son of a man who was a brother to my wife by village ties. He has had no mother since infancy; and now the other day he lost his father as well.

GAFFER. Poor thing: and so he needs me all the more.

MADHAV. The doctor says all the organs of his little body are at loggerheads with each other, and there isn't much hope for his life. There is only one way to save him and that is to keep him out of this autumn wind and sun. But you are such a terror! What with this game of yours at your age, too, to get children out of doors!

GAFFER. God bless my soul! So I'm already as bad as autumn wind and sun, eh! But, friend, I know something, too, of the game of keeping them indoors. When my day's work is over I am coming in to make friends with this child of yours. (*Exit*)

(AMAL *enters.*)

AMAL. Uncle, I say, Uncle!

MADHAV. Hullo! Is that you, Amal?

AMAL. Mayn't I be out of the courtyard at all?

MADHAV. No, my dear, no.

AMAL. See, there where Auntie grinds lentils in the quirn, the squirrel is sitting with his tail up and with his wee hands he's picking up the broken grains of lentils and crunching them. Can't I run up there?

MADHAV. No, my darling, no.

AMAL. Wish I were a squirrel!—it would be lovely. Uncle, why won't you let me go about?

MADHAV. Doctor says it's bad for you to be out.

AMAL. How can the doctor know?

MADHAV. What a thing to say! The doctor can't know and he reads such huge books!

AMAL. Does his book-learning tell him everything?

MADHAV. Of course, don't you know!

AMAL (*with a sigh*). Ah, I am so stupid! I don't read books.

MADHAV. Now, think of it; very, very learned people are all like you; they are never out of doors.

AMAL. Aren't they really?

MADHAV. No, how can they? Early and late they toil and moil at their books, and they've eyes for nothing else. Now, my little man, you are going to be learned when you grow up; and then you will stay at home and read such big books, and people will notice you and say, "he's a wonder."

AMAL. No, no, Uncle; I beg of you by your dear feet—I don't want to be learned, I won't.

MADHAV. Dear, dear; it would have been my saving if I could have been learned.

AMAL. No, I would rather go about and see everything that there is.

MADHAV. Listen to that! See! What will you see, what is there so much to see?

AMAL. See that far-away hill from our window— I often long to go beyond those hills and right away.

MADHAV. Oh, you silly! As if there's nothing more to be done but just get up to the top of that hill and away! Eh! You don't talk sense, my boy. Now listen, since that hill stands there upright as a barrier, it means you can't get beyond it. Else, what was the use in heaping up so many large stones to make such a big affair of it, eh!

AMAL. Uncle, do you think it is meant to prevent your crossing over? It seems to me because the earth can't speak it raises its hands into the sky and beckons. And those who live far and sit alone by their windows can see the signal. But I suppose the learned people——

MADHAV. No, they don't have time for that sort of nonsense. They are not crazy like you.

AMAL. Do you know, yesterday I met someone quite as crazy as I am.

MADHAV. Gracious me, really, how so?

AMAL. He had a bamboo staff on his shoulder with a small bundle at the top, and a brass pot in his left hand, and an old pair of shoes on; he was making for those hills straight across that meadow there. I called out to him and asked,

"Where are you going?" He answered, "I don't know, anywhere!" I asked again, "Why are you going?" He said, "I'm going out to seek work." Say, Uncle, have you to seek work?

MADHAV. Of course I have to. There's many about looking for jobs.

AMAL. How lovely! I'll go about, like them too, finding things to do.

MADHAV. Suppose you seek and don't find. Then——

AMAL. Wouldn't that be jolly? Then I should go farther! I watched that man slowly walking on with his pair of worn out shoes. And when he got to where the water flows under the fig tree, he stopped and washed his feet in the stream. Then he took out from his bundle some gram-flour, moistened it with water and began to eat. Then he tied up his bundle and shouldered it again; tucked up his cloth above his knees and crossed the stream. I've asked Auntie to let me go up to the stream, and eat my gram-flour just like him.

MADHAV. And what did your Auntie say to that?

AMAL. Auntie said, "Get well and then I'll take you over there." Please, Uncle, when shall I get well?

MADHAV. It won't be long, dear.

AMAL. Really, but then I shall go right away the moment I'm well again.

MADHAV. And where will you go?

AMAL. Oh, I will walk on, crossing so many streams, wading through water. Everybody will be asleep with their doors shut in the heat of the day and I will tramp on and on seeking work far, very far.

MADHAV. I see! I think you had better be getting well first; then——

AMAL. But then you won't want me to be learned, will you, Uncle?

MADHAV. What would you rather be then?

AMAL. I can't think of anything just now; but I'll tell you later on.

MADHAV. Very well. But mind you, you aren't to call out and talk to strangers again.

AMAL. But I love to talk to strangers!

MADHAV. Suppose they had kidnapped you?

AMAL. That would have been splendid! But no one ever takes me away. They all want me to stay in here.

MADHAV. I am off to my work—but, darling, you won't go out, will you?

AMAL. No, I won't. But, Uncle, you'll let me be in this room by the roadside. (*Exit* MADHAV.)

DAIRYMAN. Curds, curds, good nice curds.

AMAL. Curdseller, I say, Curdseller.

DAIRYMAN. Why do you call me? Will you buy some curds?

AMAL. How can I buy? I have no money.

DAIRYMAN. What a boy! Why call out then? Ugh! What a waste of time.

AMAL. I would go with you if I could.

DAIRYMAN. With me?

AMAL. Yes, I seem to feel homesick when I hear you call from far down the road.

DAIRYMAN (*lowering his yoke-pole*). Whatever are you doing here, my child?

AMAL. The doctor says I'm not to be out, so I sit here all day long.

DAIRYMAN. My poor child, whatever has happened to you?

AMAL. I can't tell. You see I am not learned, so I don't know what's the matter with me. Say, Dairyman, where do you come from?

DAIRYMAN. From our village.

AMAL. Your village? Is it very far?

DAIRYMAN. Our village lies on the river Shamli at the foot of the Panch-mura hills.

AMAL. Panch-mura hills! Shamli river! I wonder. I may have seen your village. I can't think when though!

DAIRYMAN. Have you seen it? Been to the foot of those hills?

AMAL. Never. But I seem to remember having seen it. Your village is under some very old big trees, just by the side of the red road—isn't that so?

DAIRYMAN. That's right, child.

AMAL. And on the slope of the hill cattle grazing.

DAIRYMAN. How wonderful! Aren't there cattle grazing in our village! Indeed, there are!

AMAL. And your women with red sarees fill their pitchers from the river and carry them on their heads.

DAIRYMAN. Good, that's right. Women from our dairy village do come and draw their water from the river; but then it isn't everyone who has a red saree to put on. But, my dear child, surely you must have been there for a walk some time.

AMAL. Really, Dairyman, never been there at all. But the first day doctor lets me go out, you are going to take me to your village.

DAIRYMAN. I will, my child, with pleasure.

AMAL. And you'll teach me to cry curds and shoulder the yoke like you and walk the long, long road?

DAIRYMAN. Dear, dear, did you ever? Why should you sell curds? No, you will read big books and be learned.

AMAL. No, I never want to be learned —I'll be like you and take my curds from the village by the red road near the old banyan tree, and I will hawk it from cottage to cottage. Oh, how do you cry— "Curd, curd, good nice curd!" Teach me the tune, will you?

DAIRYMAN. Dear, dear, teach you the tune; what an idea!

AMAL. Please do. I love to hear it. I can't tell you how queer I feel when I hear you cry out from the bend of that road, through the line of those trees! Do you know I feel like that when I hear the shrill cry of kites from almost the end of the sky?

DAIRYMAN. Dear child, will you have some curds? Yes, do.

AMAL. But I have no money.

DAIRYMAN. No, no, no, don't talk of money! You'll make me so happy if you have a little curds from me.

AMAL. Say, have I kept you too long?

DAIRYMAN. Not a bit; it has been no loss to me at all; you have taught me how to be happy selling curds. (*Exit*)

AMAL (*intoning*). Curds, curds, good nice curds—from the dairy village—from the country of the Panch-mura hills by the Shamli bank. Curds, good curds; in the early morning the women make the cows stand in a row under the trees and milk them, and in the evening they turn the milk into curds. Curds, good curds. Hello, there's the watchman on his rounds. Watchman, I say, come and have a word with me.

WATCHMAN. What's all this row you are making? Aren't you afraid of the likes of me?

AMAL. No, why should I be?

WATCHMAN. Suppose I march you off then?

AMAL. Where will you take me to? Is it very far, right beyond the hills?

WATCHMAN. Suppose I march you straight to the King?

AMAL. To the King! Do, will you? But the doctor won't let me go out. No one can ever take me away. I've got to stay here all day long.

WATCHMAN. Doctor won't let you, poor fellow! So I see! Your face is pale and there are dark rings round your eyes. Your veins stick out from your poor thin hands.

AMAL. Won't you sound the gong, Watchman?

WATCHMAN. Time has not yet come.

AMAL. How curious! Some say time has not yet come, and some say time has gone by! But surely your time will come the moment you strike the gong!

WATCHMAN. That's not possible; I strike up the gong only when it is time.

AMAL. Yes, I love to hear your gong. When it is midday and our meal is over, Uncle goes off to his work and Auntie falls asleep reading her Rāmāyana, and in the courtyard under the shadow of the wall our doggie sleeps with his nose in his curled up tail; then your gong strikes out, "Dong, dong, dong!" Tell me why does your gong sound?

WATCHMAN. My gong sounds to tell the people, Time waits for none, but goes on forever.

AMAL. Where, to what land?

WATCHMAN. That none knows.

AMAL. Then I suppose no one has ever been there! Oh, I do wish to fly with the time to that land of which no one knows anything.

WATCHMAN. All of us have to get there one day, my child.

AMAL. Have I too?

WATCHMAN. Yes, you too!

AMAL. But doctor won't let me out.

WATCHMAN. One day the doctor himself may take you there by the hand.

AMAL. He won't; you don't know him. He only keeps me in.

WATCHMAN. One greater than he comes and lets us free.

AMAL. When will this great doctor come for me? I can't stick in here any more.

WATCHMAN. Shouldn't talk like that, my child.

AMAL. No. I am here where they have left me—I never move a bit. But when your gong goes off, dong, dong, dong, it goes to my heart. Say, Watchman?

WATCHMAN. Yes, my dear.

AMAL. Say, what's going on there in that big house on the other side, where there is a flag flying high up and the people are always going in and out?

WATCHMAN. Oh, there? That's our new Post Office.

AMAL. Post Office? Whose?

WATCHMAN. Whose? Why, the King's surely!

AMAL. Do letters come from the King to his office here?

WATCHMAN. Of course. One fine day there may be a letter for you in there.

AMAL. A letter for me? But I am only a little boy.

WATCHMAN. The King sends tiny notes to little boys.

AMAL. Oh, how lovely! When shall I have my letter? How do you guess he'll write to me?

WATCHMAN. Otherwise why should he set his Post Office here right in front of your open window, with the golden flag flying?

AMAL. But who will fetch me my King's letter when it comes?

WATCHMAN. The King has many postmen. Don't you see them run about with round gilt badges on their chests?

AMAL. Well, where do they go?

WATCHMAN. Oh, from door to door, all through the country.

AMAL. I'll be the King's postman when I grow up.

WATCHMAN. Ha! ha! Postman, indeed! Rain or shine, rich or poor, from house to house delivering letters—that's very great work!

AMAL. That's what I'd like best. What makes you smile so? Oh, yes, your work is great too. When it is silent everywhere in the heat of the noonday, your gong sounds, Dong, dong, dong,—and sometimes when I wake up at night all of a sudden and find our lamp blown out, I can hear through the darkness your gong slowly sounding, Dong, dong, dong!

WATCHMAN. There's the village headman! I must be off. If he catches me gossiping with you there'll be a great to do.

AMAL. The headman? Whereabouts is he?

WATCHMAN. Right down the road

there; see that huge palm-leaf umbrella hopping along? That's him!

AMAL. I suppose the King's made him our headman here?

WATCHMAN. Made him? Oh, no! A fussy busybody! He knows so many ways of making himself unpleasant that everybody is afraid of him. It's just a game for the likes of him, making trouble for everybody. I must be off now! Mustn't keep work waiting, you know! I'll drop in again tomorrow morning and tell you all the news of the town. (*Exit*)

AMAL. It would be splendid to have a letter from the King every day. I'll read them at the window. But, oh! I can't read writing. Who'll read them out to me, I wonder! Auntie reads her Rāmāyana; she may know the King's writing. If no one will, then I must keep them carefully and read them when I'm grown up. But if the postman can't find me? Headman, Mr. Headman, may I have a word with you?

HEADMAN. Who is yelling after me on the highway? Oh, you wretched monkey!

AMAL. You're the headman. Everybody minds you.

HEADMAN (*looking pleased*). Yes, oh yes, they do! They must!

AMAL. Do the King's postmen listen to you?

HEADMAN. They've got to. By Jove, I'd like to see——

AMAL. Will you tell the postman it's Amal who sits by the window here?

HEADMAN. What's the good of that?

AMAL. In case there's a letter for me.

HEADMAN. A letter for you! Whoever's going to write to you?

AMAL. If the King does.

HEADMAN. Ha! ha! What an uncommon little fellow you are! Ha! ha! the King indeed, aren't you his bosom friend, eh! You haven't met for a long while and the King is pining, I am sure. Wait till tomorrow and you'll have your letter.

AMAL. Say, Headman, why do you speak to me in that tone of voice? Are you cross?

HEADMAN. Upon my word! Cross, indeed! You write to the King! Madhav is devilish swell nowadays. He'd made a little pile; and so kings and padishahs are everyday talk with his people. Let me find him once and I'll make him dance. Oh, you snipper-snapper! I'll get the King's letter sent to your house—indeed I will!

AMAL. No, no, please don't trouble yourself about it.

HEADMAN. And why not, pray! I'll tell the King about you and he won't be very long. One of his footmen will come along presently for news of you. Madhav's impudence staggers me. If the King hears of this, that'll take some of his nonsense out of him. (*Exit*)

AMAL. Who are you walking there? How your anklets tinkle! Do stop a while, dear, won't you?

(*A* GIRL *enters.*)

GIRL. I haven't a moment to spare; it is already late!

AMAL. I see, you don't wish to stop; I don't care to stay on here either.

GIRL. You make me think of some late star of the morning! Whatever's the matter with you?

AMAL. I don't know; the doctor won't let me out.

GIRL. Ah me! Don't then! Should listen to the doctor. People'll be cross with you if you're naughty. I know, always looking out and watching must make you feel tired. Let me close the window a bit for you.

AMAL. No, don't, only this one's open! All the others are shut. But will you tell me who you are? Don't seem to know you.

GIRL. I am Sudha.

AMAL. What Sudha?

SUDHA. Don't you know? Daughter of the flower-seller here.

AMAL. What do *you* do?

SUDHA. I gather flowers in my basket.

AMAL. Oh, flower gathering! That is why your feet seem so glad and your anklets jingle so merrily as you walk. Wish I could be out too. Then I would pick some flowers for you from the very topmost branches right out of sight.

SUDHA. Would you really? Do you know more about flowers than I?

AMAL. Yes, I *do,* quite as much. I know all about Champa of the fairy tale and his seven brothers. If only they let me, I'll go right into the dense forest where you can't find your way. And where the honey-sipping hummingbird rocks himself on the end of the thinnest branch, I will flower out as a champa. Would you be my sister Parul?

SUDHA. You are silly! How can I be sister Parul when I am Sudha and my mother is Sasi, the flower-seller? I have to weave so many garlands a day. It would be jolly if I could lounge here like you!

AMAL. What would you do then, all the day long?

SUDHA. I could have great times with my doll Benay the bride, and Meni the pussycat and—but I say it is getting late and I mustn't stop, or I won't find a single flower.

AMAL. Oh, wait a little longer; I do like it so!

SUDHA. Ah, well—now don't you be naughty. Be good and sit still and on my way back home with the flowers I'll come and talk with you.

AMAL. And you'll let me have a flower then?

SUDHA. No, how can I? It has to be paid for.

AMAL. I'll pay when I grow up—before I leave to look for work out on the other side of that stream there.

SUDHA. Very well, then.

AMAL. And you'll come back when you have your flowers?

SUDHA. I will.

AMAL. You will, really?

SUDHA. Yes, I will.

AMAL. You won't forget me? I am Amal, remember that.

SUDHA. I won't forget you, you'll see. (*Exit*)

(*A troop of* BOYS *enter.*)

AMAL. Say, brothers, where are you all off to? Stop here a little.

BOYS. We're off to play.

AMAL. What will you play at, brothers?

BOYS. We'll play at being plowmen.

FIRST BOY (*showing a stick*). This is our plowshare.

SECOND BOY. We two are the pair of oxen.

AMAL. And you're going to play the whole day?

BOYS. Yes, all day long.

AMAL. And you'll come back home in the evening by the road along the river bank?

BOYS. Yes.

AMAL. Do you pass our house on your way home?

BOYS. You come out to play with us, yes do.

AMAL. Doctor won't let me out.

BOYS. Doctor! Suppose the likes of you mind the doctor. Let's be off; it is getting late.

AMAL. Don't. Why not play on the road near this window? I could watch you then.

THIRD BOY. What can we play at here?

AMAL. With all these toys of mine lying about. Here you are, have them. I can't play alone. They are getting dirty and are of no use to me.

BOYS. How jolly! What fine toys! Look, here's a ship. There's old mother Jatai; say, chaps, ain't he a gorgeous sepoy? And you'll let us have them all? You don't really mind?

AMAL. No, not a bit; have them by all means.

BOYS. You don't want them back?

AMAL. Oh, no, I shan't want them.

[144]

BOYS. Say, won't you get a scolding for this?

AMAL. No one will scold me. But will you play with them in front of our door for a while every morning? I'll get you new ones when these are old.

BOYS. Oh, yes, we will. Say, chaps, put these sepoys into a line. We'll play at war; where can we get a musket? Oh, look here, this bit of reed will do nicely. Say, but you're off to sleep already.

AMAL. I'm afraid I'm sleepy. I don't know, I feel like it at times. I have been sitting a long while and I'm tired; my back aches.

BOYS. It's only early noon now. How is it you're sleepy? Listen! The gong's sounding the first watch.

AMAL. Yes, dong, dong, dong, it tolls me to sleep.

BOYS. We had better go then. We'll come in again tomorrow morning.

AMAL. I want to ask you something before you go. You are always out—do you know of the King's postmen?

BOYS. Yes, quite well.

AMAL. Who are they? Tell me their names.

BOYS. One's Badal, another's Sarat. There's so many of them.

AMAL. Do you think they will know me if there's a letter for me?

BOYS. Surely, if your name's on the letter they will find you out.

AMAL. When you call in tomorrow morning, will you bring one of them along so that he'll know me?

BOYS. Yes, if you like.

CURTAIN

ACT II

(AMAL in Bed)

AMAL. Can't I go near the window today, Uncle? Would the doctor mind that too?

MADHAV. Yes, darling, you see you've made yourself worse squatting there day after day.

AMAL. Oh, no, I don't know if it's made me more ill, but I always feel well when I'm there.

MADHAV. No, you don't; you squat there and make friends with the whole lot of people round here, old and young, as if they are holding a fair right under my eaves—flesh and blood won't stand that strain. Just see—your face is quite pale.

AMAL. Uncle, I fear my fakir'll pass and not see me by the window.

MADHAV. Your fakir, whoever's that?

AMAL. He comes and chats to me of the many lands where he's been. I love to hear him.

MADHAV. How's that? I don't know of any fakirs.

AMAL. This is about the time he comes in. I beg of you, by your dear feet, ask him in for a moment to talk to me here.

(GAFFER enters in a FAKIR's guise.)

AMAL. There you are. Come here, Fakir, by my bedside.

MADHAV. Upon my word, but this is——

GAFFER (winking hard). I am the fakir.

MADHAV. It beats my reckoning what you're not.

AMAL. Where have you been this time, Fakir?

FAKIR. To the Isle of Parrots. I am just back.

MADHAV. The Parrots' Isle!

FAKIR. Is it so very astonishing? Am I like you, man? A journey doesn't cost a thing. I tramp just where I like.

AMAL (clapping). How jolly for you! Remember your promise to take me with you as your follower when I'm well.

FAKIR. Of course, and I'll teach you such secrets too of traveling that nothing in sea or forest or mountain can bar your way.

MADHAV. What's all this rigmarole?

GAFFER. Amal, my dear, I bow to nothing in sea or mountain; but if the doctor joins in with this uncle of yours, then I with all my magic must own myself beaten.

AMAL. No. Uncle shan't tell the doctor. And I promise to lie quiet; but the day I am well, off I go with the Fakir and nothing in sea or mountain or torrent shall stand in my way.

MADHAV. Fie, dear child, don't keep on harping upon going! It makes me so sad to hear you talk so.

AMAL. Tell me, Fakir, what the Parrots' Isle is like.

GAFFER. It's a land of wonders; it's a haunt of birds. There's no man; and they neither speak nor walk, they simply sing and they fly.

AMAL. How glorious! And it's by some sea?

GAFFER. Of course. It's on the sea.

AMAL. And green hills are there?

GAFFER. Indeed, they live among the green hills; and in the time of the sunset when there is a red glow on the hillside, all the birds with their green wings flock back to their nests.

AMAL. And there are waterfalls!

GAFFER. Dear me, of course; you don't have a hill without its waterfalls. Oh, it's like molten diamonds; and, my dear, what dances they have! Don't they make the pebbles sing as they rush over them to the sea. No devil of a doctor can stop them for a moment. The birds looked upon me as nothing but a man, quite a trifling creature without wings—and they would have nothing to do with me. Were it not so I would build a small cabin for myself among their crowd of nests and pass my days counting the sea waves.

AMAL. How I wish I were a bird! Then——

GAFFER. But that would have been a bit of a job; I hear you've fixed up with the dairyman to be a hawker of curds when you grow up; I'm afraid such business won't flourish among birds; you might land yourself into serious loss.

MADHAV. Really this is too much. Between you two I shall turn crazy. Now, I'm off.

AMAL. Has the dairyman been, Uncle?

MADHAV. And why shouldn't he? He won't bother his head running errands for your pet fakir, in and out among the nests in his Parrots' Isle. But he has left a jar of curd for you saying that he is rather busy with his niece's wedding in the village, and he has got to order a band at Kamlipara.

AMAL. But he is going to marry me to his little niece.

GAFFER. Dear me, we are in a fix now.

AMAL. He said she would find me a lovely little bride with a pair of pearl drops in her ears and dressed in a lovely red saree; and in the morning she would milk with her own hands the black cow and feed me with warm milk with foam on it from a brand new earthen cruse; and in the evenings she would carry the lamp round the cow-house, and then come and sit by me to tell me tales of Champa and his six brothers.

GAFFER. How delicious! The prospect tempts even me, a hermit! But never mind, dear, about this wedding. Let it be. I tell you when you wed there'll be no lack of nieces in his household.

MADHAV. Shut up! This is more than I can stand. (*Exit*)

AMAL. Fakir, now that Uncle's off, just tell me, has the King sent me a letter to the Post Office?

GAFFER. I gather that his letter has already started; but it's still on the way.

AMAL. On the way? Where is it? Is it on that road winding through the trees which you can follow to the end of the forest when the sky is quite clear after rain?

GAFFER. That's so. You know all about it already.

AMAL. I do, everything.

GAFFER. So I see, but how?

AMAL. I can't say; but it's quite clear to me. I fancy I've seen it often in days long gone by. How long ago I can't tell. Do you know when? I can see it all: there, the King's postman coming down the hillside alone, a lantern in his left hand and on his back a bag of letters; climbing down for ever so long, for days and nights, and where at the foot of the mountain the waterfall becomes a stream he takes to the footpath on the bank and walks on through the rye; then comes the sugarcane field and he disappears into the narrow lane cutting through the tall stems of sugarcanes; then he reaches the open meadow where the cricket chirps and where there is not a single man to be seen, only the snipe wagging their tails and poking at the mud with their bills. I can feel him coming nearer and nearer and my heart becomes glad.

GAFFER. My eyes aren't young; but you make me see all the same.

AMAL. Say, Fakir, do you know the King who has this Post Office?

GAFFER. I do; I go to him for my alms every day.

AMAL. Good! When I get well, I must have my alms too from him, mayn't I?

GAFFER. You won't need to ask, my dear, he'll give it to you of his own accord.

AMAL. No, I would go to his gate and cry, "Victory to thee, O King!" and dancing to the tabor's sound, ask for alms. Won't it be nice?

GAFFER. It would be splendid, and if you're with me, I shall have my full share. But what'll you ask?

AMAL. I shall say, "Make me your postman, that I may go about lantern in hand, delivering your letters from door to door. Don't let me stay at home all day!"

GAFFER. What is there to be sad for, my child, even were you to stay at home?

AMAL. It isn't sad. When they shut me in here first I felt the day was so long. Since the King's Post Office I like it more and more being indoors, and as I think I shall get a letter one day, I feel quite happy and then I don't mind being quiet and alone. I wonder if I shall make out what'll be in the King's letter?

GAFFER. Even if you didn't wouldn't it be enough if it just bore your name?

(MADHAV enters.)

MADHAV. Have you any idea of the trouble you've got me into, between you two?

GAFFER. What's the matter?

MADHAV. I hear you've let it get rumored about that the King has planted his office here to send messages to both of you.

GAFFER. Well, what about it?

MADHAV. Our headman Panchanan has had it told to the King anonymously.

GAFFER. Aren't we aware that everything reaches the King's ears?

MADHAV. Then why don't you look out? Why take the King's name in vain? You'll bring me to ruin if you do.

AMAL. Say, Fakir, will the King be cross?

GAFFER. Cross, nonsense! And with a child like you and a fakir such as I am. Let's see if the King be angry, and then won't I give him a piece of my mind.

AMAL. Say, Fakir, I've been feeling a sort of darkness coming over my eyes since the morning. Everything seems like a dream. I long to be quiet. I don't feel like talking at all. Won't the King's letter come? Suppose this room melts away all on a sudden, suppose——

GAFFER (fanning AMAL.) The letter's sure to come today, my boy.

(DOCTOR enters.)

DOCTOR. And how do you feel today?

AMAL. Feel awfully well today, Doctor. All pain seems to have left me.

DOCTOR (*aside to* MADHAV). Don't quite like the look of that smile. Bad sign that, his feeling well! Chakradhan has observed——

MADHAV. For goodness sake, Doctor, leave Chakradhan alone. Tell me what's going to happen?

DOCTOR. Can't hold him in much longer, I fear! I warned you before— This looks like a fresh exposure.

MADHAV. No, I've used the utmost care, never let him out of doors; and the windows have been shut almost all the time.

DOCTOR. There's a peculiar quality in the air today. As I came in I found a fearful draft through your front door. That's most hurtful. Better lock it at once. Would it matter if this kept your visitors off for two or three days? If someone happens to call unexpectedly— there's the back door. You had better shut this window as well, it's letting in the sunset rays only to keep the patient awake.

MADHAV. Amal has shut his eyes. I expect he is sleeping. His face tells me— Oh, Doctor, I bring in a child who is a stranger and love him as my own, and now I suppose I must lose him!

DOCTOR. What's that? There's your headman sailing in!—What a bother! I must be going, brother. You had better stir about and see to the doors being properly fastened. I will send on a strong dose directly I get home. Try it on him— it may save him at last, if he can be saved at all. (*Exeunt* MADHAV *and* DOCTOR.)

(*The* HEADMAN *enters.*)

HEADMAN. Hello, urchin!——

GAFFER (*rising hastily*). 'Sh, be quiet.

AMAL. No, Fakir, did you think I was asleep? I wasn't. I can hear everything; yes, and voices far away. I feel that mother and father are sitting by my pillow and speaking to me.

(MADHAV *enters.*)

HEADMAN. I say, Madhav, I hear you hobnob with bigwigs nowadays.

MADHAV. Spare me your jests, Headman, we are but common people.

HEADMAN. But your child here is expecting a letter from the King.

MADHAV. Don't you take any notice of him, a mere foolish boy!

HEADMAN. Indeed, why not! It'll beat the King hard to find a better family! Don't you see why the King plants his new Post Office right before your window? Why there's a letter for you from the King, urchin.

AMAL (*starting up*). Indeed, really!

HEADMAN. How can it be false? You're the King's chum. Here's your letter (*showing a blank slip of paper*). Ha, ha, ha! This is the letter.

AMAL. Please don't mock me. Say, Fakir, is it so?

GAFFER. Yes, my dear. I as Fakir tell you it *is* his letter.

AMAL. How is it I can't see? It all looks so blank to me. What is there in the letter, Mr. Headman?

HEADMAN. The King says, "I am calling on you shortly; you had better arrange puffed rice offerings for me.— Palace fare is quite tasteless to me now." Ha! ha! ha!

MADHAV (*with folded palms*). I beseech you, headman, don't you joke about these things——

GAFFER. Cutting jokes indeed, dare he!

MADHAV. Are you out of your mind too, Gaffer?

GAFFER. Out of my mind, well then I am; I can read plainly that the King writes he will come himself to see Amal, with the state physician.

AMAL. Fakir, Fakir, 'sh, his trumpet! Can't you hear?

HEADMAN. Ha! ha! ha! I fear he won't until he's a bit more off his head.

AMAL. Mr. Headman, I thought you were cross with me and didn't love me. I never could think you would fetch me the King's letter. Let me wipe the dust off your feet.

HEADMAN. This little child does have an instinct of reverence. Though a little silly, he has a good heart.

AMAL. It's hard on the fourth watch now, I suppose— Hark the gong, "Dong, dong, ding," "Dong, dong, ding." Is the evening star up? How is it I can't see——

GAFFER. Oh, the windows are all shut, I'll open them.

(*A knocking outside.*)

MADHAV. What's that?—Who is it—what a bother!

VOICE (*from outside*). Open the door.

MADHAV. Say, Headman— Hope they're not robbers.

HEADMAN. Who's there?—It's Panchanan, the headman, calls— Aren't you afraid of the like of me? Fancy! The noise has ceased! Panchanan's voice carries far.—Yes, show me the biggest robbers!——

MADHAV (*peering out of the window*). I should think the noise has ceased. They've smashed the door.

(*The* KING'S HERALD *enters.*)

HERALD. Our Sovereign King comes tonight!

HEADMAN. My God!

AMAL. At what hour of the night, Herald?

HERALD. On the second watch.

AMAL. When from the city gates my friend the watchman will strike his gong, "ding dong ding, ding dong ding"—then?

HERALD. Yes, then. The King sends his greatest physician to attend on his young friend.

(STATE PHYSICIAN *enters.*)

STATE PHYSICIAN. What's this? How close it is here! Open wide all the doors and windows. (*Feeling* AMAL's *body*) How do you feel, my child?

AMAL. I feel very well, Doctor, very well. All pain is gone. How fresh and open! I can see all the stars now twinkling from the other side of the dark.

PHYSICIAN. Will you feel well enough to leave your bed with the King when he comes in the middle watches of the night?

AMAL. Of course, I'm dying to be about for ever so long. I'll ask the King to find me the polar star.—I must have seen it often, but I don't know exactly which it is.

PHYSICIAN. He will tell you everything. (*To* MADHAV) Will you go about and arrange flowers through the room for the King's visit? (*Indicating the* HEADMAN) We can't have that person in here.

AMAL. No, let him be, Doctor. He is a friend. It was he who brought me the King's letter.

PHYSICIAN. Very well, my child. He may remain if he is a friend of yours.

MADHAV (*whispering into* AMAL's *ear*). My child, the King loves you. He is coming himself. Beg for a gift from him. You know our humble circumstances.

AMAL. Don't you worry, Uncle.—I've made up my mind about it.

MADHAV. What is it, my child?

AMAL. I shall ask him to make me one of his postmen that I may wander far and wide, delivering his message from door to door.

MADHAV (*slapping his forehead*). Alas, is that all?

AMAL. What'll be our offerings to the King, Uncle, when he comes?

HERALD. He has commanded puffed rice.

AMAL. Puffed rice! Say, Headman, you're right. You said so. You knew all we didn't.

HEADMAN. If you send word to my house then I could manage for the King's advent really nice——

PHYSICIAN. No need at all. Now be quiet all of you. Sleep is coming over him. I'll sit by his pillow; he's dropping into slumber. Blow out the oil-lamp. Only let the star-light stream in. Hush, he slumbers.

MADHAV (*addressing* GAFFER). What are you standing there for like a statue, folding your palms.—I am nervous.— Say, are they good omens? Why are they darkening the room? How will star-light help?

GAFFER. Silence, unbeliever.

(SUDHA *enters.*)

SUDHA. Amal!

PHYSICIAN. He's asleep.

SUDHA. I have some flowers for him. Mayn't I give them into his own hand?

PHYSICIAN. Yes, you may.

SUDHA. When will he be awake?

PHYSICIAN. Directly the King comes and calls him.

SUDHA. Will you whisper a word for me in his ear?

PHYSICIAN. What shall I say?

SUDHA. Tell him Sudha has not forgotten him.

CURTAIN

THE LIFE AND WORKS OF
RABINDRANATH TAGORE

By AMIYA CHAKRAVARTY

RABINDRANATH TAGORE in *Jiban-Smriti* (*My Reminiscences,* 1917), and later in *Chele-bela* (*My Boyhood Days,* 1940) gives us many of his own memories of childhood and youth. He paints a vivid picture of Calcutta, where he was born on May 6, 1861. It was truly an ancient city, he wrote, with horse carriages rolling heavily through the streets, lifting great clouds of dust. The more fortunate citizens had their monograms painted on their leather-hooded coaches. The coachman flaunted a turban draped over his ears: two footmen stood up behind, shouting "Hey-yo!" to frighten the pedestrians, who would jump out of the way. Separated from the men, the women moved about in closed palanquins. Few would have been so daring as to wear a modern blouse or shoes, which were symbols of immodesty.

He etches many details of a vanished feudal past—an atmosphere which outraged him—including the daily wonder of being early awakened by the kerosene lamps, so different from the castor-oil lamps whose fitful glare lighted the lessons in which his teacher gave him his first contact with literature. The boy would yawn over his book, finally falling asleep in spite of warnings against becoming "the family pack-mule." In the

various schools he later attended, he continued to be a slow learner, incapable of accepting a disciplinary system that looked upon the students as bodies with no regard for their individual personalities. For him the schoolrooms were brick dungeons, with no gardens or trees: for no reason, children were banished there, away from the life of nature and human relationships, and treated with dry hostility by elderly, unimaginative tyrants. The Oriental Seminary, given to rather barbarous corporal punishment— which he somehow escaped—dug the deepest scars in his memory.

Tagore, however, could afford the luxury of being a bad scholar, for at home, with his twelve older brothers and sisters, he found an atmosphere of high spiritual culture. Art, social service, patriotic schemes for freedom from foreign rule, were discussed and practiced. Being the youngest he was largely ignored but still he responded inwardly. His father was a remarkable man, venerated under the name of *Maharishi* ("the great saint"), and his liberalism, rare in a period when caste and class prevailed to an acute degree, had earned him the affection of the people. In a pioneering family, inspired by the first generation of Indian reformers in the early nineteenth century, the saintly father whose religious faith ignited a revolutionary ardor—to be far surpassed by his young son and by Gandhi at a much later period—was a creative influence.

Tagore was a lonely adolescent. He lost his mother when he was only fourteen—his only joy had often been to go to her and talk or recite, showing off his secret knowledge—and with her passing he had no one to go to. His poetic gifts were slowly maturing; when he was only eight he had started writing verses. One of his brothers had taught him the technique of the fourteen-syllable *payar,* and he immediately started improvising patterns of words on a small black slate. He remarked once that he must have made a pest of himself with his "newborn poetry," but a great Indian poet had been born. From that time on the passion for poetry never left him.

The world of trees and the sky, the far reality of nature which was also near to him, nourished his sensitive mind. Alone or in the care of servants much of the time, he spent long hours rummaging about the old house and then tiptoeing to the far corner of the veranda from where he could watch the garden and the pond, and observe the people who came there to bathe or to gather flowers. Overhead the kites flew, clouds gathered, and the lighted blue air was an unending mystery. The vendor's cry, selling green mangos, silver bangles, or other wares came from across the street.

Thus an independent and lonely companionship was built up with the great world. While most children thought only of play—his playmates, as he tenderly puts it in a later poem, never left him from "seven to seventy"—the decades deepened a childlike wonder which sustained his entire life, actually up to his eightieth year. Each morning when he wakened, he tells us in his autobiog-raphy, the day seemed to him a gilt-edged envelope with a secret message inside. "It was as if nature held something in her closed hands and was smilingly asking us: 'What d'you think I have?'" He shared in the mystery of creation, to be colored by great joy and great sorrow, but the assurance remained.

Tagore's first journey outside India was a trip to the Himalayas. He traveled with his father, who taught him on this trip the Vedas and Upanishads—which he learned to recite in the original Sanskrit—acquainted him with astronomy, made him take rigorous exercises to train his body, and took him to several cultural and spiritual centers in Northern India. He always remembered his visit to Amritsar, the holy city of the Sikhs, where he listened to the chanting in the golden temple. Tagore's consciousness of the inheritances of India's past, of the living streams of faith deepened; he also sensed the beauty and spaciousness of his homeland. A further chapter in his life was opened; the young poet's consciousness touched an immemorial civilization and its scenic grandeur. He was also initiated into the problems of India, its multitudes, its poverty—although his encounters with that side of his country's life were not as agonizing as they became later on.

Then, after a rather disappointing interlude in school, he left with a brother for England in 1878 to study and to familiarize himself with British civilization. There was a brief and rather futile stay in a school at Brighton; then he was on his own in London lodgings, where he rather listlessly began to study Latin. His greatest enthusiasm was reserved for literature at the University of London. Sensitive to the human character and expressive power of English poetry, he was particularly fond of Shakespeare and

Shelley because of "the wave of passion that breaks from their works." He also felt an affinity for Chatterton and this inspired his technique of presenting one of his first books of poems as extracts from an ancient manuscript. Later, however, freed from excessive enthusiasm, his judgment of English literature became more critical; he reserved his deepest admiration for creative artists like Keats, Shelley, and Wordsworth, and he was influenced by the Romantic tradition which also found expression in Continental European literature.

Tagore returned home without earning the university diploma his brothers had hoped for, but his mind was nevertheless considerably enriched. He had arrived at a point of maturity which marked the first authentic products of his creative writing. The years that followed were happy: "All about me everything was eighteen!" Under the influence of both European and Indian music he composed a musical drama, *Valmiki Pratibha* (*The Genius of Valmiki*, 1881), written for performance at family *soirées*. "At that time," he wrote, "a veritable cascade of creative impulse ceaselessly played upon us. We wrote, we sang, we played, we carried on all sorts of dialogue among ourselves."

At the age of twenty he published his *Sandhya-Sangeet* (*Evening Songs*, 1881), a volume of verse written with complete freedom from any preoccupation with pleasing a traditional public. Here he explains the break in harmony which is produced between the outer and inner worlds when the soul endeavors to escape from the body's prison and when the heart cries out its raging thirst for love. *Prabhat-Sangeet* (*Morning Songs*, 1882) exalts the mystical dawn that opens a symbolic door onto the night and through which the pure spirit enters. Tagore himself later expressed certain reservations about these early works,

recognizing in them a tendency toward obscurity, but at the same time insisting on his total lack of literary affectation.

This was a period that was to prove vital in the development of his thought and the growth of his genius. A new form of humanism was taking shape in his mind, and he began to develop one of the ideas which was to be among the most cherished throughout his life, inspired moreover by the cosmic and yet ethically related themes given him by his family. True greatness, he felt, is to be sought in the very small; God's truth is often expressed in the humblest, tiniest creation, whether it be a bird, a blade of grass, a flower. A human child is a perennial wonder. At the same time he discovered that it is through love, spiritualized and mysticized, that the eternal freedom of the soul is developed.

In 1881 he left for Chandernagore to stay with his favorite brother, Jyotirindra, and his wife. They boated together on the Ganges, singing to the accompaniment of a violin. Tagore recited his verses from *Evening Songs*—"The Complaint of Happiness," inspired by the moon; "Separation," with its intense lyricism; "Suicide of a Star." He made a start on his first novel, *Bou Thakuranir Hat* (*The Young Queen's Market*, 1883), then left to live for a while near Calcutta, where he collaborated in founding a literary academy promoting the development of regional studies and the free expression of the Bengali colloquial tradition.

Soon he was living on a beach on the west coast, at Karwar, with his second brother. The surroundings were inspiring; the seashore ringed by mountains, furrowed by a river. In this landscape his lyric outpouring reached a new height: the book of poems, *Pictures and Songs* (*Chabi O Gan*, 1883), blends visual beauty with intensive perception. At this time he also wrote the poetic drama

Nature's Revenge (*Prakitir Parishodh*, 1883), which was his first clear expression, through character and dramatized situation, of the futility of denying life in order to gain spiritual truth; the ascetic fails because he is unable to take a larger view of life and nature takes her revenge.

On his return from Karwar, Tagore was married. He has told us little about this phase of his life. We know only that his wife died fifteen years later, as did two of the three children born to them. His tenderness for her, his deep sense of loss and loneliness found expression in *Remembrance* (*Smaran*, 1902), a dedicatory volume of lyrics published shortly after her death. In the phase that followed, Tagore seems to have been a spectator of life, welcoming every outer impression without misgiving in order to use it as a source of inner experience. His life was touched with inwardness, and a sense of interconnections; love and life, nature and the mysterious universe, though tinged with sorrow, never obscured an abiding reality.

Some of the poems written during that period were to be included much later in *The Gardener, Lyrics of Love and Life* (1913), published in English. Without chronicling Tagore's great output of songs, poems, stories, dramas and his varied and magnificent prose discourses, we can pause here and record the fact that he had now arrived: the full plenitude of his writings would now open up year by year in original Bengali and later, from 1912, in his own English translations. A few of his novels, plays, and stories can be mentioned here as landmarks of his creative life, and then the English translations can be traced in later sequence.

Briefly speaking, the main phases of his poetry are described as the period of *Golden Boat* (*Sonar Tari*, 1894) and *Moments* (*Ksanika*, 1901). These books and others published in between include romantic lyrics, odes, and ballads, ranging from the sonorous and ornamental to the seemingly light but passionate unification of love and life.

The second great period is often described as belonging to *The Flight of Swans* (*Balaka*, 1916), where he broke into experiments in meditational lyrics; life and art are heightened in the context of the heart's wisdom. An outreach of philosophy transforms and yet maintains a high meridian of spontaneous poetry. Also, the technique is diversified, reaching the border of free verse without renouncing meter and rhyme. The famous poem "Tajmahal" and "The Picture" were printed in that volume, as was also the title poem "Balaka," which celebrates the sudden flight of a flock of birds on the Jhelum River in Kashmir. This migratory flash of wings reminded him of a home away from home, toward which all creation is speeding. The usual descriptive recording, not an accurately measured one, could now be extended and include a much later volume, *Evening Melody* (*Puravi*, 1925). Most of the solemn, sunset-colored, and richly harmonized poems of this volume were written during his trip to Latin America, on the boat and in San Isidro, near Buenos Aires. This period ends with his *Last Poems*, most of which were published in book form after his death in 1941. Terse and unadorned, chiseled with a mastery gained through almost seven decades of thought and craft, these poems mark yet another level of poetic expression.

In the fewest words they transmit a radiance that is evocative of the Vedic and Upanishadic *mantras* (hymns). Most of these poems remain untranslated, but one or two, like "The Last Day's Sun," are widely known to Indian readers in English translation.

Turning to the other literary aspects of

Tagore's art and life, one can begin with his dramas, one of which has already been mentioned. *Sacrifice* (*Visarjan*, published in Bengali in 1890) depicts the struggle between the deeper meaning of religion as contrasted to orthodox Hindu practices. Because of Tagore's scrupulous fairness the priest does not appear as a mere paper figure, embossed with scriptural quotations. The power of tradition as embodied in a narrow religious conformist is exposed by the simple humanity of a young devotee who in turn was brought close to spiritual truth through the love of Aparna, a courageous beautiful girl. Jaising, the young devotee, his master Raghupati, the priest, and the unaffected strength of Aparna reach a tragic climax which as in a Shakespearean drama redeems even when no victory is in sight. *Sacrifice* is recognized as one of his best plays.

Chitra (*Chitrangada*, 1913) is a delicate, sensuous, and highly symbolic play of love. *Post Office* (*Dakghar*, 1912), a subtle and wistful playlet, portrays a young boy, Amal, who waits for the king's letter while he watches the procession of life from his sickroom window. The letter arrives. Amal is asleep, his time is over; at that point a little girl, his playmate, comes and leaves a flower at his bedside, asking people to tell him when he awoke "Sudha has not forgotten him." These short plays are favorites both in India and the West.

Tagore wrote many other dramas, some of them based on mystical themes and others, like *Red Oleanders* (*Rakta-Karabi*, 1925), are dramas socially and politically oriented, written as a protest against mechanistic civilization. But most of them are suited more for profound and imaginative study rather than for acting. And yet his dramas always seem to gain new power when they are staged. Tagore, who wrote plays and acted them in his family theater from his youthful

days, had a keen sense of character, plot, and the technique of dramatic presentation.

Among Tagore's short stories published in different English translations, such as *Hungry Stones and Other Stories* (1916), *House-Warming and Other Selected Writings* (1965), some individual stories like "Cabuliwallah" and "Hungry Stones" are perennial favorites. Between the last two lie scores of stories drawn from the river region of Bengal, with simple rural characters whom he got to know and love when he lived in a houseboat and watched village India at close range. Tagore has not been matched or rivaled in the domain of the short story in the rich literature of Bengal or, actually, in any other part of the world. "Wife's Letter" is a masterly, modern portrait of a Bengali woman, a housewife who breaks out of the fetters of narrow domesticity: the depth of character, the social context and the irony no less than the utter humanity of the story reveal the sensitive iconoclast and the artist in Tagore.

Not much is known in English about Tagore's novels. And yet *Gora* (1923), poorly translated by an English friend, is accepted by Bengali critics as the greatest novel that has been written in their literature. Originally written in 1910 when Bengal—and India as a whole—was seething with patriotism, he took the whole canvas of the conservative as well as revolutionary movements to depict a nationalist, Gora, who stood for freedom. But his freedom, noble as it was in conception, was identified with one country only and with the order of traditional Indian society only, a society seeking freedom from foreign rule while not fully realizing the need of acquiring and giving full freedom to all sections of Indian society as well. Gora discovers, at the height of his zealous nationalism, that he is the son of an Irish father and a

Hindu mother whose union was perhaps never legitimized. This makes him confront the larger humanity of which India was a part. *Ghare-Baire* (*Home and the World,* 1910) is a more discursive and deeply philosophical novel written in the form of letters, on the same general theme of patriotism seen in the context of the new international world. *Chaturanga* (*Broken Ties,* 1916) is a collection of stories or novelettes. Its first short novel is one of the finest creations of Tagore: it is quintessential, and is yet detailed in observation and analysis. The whole field of religion—including group-ecstasy and collective tradition, as well as the all too individual path of spiritual realization—is brought into the story with humor and passionate veracity.

How did an Indian poet—and that was Tagore's lifelong identity—who had hardly ever written a line in English reach the Western world? In May 1912, for various reasons, he went to his favorite estate in Bengal for quietness. During this short period of spare days and hours, Tagore remembered a promise he had once made to an English artist and writer who had come to his family home in Calcutta: namely, that he would translate a few of his Bengali poems into English. Let us hear of the genesis of *Gitanjali* (*Song Offerings,* 1913) in the poet's own words:

. . . You have alluded to the English translation of *Gitanjali.* To this day I have not been able to imagine how I came to do it and how people came to like it so much. That I cannot write English is such a patent fact, that I never had even the vanity to feel ashamed of it. If anybody wrote an English note asking me to tea, I have never felt equal to answering it. Perhaps you think that by now I have gotten over that delusion, but in no way am I deluded that I have composed in English. . . . I went to Shelidah to rest, but unless the mind is active, one does not feel strong enough to relax completely, so the only way to keep myself calm was to do some light work.

So I took up the poems of *Gitanjali* and set myself to translate them one by one. You may wonder why such a crazy ambition should possess one in such a weak state of health. But believe me, I did not undertake this task in a spirit of reckless bravery; I simply felt an urge to recapture, through the medium of another language, the feelings and sentiments which had created such a feast of joy within me in past days. The pages of a small exercise-book came gradually to be filled, and with it in my pocket I boarded the ship. The idea of keeping it in my pocket was that when my mind became restless on the high seas, I could recline on a deck-chair and set myself to translate one or two poems. And this is what actually happened. . . . Rothenstein already had an inkling of my reputation as a poet; therefore, when in the course of conversation he expressed a desire to see some of my poems, I handed him my manuscript, with some reluctance. I could hardly believe the opinion he expressed after reading it. He then gave my book to Yeats. The story of what followed is known to you. From this explanation of mine you will see that I was not responsible for the offense, but that it was due mainly to the force of circumstances . . .

Yeats in his introduction to *Gitanjali* told the world about the overwhelming impact these translations made on him. Not only Tagore's genius, but the immemorial traditions of Indian life and lyricism which he represented, Tagore's natural gift of symbolism at once simple and deep, and his incomparable choice of English words impressed the Irish poet. The climax came when Rothenstein invited a few friends—some of the most notable thinkers, artists, and literary men in or near London—to meet Tagore and hear his poems. Yeats recited some of Tagore's translations. The effect was an immediate recognition and a recommendation, soon to follow, for awarding the Nobel Prize to the Indian poet. Indeed the Nobel award was announced a year later in 1914 when the poet had returned to Santiniketan, his educational center in India.

Even through the opaque and somewhat distorted, abbreviated and intellectualized medium of translation the Indian poet was able to transmit the original glow of his Bengali lyrics. He was his own translator and could change metaphors and words in a way that others could not, and this he often did without any adverse effect. Indeed, some of his translations read like originals, carrying a spontaneity and elusive beauty that continue to move us today.

We need yet to consider Tagore's influence as an educationist, as a social pioneer in India and as an uncompromising worker for the freedom of all races, peoples, and cultures as an inalienable human right. His educational center, started in rural West Bengal in 1901, grew into a pioneer school; he had introduced coeducation, abolition of all caste or class distinctions, and he invited literary, scholarly, and artistic talent from all over India and the world to come and teach. *Santiniketan* (literally, the abode of peace) thus united his life's work and vision; it played an increasing role as India's and Asia's—"guest-house" where

humanity could meet. *"Yatra Visvam Bhavati Eka Needam,"* "there where the world finds its home," is a passage from the ancient Vedic age which Tagore accepted and applied in the modern age. *Visva-Bharati* (World University), as he later named the educational center, was an achievement in depth and inclusiveness; scholars and artists came from many countries to help its growth. Gandhi and Nehru gave Tagore their firm support at a later stage; now it is a chartered university.

Tagore's repeated visits to Europe, the United States, and to all the countries of Asia allowed him to understand the needs of peoples, to share with them their frustrations in a divisive world. It would be apposite to mention that the entire sum given to him as a Nobel award was spent in building this center; also his earnings from world lecture tours and from performances of his plays were quietly used for adding new departments or for inviting scholars from different parts of India and from abroad.

A poet, a patriot, and a revered personality whose generous gifts to our times are a part of our civilization, Rabindranath Tagore died in 1941 in the city of his birth, Calcutta. As he loved to say, his greatest pride was that he had already become "anonymous" in his lifetime; people in remote Indian villages sang his songs, recited his poems, used his thoughts without knowing the authorship; bullock-cart drivers, ferry boatmen, workers in the fields thus accepted his gifts as a part of their perennial inheritance. All modern civilizations came to know him through *Gitanjali* and the Nobel Prize, and gave him a permanent place; his vision of human truth will long continue to challenge and inspire mankind.

Amiya Chakravarty was literary secretary to Rabindranath Tagore for twenty years. He is now a professor of philosophy at New Paltz State College in New York.

THE 1913 PRIZE

By GUNNAR AHLSTRÖM

RABINDRANATH TAGORE's *Gitanjali,* as related earlier in this section, was shown to William Butler Yeats in manuscript by William Rothenstein. Yeats in turn showed it to the poet and artist Thomas Sturge Moore. In 1911 Sturge Moore was elected to an important post in the Royal Society of Literature, whose concern it had been, since 1912, to watch over the interests of England with regard to the Nobel Prize. It would have been natural that Yeats himself should propose Tagore for the Prize, but perhaps he considered himself to be too personally involved. So Tagore's nomination, sent to the Swedish Academy in January 1913, was signed by Sturge Moore.

England's principal candidate for that year was Thomas Hardy, and it was the subject of concerted action on the part of no less than ninety-seven signatories. In all, twenty-eight names of varying importance were proposed. In Spain, there was a mass rising in favor of Benito Pérez Galdos, the petitions for whom carried a total of seven hundred signatures. Italy's principal candidate was Grazia Deledda; Switzerland again produced Carl Spitteler. There were candidates from Denmark, Finland, and Sweden, and Belgium stuck up for its rights. France as usual sent eminent representatives of the literary school of the period: Ernest Lavisse, Pierre Loti, and Anatole France, this year proposed by Germany. It might have been feared that the faraway author of *Gitanjali* would be submerged by so many candidates from the West. That it was not so is a high tribute to the conscientious work and the fairness of mind of the people whose task it was to award the Prize.

The Nobel Committee of the Swedish Academy was in the singularly happy position of having among its members an expert orientalist who understood Bengali and already knew of Tagore. The Swedish Academy had been rejuvenated during the course of the last few years, and one of its members at that time was a greatly admired poet, Verner von Heidenstam, of whom more was to be heard in connection with the Nobel Prize in 1916. He had been enchanted by the message of *Gitanjali,* a message inspired by an orientalism whose inspiration he could discover in his own youthful poems. With praiseworthy independence of mind, he seized his pen and drew up a special report and sent it in for the consideration of his colleagues.

His reasoning hit home, and recalled certain criticisms of decisions made in earlier years. He was also strongly backed up by the enthusiasm issuing from a document presented by a colleague who belonged to the same generation of writers. Among the Committee's collection of university professors, bishops, officials, and retired poets, these two writers were the only ones who represented the active contemporary literature of the country. Their opinion held weight. More and more of the Academicians began to read *Gitanjali* and gradually succumbed to the charm of these rhythmic ideas. Then the unexpected happened. The Committee's recommendation in behalf of Emile Faguet was rejected by a decision of the Academy *in pleno*. Of the thirteen who voted on November 13, twelve were in favor of Rabindranath Tagore.

It was afternoon at the school of Santiniketan, the institution founded by Tagore in a small village in West Bengal. The sun would soon disappear over the horizon; the master had returned from an expedition into the forest accompanied by his pupils. On the homeward road they passed by the village post office, and an official dashed out to deliver a telegram. Tagore absentmindedly put the envelope in his pocket, but the telegraph operator eagerly insisted on his opening it immediately. The students listened to its contents. Their pride knew no bounds.

Their teacher had been the recipient of a worldwide honor: "because of his profoundly sensitive, fresh, and beautiful verse, by which, with consummate skill, he has made his poetic thought, expressed in his own English words, a part of the literature of the West."

The award ceremony took place on December 10, 1913, but Tagore did not take part in it. The authorities had to content themselves with accepting his telegram of apology, pleading the distance of a whole hemisphere separating him from the laureate's platform. When Tagore finally visited Sweden in the spring of 1921, in Stockholm he was treated like an oriental Magus. School children sang in his honor; enthusiastic audiences applauded him at his lectures; King Gustavus granted him an audience, and the Academy arranged a dinner for him. The honored guest's hair and beard had had time to turn white and his work, which had reached a vast output and was by now more fully translated, was even more impressive than on that happy day in 1913 when he had won the Nobel Prize.

Translated by Camilla Sykes.

Sigrid Undset

1928

"Principally for her powerful

descriptions of Northern life

during the Middle Ages"

Illustrated by HERMINE DAVID

PRESENTATION ADDRESS

By PER HALLSTRÖM

CHAIRMAN OF THE NOBEL COMMITTEE
OF THE SWEDISH ACADEMY

In HER FIRST NOVELS or novellas, all of them remarkable works, Sigrid Undset painted the present-day world of young women in the environs of Christiania. It was a restless generation, prompt to make the gravest decisions as soon as its aspirations for happiness were at stake, ready to take the ultimate logical and sentimental consequences of its impulsive nature, and impassioned for truth. This generation had to pay dearly for the sense of reality it acquired. It had to pass through many trials before regaining its inner unity, and some of its representatives succumbed in the struggle. The women of this generation were strangely isolated in this disconcerting world. Far from finding support in a firmly established social rule, they had, in full consciousness, renounced the heritage of the past. Hostile to all established social order, which they considered a useless yoke, they counted only on themselves to create a new society, consistent with a conviction, doubtless sincere at bottom, but easily misled.

With a lively imagination, Sigrid Undset lived the life of these women; she portrayed them sympathetically but with merciless truthfulness. She traced the tragedy of their lives without embellishing or amplifying it; and she conveyed the evolution of their destinies with the most implacable logic, which implied the condemnation of her heroines and of the world in which they were living. The picture is gripping, as far as the scope of the personages permits; it is attractive only in its marvelously fresh and brilliant descriptions of nature. Remaining forever in the reader's memory are the excursions on skis in the Norwegian solitude, the effects of the capricious play of the winter light, the exhilaration of the icy wind during the run, the mad dance of the blood in the veins, the spirit of adventure, the joy, the feeling of life and strength which makes the heart pound. And Sigrid Undset describes with the same mastery the splendors of spring, saturated with light and full of promises. In this domain her art attained greatness quite early.

This greatness began to extend to her entire work as soon as she abandoned the disunified and uprooted beings of the present time who had attracted her attention, in order to dedicate herself to the life of a distant past. She was destined by birth to do pioneer work in this area. Her father was a gifted historian, and from childhood she had lived in an atmosphere of historic legend and folklore. Moreover, she acquired a solid historical knowledge, guided, it would seem, by this premonition of the task her genius had set for her.

There she found the material which truly suited her nature, and her imagination was confronted with a task adequate to its scope. The characters she was going to make appear out of the past would offer a more complete unity and would be of a firmer cast than the contemporary characters. Far from being confined in a sterile isolation, they would participate in the great solidarity of past generations. These great masses would come alive in her work in a more vivid, firmer shape than the amorphous society of our era. Here was a great challenge to a writer who felt capable of carrying a heavy burden.

In their fashion, the generations of the Middle Ages also enjoyed a more varied inner life than the present generation, which Sigrid Undset found obsessed with the pursuit of sexual happiness, a quest which also determined their concepts of truth. These ancestors were strongly determined by the sentiment of honor and by faith. Here was the rich field for a psychology adequate to them. Moreover, the author's imagination was bound to be attracted by the difficult task of conjuring out of the darkness of a little-known past the external life of former generations in all its diversity. Sigrid Undset has done so to an extent that has aroused general admiration.

Insofar as the inner life is concerned, her work can hardly be criticized. Intimately combined with the consciousness of the nation, in her depiction, honor retains all the rigor and all the weight that it had for the chevaliers and great landowners of the fourteenth century. The demands of honor are clearly stated, and the conflicts it creates are worked out regardless of their brutal consequences. Religious life is described with startling truth. Under Sigrid Undset's pen it does not become a continuous holiday of the mind, penetrating and dominating human nature; it remains, as in our day, insecure and rebellious, and is often even harsher. Profoundly conscious of the hold of faith on these inexperienced and unpolished souls, the author has given it, in the grave hours of existence, an overwhelming power.

The erotic life, the problem common to the two sexes, which constitutes the center of Sigrid Undset's psychological interest, is found again, almost without modifications, in her historical novels. In this respect, objections naturally come to mind. In medieval documents, the feminist question is not known; one never finds hints of the inner personal life which later was to raise this question. The historian, demanding proofs, has the right to note this discrepancy. But the historian's claim is not absolute; the poet has at least an equal right to express himself when he relies on a solid and intuitive knowledge of the human soul. The archaeologist must admit that there existed in the past instruments of a nature other than those which have come down to us, not to mention the often fortuitous ways in which the memories of the past have reached us. The poet has the right to suppose that human nature has hardly varied in the course of ages, even if the annals of the past are silent in certain regards.

In spite of the laws imposed by necessity, the common life of man and woman could scarcely have been peaceful and simple. It was no doubt less noisy than in our day, but it was exempt from neither conflicts nor bloody disturbances. To these conflicts and disturbances Sigrid Undset gave a voice, although it sometimes seems that the voice had accents far too modern and that the sentiments were too subtle for an era in which the influence of poetry had not yet manifested itself. The heavier and harsher environment seems also to have been of a nature which hardened the characters more firmly. But it is to this dissemblance, if indeed one can speak of dissemblance, that her poetic work owes its poignant and evocative life. In the inevitable compromise between the present and the past, from which the historical novel cannot escape, Sigrid Undset has chosen a richly rewarding way.

Her narrative is vigorous, sweeping, and at times heavy. It rolls on like a river, ceaselessly receiving new tributaries whose course the author also describes, at the risk of overtaxing the reader's memory.

This stems in part from the very nature of the subject. In the series of generations, conflicts and destinies assume a very concentrated form; these are whole masses of clouds which collide when the lightning flashes. However, this heaviness is also a result of the author's ardent and instant imagination, forming a scene and a dialogue of each incident in the narrative without taking the necessary backward look at the general perspective. And the vast river, whose course is difficult to embrace comprehensively, rolls its powerful waves which carry along the reader, plunged into a sort of torpor. But the roaring of its waters has the eternal freshness of nature. In the rapids and in the falls, the reader finds the enchantment which emanates from the power of the elements, as in the vast mirror of the lakes he notices a reflection of immensity, with the vision there of all possible greatness in human nature. Then, when the river reaches the sea, when Kristin Lavransdatter has fought to the end the battle of her life, no one complains of the length of the course which accumulated so overwhelming a depth and profundity in her destiny. In the poetry of all times, there are few scenes of comparable excellence.

Sigrid Undset's last novel, the two-volume story of *Olav Audunssøn* (1925–27), is generally on a level with the preceding novel, although it does not soar to its tragic finale. It attains, however, almost the same height in the scene in which Olav kills the Icelander. This scene constitutes a magnificent tableau, a masterly expression of the inner life, with a loftiness, a justice, an almost superhuman breadth of view rising above all the atrocities. One rediscovers here the same ripening of power as in *Kristin Lavransdatter* (1920–22). As far as the character studies are concerned, it seems impossible to reach higher than the portrayal of Eirik, the principal personage of the last part of the novel. Here is the complete evolution of a human being, from the first manifestations of childhood which are recorded not only with a vigorous strictness but also with a surprising superimposition of new traits, proportionate to the increasing clarity in the character delineation. One sees a human soul freely develop under one's eyes, a true creation of a truly superior art.

Sigrid Undset has received the Nobel Prize for Literature while still in her prime, an homage rendered to a poetic genius whose roots must be in a great and well-ordered spirit.

ACCEPTANCE SPEECH

By SIGRID UNDSET

THE PRECEDING SPEAKERS have far better expressed our gratitude for the Prizes awarded to us than I could have done, and I subscribe to their words. I write more readily than I speak and I am especially reluctant to talk about myself. Instead, I wish to offer a salute to Sweden. Before I left for Sweden, a party was given for me—that is to say, not strictly speaking for me but because I was going to leave for Sweden—and everybody, the President of the Council of Ministers of Norway as well as my personal friends, asked me to give regards to Sweden. After all, the people of our peninsula form a distinct part of the world. Our forests and our mountains run into each other and our rivers carry their waters from one country to the other. Our houses in Norway resemble those in Sweden. God be praised! We have always lived in a great number of small, private dwellings spread all over our countries. Modern technology has not yet completely intruded on the humanity of the North.

But what I wished to say here is that I have been asked to give regards to Sweden, the country we think of with joy, and to Stockholm, which we Norwegians consider the most beautiful city in the world.

THE GARLAND

By SIGRID UNDSET

Translated by Charles Archer and J. S. Scott

[From *Kristin Lavransdatter*]

1

Aasmund Björgulfsön's church-boat stood in round the point of Hovedö early one Sunday at the end of April, while the bells were ringing in the cloister-church and were answered from across the bay by the chime of bells from the town, now louder and now fainter as the breeze rose or fell.

Light, fluted clouds were floating over the high, pale-blue heavens, and the sun was glittering on the dancing ripples of the water. It was quite spring-like along the shores; the fields lay almost bare of snow, and over the leaf-tree thickets the light had a yellow shimmer and the shadows were blue. But in the pine-forests up on the high ridges, which framed in the settled lands of Akersbygd, there were glimpses of snow, and on the far blue fells to the westward, beyond the fjord, there still showed many flashes of white.

Kristin was standing in the bow of the boat with her father, and Gyrid, Aasmund's wife. She gazed at the town, with all the light-hued churches and stone buildings that rose above the swarm of gray-brown wooden houses and bare tree-tops. The wind ruffled the skirts of her cloak and snatched at her hair beneath her hood.

They had let the cattle out at Skog the day before, and a great longing had come on her to be at Jörundgaard. It would be a long time still before they could let the cattle out there—she longed with tender pity for the lean, winter-worn cows in the dark byres; they would have to wait and suffer a long while yet. Her mother, Ulvhild, who had slept in her arms each night all these years, little Ramborg—she yearned so much for them; she longed for all the folk at home, and the horses and the dogs, for Kortelin, whom Ulvhild was to have while she was gone, and for her father's hawks as they sat there on their perches with their hoods over their heads. She saw the horse-hide gloves that hung beside them to wear when you took them on to your wrist, and the ivory staves to scratch them with.

It was as if all the woe of the last winter had gone far away from her, and she only saw her home as it used to be. They had told her, too, that none thought ill of her in the parish—Sira Eirik did not believe that story; he was angry and grieved at what Bentein had done. Bentein had fled from Hamar; 'twas said he had gone to Sweden. So things were not so bad between them and their neighbor as she had feared.

On the journey down to Oslo they had stayed as guests at Simon's home, and she had come to know his mother and sisters—Sir Andres was in Sweden still. She had not felt at ease there, and her dislike of the Dyfrin folk was all the stronger that she could think of no good ground for it. All the way thither, she had said to herself that they had no cause to be proud or to think themselves better than her kin—no man knew aught of Reidar Darre, the Birch-leg, before King Sverre got him the widow of the Dyfrin Baron to wife. But lo! they were not proud at all; and when Simon himself spoke one night of his forefather: "I have found out now for sure—he was a comb-maker—so 'tis as though you were to come into a kingly stock—almost, Kristin," said he. "Take heed to your tongue, boy," said his mother, but they all laughed together. It vexed her strangely when she thought of her father; he laughed much, if Simon gave him the least cause—a thought came to her dimly that maybe her father would gladly have had more laughter in his life. But 'twas not to her mind that he should like Simon so much.

They had all been at Skog over Easter. She had found that her uncle was a hard master to his farmers and serving-folk—she had met one and another who asked after her mother and spoke lovingly of Lavrans; they had better times when he lived here. Aasmund's mother, Lavrans' stepmother, lived on the manor in a house by herself; she was not so very old, but sickly and failing. Lavrans had but seldom spoken of her at home. Once when Kristin asked him if he had had a hard stepmother, her father answered: "She never did much to me of either good or ill."

Kristin felt for her father's hand, and he pressed hers:

"You will be happy soon enough, my daughter, with the good Sisters—you will have other things to think of besides longing to be home with us—"

They sailed so near by the town that the smell of tar and salt fish was borne out to them from the wharves. Gyrid named all the churches, the traders' quarters, and the open places which run up from the water's edge—Kristin remembered nothing from the time she was here before but the great heavy towers of St. Halvard's Church. They sailed westward past the whole town and laid to at the convent pier.

Kristin walked between her father and her uncle through a cluster of warehouses, and came out upon a road which led up through the fields. Simon came after, leading Gyrid by the hand. The serving-folk stayed behind to help some men from the convent load the baggage upon a cart.

Nonneseter and the whole Leiran quarter lay within the boundaries of the town grazing-grounds, but there were but a few clusters of houses here and there along the roadside. The larks were trilling over their heads in the pale-blue sky, and the small yellow flowers of the coltsfoot were thickly sprinkled over the wan clay slopes, but along by the fences the roots of the grass were green.

When they were through the gate and were come into the cloister, all the nuns came marching two by two towards them from the church, while song and music streamed out after them through the open door.

Ill at ease, Kristin watched the many black-robed women with white linen wimples about their faces. She curtsied low, and the men bowed with their hats held close to their breasts. After the nuns came a flock of young maidens—some of them but children—in gowns of undyed wadmal, their waists bound with belts of twined black and white, and their hair braided tightly back from their faces with cords of the same black and white. Without thinking, Kristin put on a bold and forward look as the young maids passed, for she felt bashful, and was afraid they must think she looked countrified and foolish.

The convent was so glorious that she was quite overcome. All the buildings round the inner court were of gray stone; on the north side the main wall of the church stood up high above the other houses; it had two tiers of roofs and towers at the west end. The court itself was laid with stone flags, and round the whole there ran a covered way, whose roof was borne on pillars fairly wrought. In the midst of the court stood a stone statue of the Mater Misericordiæ, spreading her cloak over some kneeling figures.

Then a lay-sister came and prayed them to go with her to the Abbess' parlor. The Lady Groa Guttormsdatter was a tall and stoutly made old woman—she would have been comely had she not had so many hairs about her mouth. Her voice was deep like a man's. But her bearing was gentle and kindly—she called to mind that she had known Lavrans' father and mother, and asked after his wife and his other children. Last she spoke to Kristin in friendly wise:

"I have heard good report of you, and you look to be wise and well nurtured—sure I am you will give us no cause for miscontent. I have heard that you are plighted to this good and well-born man, Simon Andressön, whom I see here—it seems to us that 'twas wise counsel of your father and your husband to be, to grant you leave to live here awhile in the Virgin Mary's house, that you may learn to obey and serve before you are called to rule and to command. Now would I have to lay to heart this counsel: that you learn to find joy in prayer and the worship of God, that you may use yourself in all your doings to remember your Creator, God's gentle Mother, and all the Saints who have given us the best patterns of strength, uprightness, faithfulness and all the virtues you must show forth in guiding your people and your goods and nurturing your children. And you will learn in this house, too, to take good heed of time, for here every hour has its use and its task also. Many young maids and women love all too well to lie abed late of a morning, and sit long at table of an evening in idle talk—yet look not you as you were one of these. Yet may you learn much in the year you are here that may profit you both here on earth and in our heavenly home."

Kristin curtsied and kissed her hand. After that Lady Groa bade Kristin go with a monstrously fat old nun, whom she called Sister Potentia, over to the nuns' refectory. The men and Gyrid she asked to dine with her in another house.

The refectory was a great and fair room with a stone floor and pointed windows with glass panes. There was a doorway into another room, where, Kristin could see, there must be glass windows too, for the sun shone in.

The Sisters were already seated at the table waiting for their food—the elder nuns upon a cushioned stone-bench along the wall under the windows; the younger Sisters and the bareheaded maidens in light-hued wadmal dresses sat upon a wooden bench on the outer side of the board. In the next room a board was laid too; this was for the commoners and the lay-servants; there were a few old men among them. These folk did not wear the convent habit, but were none the less clad soberly in dark raiment.

Sister Potentia showed Kristin to a seat on the outer bench, but went and placed herself near to the Abbess' high-seat at the end of the board—the high-seat was empty today.

All rose, both in this room and in the side-room, while the Sisters said grace. After that a fair, young nun went and stood at a lectern placed in the doorway between the two chambers. And while the lay-sisters in the greater room, and two of the youngest nuns in the side-room, bore in food and drink, the nun read in a high and sweet voice, and without stopping or tripping at a single word, the story of St. Theodora and St. Didymus.

At first Kristin was thinking most of minding her table-manners, for she saw all the Sisters and the young maids bore them as seemly and ate as nicely as though they had been sitting at the finest feast. There was abundance of the best food and drink, but all helped themselves modestly, and dipped but the very tips of their fingers into the dishes; no one spilled the broth either upon the cloths or upon their garments, and all cut up the meat so small that they did not soil their mouths, and ate with so much care that not a sound was to be heard.

Kristin grew hot with fear that she might not seem as well behaved as the others; she was feeling ill at ease, too, in her bright dress in the midst of all these women in black and white—she fancied they were all looking at her. So when she had to eat a fat piece of breast of mutton, and was holding it by the bone with two fingers, while cutting morsels off with her right hand, and taking care to handle the knife lightly and neatly—suddenly the whole slipped from her fingers; her slice of bread and the meat flew on to the cloth, and the knife fell clattering on the stone flags.

The noise sounded fearfully in the quiet room. Kristin flushed red as fire and would have bent to pick up the knife, but a lay-sister came noiselessly in her sandals and gathered up the things.

But Kristin could eat no more. She found, too, that she had cut one of her fingers, and she was afraid of bleeding upon the cloth; so she sat with her hand wrapped in a corner of her skirt, and thought of how she was staining the goodly light blue dress she had gotten for the journey to Oslo, and she did not dare to raise her eyes from her lap.

Howbeit, in a little she began to listen more to what the nun was reading. When the ruler found he could not shake the steadfastness of the maid, Theodora—she would neither make offerings to the false gods nor let herself be given in marriage —he bade them lead her to a brothel. Yet while on the way thither he exhorted her to think of her freeborn kindred and her honored father and mother, upon whom everlasting shame must now be brought, and gave his word she should be let live in peace and stay a maid, if she would but join the service of a heathen goddess, whom they called Diana.

Theodora answered fearlessly: "Chastity is like a lamp, but love of God is the flame; were I to serve the devil-woman whom you call Diana, my chastity were no more worth than a rusty lamp without flame or oil. Thou callest me freeborn, but we are all born bondsmen, since our first parents sold us to the devil; Christ has bought me free, and I am bound to serve Him, so that I cannot wed me with His foes. He will guard His dove; but should He even suffer you to break my body, that is the temple of His Holy Spirit, it shall not be counted to me for shame, if so be that I consent not to betray what is His into the hands of His enemies."

Kristin's heart began to throb, for this in some way reminded her of her meeting with Bentein—she was smitten by the thought that this perhaps was her sin— she had not for a moment thought of God nor prayed for His help. And now Sister Cecilia read further of St. Didymus. He was a Christian knight, but heretofore he had kept his faith hidden from all save a few friends. He went now to the house where the maid was; he gave money to the woman who owned the house, and thus was the first to be let in to Theodora. She fled into a corner like a frightened hare, but Didymus hailed her as his sister and as his Lord's bride, and said he was come to save her. Then he spoke with her awhile, saying: Was it not meet that a brother should wage his life for his sister's honor? And at last she did as he bade her, changed clothes with him, and let herself be clad in Didymus' coat of mail; he pulled the hat down over her eyes and drew the cape up about her chin, and bade her go out with her face hidden, like a youth who is abashed at having been in such a place.

Kristin thought of Arne, and was scarce able to hold back her tears. She gazed straight before her with wet eyes while the nun was reading to the end— how Didymus was led to the place of execution, and how Theodora came hastening down from the mountains, cast herself at the headsman's feet and begged that she might die in his stead. And now the holy man and maid strove together who should first win the crown; and both were beheaded on the one day. This was the eighth-and-twentieth day of April in the year 304 after the birth of Christ, in Antioch, as was written by St. Ambrosius.

When they rose from the table, Sister Potentia came and patted Kristin kindly on the cheek: "Ay, you are longing for your mother, I can well believe." And on that Kristin's tears began to fall. But the nun made as though she did not see them, and led Kristin to the hostel where she was to dwell.

It was in one of the stone houses by the cloisters; a goodly room with glass windows and a big fireplace in the short wall at the far end. Along one main wall stood six bedsteads, and along the other all the maidens' chests.

Kristin wished they would let her sleep with one of the little girls, but Sister Potentia called a fat, fair-haired, grown maiden: "Here is Ingebjörg Filippusdatter, who is to be your bed-fellow—you must see now and learn to know each other." And with that she went out.

Ingebjörg took Kristin at once by the hand and began to talk. She was not very tall, and was much too fat, above all in the face—her cheeks were so plump that her eyes looked quite small. But her skin was clear, red and white, and her hair was yellow as gold, and so curly that her thick plaits twisted and twined together like strands of rope, and small locks kept ever slipping from under her snood.

She began straightway to question Kristin about many things, but never waited for an answer; instead she talked about herself, reckoned out the whole of her kindred in all its branches—they were naught but fine and exceeding rich folk. She was betrothed, too, to a rich and mighty man, Einar Einarssön of Aganæs—but he was far too old, and twice widowed; this was her greatest sorrow, she said. Yet could Kristin not mark that she took it much to heart. Then she talked a little of Simon Darre—'twas a marvel how closely she had looked him over in the short moment when they were passing in the cloisters. After that she had a mind to look into Kristin's chest— but first she opened her own and brought forth all her clothes. While they were ransacking their chests, Sister Cecilia came in—she rebuked them and said that this was no seemly Sunday pastime. This made Kristin unhappy again—she had never been taken to task by any but her own mother, and that was not the same as being chid by a stranger.

Ingebjörg was not abashed. After they were come to bed in the evening, she lay chattering until Kristin fell asleep. Two elder lay-sisters slept in a corner of the room; they were to see that the maidens did not take their shifts off at night—for it was against the rules for the girls to undress entirely—and to see that they were up in time for matins in the church. But else they did not trouble themselves to keep order in the hostel, and made as though they marked it not when the maids were lying talking, or eating the dainties which they had hidden in their chests.

When Kristin was awakened next morning, Ingebjörg was in the midst of a long tale already, so that Kristin almost wondered whether the other had been talking the whole night through.

2

The foreign merchants who lay in Oslo during the summer and trafficked there, came to the town in the spring about Holy Rood Day, which is ten days before the Halvards-wake Fair. To this folk streamed in from all the parishes between Mjösen and the Swedish marches, so that the town swarmed with people in the first weeks of May. This was the best time to buy from the strangers, before they had sold too many of their wares.

Sister Potentia had the care of the marketing for Nonneseter, and she had promised Ingebjörg and Kristin that they should go with her down to the town the day before the Halvards-wake. But about midday some of Sister Potentia's kin came to the convent to see her; and so she could not go that day. Then Ingebjörg begged and prayed till at last she let them go alone—although it was against the rules. An old peasant who was a commoner of the convent was sent with them as escort—Haakon was his name.

Kristin had been three weeks now at Nonneseter, and in all that time she had not set foot outside the convent grounds and gardens. She wondered to see how spring-like it was outside. The little

woods out in the fields were pale-green; the wood anemones grew thick as a carpet round the light-colored tree stems; white fair-weather clouds came sailing up over the islands in the fjord, and the water lay fresh and blue, slightly ruffled here and there by the light flaws of wind.

Ingebjörg skipped about, plucked bunches of leaves from the trees and smelled them, and peeped round after the folk they met; till Haakon chid her— were these seemly goings-on for a well-born maid, and in the convent habit too? The maidens were made to walk just behind him, hand in hand, quietly and seemly; but Ingebjörg used her eyes and her tongue all the same—Haakon was somewhat deaf. Kristin, too, was wearing the novices' garb now—an undyed, light-gray wadmal dress, woolen belt and head-band, and a plain, dark blue cloak over all, with a hood turned up so that the plaited hair was quite hid. Haakon strode in front with a stout brass-knobbed staff in his hand. He was dressed in a long black gown, had a leaden Agnus Dei hanging on his breast and an image of St. Christopher in his hat—his white hair and beard were so well brushed that they shone like silver in the sunshine.

The upper part of the town between the Nunsbeck and the bishop's palace was a quiet neighborhood; there were here neither shops nor taverns; most of the dwelling-places belonged to great folk from the parishes around, and the houses turned dark, windowless, timber gables to the street. But on this day whole crowds of people were roaming about the roads even up here, and the serving-folk stood loitering about the courtyard gates gossiping with the passers-by.

When they were come out near the bishop's palace, there was a great crush upon the place in front of Halvard's Church and the Olav-cloister—booths had been set up on the grassy slopes, and there were showmen making trained dogs jump through barrelhoops. But Haakon would not have the maids stand and look at these things, and he would not let Kristin go into the church—he said 'twould be better worth her seeing on the great Feast-day itself.

As they came down over the open space by St. Clement's Church, Haakon took them by the hands, for here was the greatest press of folk coming from the wharves or out from the alleys between the traders' yards. The maidens were bound for the Mickle Yard, where the shoemakers plied their trade. For Ingebjörg had found the clothes Kristin had brought from home very good and sightly, but she said the shoes she had with her from the Dale were not fit to wear for best. And when Kristin had seen the shoes from the outland Ingebjörg had in her chest—more pairs than one—she felt she could not rest until she too had bought some like them.

The Mickle Yard was one of the largest in Oslo; it stretched from the wharves up to the Souters' Alley, with more than forty houses round two great courts. And now they had set up booths with wadmal roofs in the courts as well. Above the roofs of these tents there rose a statue of St. Crispinus. Within the courts was a great throng of folk buying and selling, women running between the kitchens with pots and pails, children getting in the way of folks' feet, horses being led in and out of the stables, and serving-men carrying packages to and from the warehouses. From the balconies of the lofts above, where the finest wares were sold, shoemakers and their apprentices shouted to the two maids and dangled small gaily-colored or gold-embroidered shoes before them.

But Ingebjörg made her way toward the loft where Didrek the shoemaker sat; he was a German, but had a Norse wife and owned a house in the Mickle Yard.

The old man was standing bargaining with an esquire wearing a traveler's cloak, and a sword at his belt; but Ingebjörg went forward unabashed, bowed, and said:

"Good sir, will you not suffer us of your courtesy to have speech with Didrek first? We must be home in our convent by vespers; you, perchance, have no such great haste?"

The esquire bowed and stepped aside. Didrek nudged Ingebjörg with his elbow and asked, laughing, whether they danced so much in the convent that she had worn out already all the shoon she had of him the year before. Ingebjörg nudged him again and said they were still unworn, thank Heaven, but here was this other maid—and she pulled Kristin forward. Then Didrek and his lad bore forth a box into the balcony; and out of it he brought forth shoes, each pair finer than the last. They had Kristin sit down upon a chest that he might try them on her— there were white shoes and brown and red and green and blue, shoes with painted wooden heels and shoes without heels, shoes with buckles and shoes with silken laces in them, shoes in leather of two or of three hues. Kristin felt she would fain have had them all. But they cost so dear she was quite dismayed—not one pair cost less than a cow at home. Her father had given her a purse with a mark of silver in counted money when he left—that was for pocket money, and Kristin had deemed it great riches. But she soon saw that Ingebjörg thought it no great store to go a-marketing with.

Ingebjörg, too, must try on some shoes for the jest of it; that cost no money, said Didrek laughing. She did buy one pair of leaf-green shoes with red heels—she said she must have them on trust, but then Didrek knew her and her folks.

Kristin thought, indeed, that Didrek liked this none too well, and that he was vexed too, that the tall esquire in the traveling cloak had left the loft—much time had been taken up with the trying-on. So she chose for herself a pair of heelless shoes of thin purple-blue leather, broidered with silver and with rose-red stones. But she liked not the green silk laces in them. Didrik said he could change these, and took the maids with him into a room at the back of the loft. Here he had coffers full of silk ribbons and small silver buckles—'twas against the law, strictly, for shoemakers to trade in these things—and the ribbons, too, were many of them too broad and the buckles too big for footgear.

They felt they had to buy one or two of the smaller things, and when they had drunk a cup of sweet wine with Didrek and he had packed the things they had brought into a wadmal cloth, the hour was grown somewhat late, and Kristin's purse much lighter.

When they were come to the Ostre Stræte again the sunlight was turned golden, and, by reason of the traffic in the town, the dust hung over the street in a bright haze. The evening was warm and fair, and folk were coming down from Eikaberg with great armfuls of young green branches wherewith to deck their houses for the holy-day. And now the whim took Ingebjörg that they should go out to the Gjeita bridge—at fair-times there was wont to be so much merry-making in the fields on the farther side of the river, both jugglers and fiddlers—nay, Ingebjörg had heard there was come a whole shipful of outlandish beasts that were being shown in booths down by the waterside.

Haakon had had a pot or two of Ger-man beer at the Mickle Yard, and was now easy and mild of mood; so when the maidens took him by the arm and begged him sweetly, he gave way at last, and the three went out towards Eikaberg.

Beyond the stream there were but a few small dwelling-places scattered about the green slopes between the river and the steep hillside. They went past the Minorite monastery, and Kristin's heart sank with shame as she bethought her how she had meant to give most of her silver for the good of Arne's soul. But she had had no mind to speak of it to the priest at Nonneseter; she feared to be asked questions—she had thought that she could maybe come out to the bare-foot friars and find if by chance Brother Edvin were in the cloister now. She was fain to meet him again—but she knew not, either, what would be the most seemly way to get speech with one of the monks and tell him her desire. And now she had so little money she knew not whether she could buy a mass—maybe she must be content to offer a thick wax-candle.

Of a sudden they heard a fearful yell from countless throats down by the shore —a storm seemed to sweep over the press of human beings down there—and now the whole mass rushed towards them, shrieking and shouting. All seemed wild with terror, and some of the runners-by cried out to Haakon and the maids that the pards were loose. . . .

They set out running back to the bridge, and heard folk shout to one an-other that a booth had fallen down and two pards had broken loose—some spoke of a serpent, too. The nearer they came to the bridge the worse became the crush. Just in front of them a woman dropped a little child out of her arms—Haakon stood astride the little one to shield it— soon after they caught sight of him far away with the child in his arms, and then they lost him.

At the narrow bridge the press of peo-ple was so great that the maids were pushed right out into a field. They saw folks run down to the river-bank; young men jumped in and swam, but elder folk sprang into boats that lay there, and these were overladen in a trice.

Kristin tried to make Ingebjörg hear—

she cried out to her that they should run up to the Minorite cloister—they could see the Gray Friars come running out from it, striving to gather in the terrified people. Kristin was not so frightened as the other girl—they saw nothing, either, of the wild beasts—but Ingebjörg had quite lost her wits. And now, when there was a fresh uproar in the throng, and it was driven back by a whole troop of men from the nearest dwellings, who had armed themselves and forced their way back over the bridge, some riding and some running, and Ingebjörg was nigh coming under the feet of a horse—she gave a scream and set off running for the woods. Kristin had never thought the girl could have run so fast—it made her think of a hunted pig. She ran after her, so that they two, at least, should not be parted.

They were deep in the woods before Kristin could get Ingebjörg to stop—they were on a little path which seemed to lead down toward the road to Trælaborg. They stood still for a little to get their breath again; Ingebjörg was sniveling and weeping, and said she dared not go back alone through the town and all the way out to the convent.

Nor did Kristin deem that this would be well, with the streets in such commotion; she thought they must try to find a house where they might hire a lad to take them home. Ingebjörg thought there was a bridle-path to Trælaborg farther down by the short, and along it there lay some houses she knew. So they followed the path downward, away from the town.

Fearful and uneasy as they both were, it seemed to them they had gone far ere at last they came to a farmstead lying off in a field. In the courtyard there they found a band of men sitting drinking at a board under some ash trees, while a woman came and went, bearing out tankards to them. She looked wonderingly and sourly at the two maids in convent habit, and none of the men seemed to have a mind to go with them when Kristin told their need. At last, though, two young men stood up and said they would bring the girls to Nonneseter, if Kristin would give them a silver ducat.

She heard by their speech that they were not Norse, but she thought they seemed honest folk enough. 'Twas a shameless sum they asked, she thought, but Ingebjörg was beside herself with fright and she saw not how they could go home alone so late; and so she struck the bargain.

No sooner were they come to the forest-path than the men drew closer to them and began to talk. Kristin liked this but ill, but she would not show she was afraid; so she answered them quietly, told of the pards and asked the men where they were from. She spied about her, too, and made as though she looked each moment to meet the serving-men they had had with them—she talked as though there had been a whole band. As they went on the men spoke less and less—nor did she understand much of their speech.

After a while she became aware that they were not going the same way she had come with Ingebjörg—the course their path took was not the same; 'twas more northerly—and she deemed they had already gone much too far.

Deep within her there smoldered a fear she dared not let herself think upon—but it strengthened her strangely to have Ingebjörg with her, for the girl was so foolish that Kristin knew she must trust in herself alone to find a way out for them both. Under her cloak, she managed by stealth to pull out the cross with the holy relic she had had of her father; she clasped it in her hand, praying fervently in her heart that they might soon meet some one, and in all ways sought to gather all her courage and to make no sign.

Just after this she saw that the path

came out on to a road and there was a clearing in the forest. The town and the bay lay far below. The men had led them astray, whether wilfully or because they knew not the paths—they were high up on the mountain-side and far north of Gjeita bridge, which she could see below; the road they had now met seemed to lead thither.

Thereupon she stopped, drew forth her purse and made to count out ten silver pennies into her hand.

"Now, good fellows," said she, "we need you not any more to guide us; for we know the way from here. We thank you for your pains, and here is the wage we bargained for. God be with you, good friends."

The men looked at one another so foolishly, that Kristin was near smiling. Then one said with an ugly grin that the road down to the bridge was exceedingly lonely; 'twas not wise for them to go alone.

"None, surely, are such nithings or such fools that they would seek to stop two maids, and they in the convent habit," answered Kristin. "We would fain go our own way alone now—" and she held out the money.

The man caught her by the wrist, thrust his face close up to hers, and said somewhat of "kuss" and "beutel"—Kristin made out he was saying they might go in peace if she but gave him a kiss and her purse.

She remembered Bentein's face close to hers like this, and such a fear came on her for a moment that she grew faint and sick. But she pressed her lips together, and called in her heart upon God and the Virgin Mary—and in the same instant she thought she heard hoof-falls on the path from the north.

She struck the man in the face with her purse so that he staggered—and then she pushed him in the breast with all her strength so that he tumbled off the path

and down into the wood. The other German gripped her from behind, tore the purse from her hand and her chain from her neck so that it broke—she was near falling, but clutched the man and tried to get her cross from him again. He struggled to get free—the robbers, too, had now heard folk coming—Ingebjörg screamed with all her might, and the riders on the path came galloping forward at full speed. They burst out of the thicket—three of them—and Ingebjörg ran shrieking to meet them as they sprang from their horses. Kristin knew one for the esquire of Didrek's loft; he drew his sword, seized the German she was struggling with by the back of the neck, and thrashed him with the flat of his blade. His men ran after the other, caught him and beat him to their heart's content.

Kristin leaned against the face of the rock; she was trembling now that all was over, but what she felt most was marvel that her prayer had brought such speedy help. Then she caught sight of Ingebjörg, who had thrown back her hood, hung her cape loosely over her shoulders and was in the act of bringing her heavy, shining plaits of hair forward into sight upon her breast. At this sight Kristin burst out a-laughing—her strength left her and she had to hold on to a tree to keep her feet, for 'twas as though the marrow of her bones was turned to water, she felt so weak; and so she trembled and laughed and cried.

The esquire came forward and laid a hand warily upon her shoulder:

"You were more frightened, I see, than you would show," said he, and his voice was kindly and gentle. "But now you must take a hold on yourself—you bore you so bravely while yet there was peril—"

Kristin could only look up at him and nod. He had fine, bright eyes set in a narrow, pale-brown face, and coal-black hair clipped somewhat short over the forehead and behind the ears.

Ingebjörg had her hair in order now; she came and thanked the stranger with many fair words. He stood there still with a hand on Kristin's shoulder while he answered her comrade.

"We must take these birds along," said he to his men, who stood holding the two Germans—they were from a Rostock ship, they said—"we must have them along with us to the town that they may be sent to the black hole. But first must we take these two maids home to the convent. You can find some thongs, I trow, to bind them with—"

"Mean you the maids, Erlend?" asked one of the men. They were young, stout, well-appointed yeomen, and were in high feather from the tussle.

Their master frowned and seemed about to answer sharply, but Kristin laid her hand upon his sleeve:

"Let them go, dear sir!" She shuddered a little. "Loth would we be, in truth, both my sister and I, this matter should be talked of."

The stranger looked down at her—he bit his lip and nodded, as though he understood her. Then he gave each of the captives a blow on the nape with the flat of his sword which sent them sprawling forwards. "Run for it, then," he said, kicking them, and both scrambled up and took to their heels as fast as they could. Then he turned again to the maidens and asked if they would please to ride.

Ingebjörg let herself be lifted into Erlend's saddle, but it was soon plain that she could not keep her seat—she slid down again at once. He looked at Kristin doubtfully, and she said that she was used to ride on a man's saddle.

He took hold of her below the knees and lifted her up. A sweet and happy thrill ran through her to feel how carefully he held her from him, as though afraid to come near her—at home, no one ever minded how tight they held her when they helped her on to a horse. She felt marvelously honored and uplifted.

The knight—as Ingebjörg called him, though he had but silver spurs—now offered that maiden his hand, and his men sprang to their saddles. Ingebjörg would have it that they should ride round the town to the northward below the Ryenberg and Martestokke, and not through the streets. First, she gave as a reason that Sir Erlend and his men were fully armed—were they not? The knight answered gravely that the ban on carrying arms was not over strict at any time—for travelers at least—and now everyone in the town was out on a wild beast hunt. Then she said she was fearful of the pards. Kristin saw full well that Ingebjörg was fain to go by the longest and loneliest road, that she might have the more talk with Erlend.

"This is the second time this evening that we hinder you, good sir," said she, and Erlend answered soberly:

" 'Tis no matter, I am bound no farther than to Gerdarud tonight—and 'tis light the whole night long."

It liked Kristin well that he jested not, nor bantered them, but talked to her as though she were his like or even more than his like. She thought of Simon; she had not met other young men of courtly breeding. But 'twas true, this man seemed older than Simon.

They rode down into the valley below the Ryenberg hills and up along the beck. The path was narrow, and the young bushes swung wet, heavily scented branches against her—it was a little darker down here, and the air was cool and the leaves all dewy along the beck-path.

They went slowly, and the horses' hoofs sounded muffled on the damp, grass-grown path. She rocked gently in the saddle; behind her she heard Inge-björg's chatter, and the stranger's deep, quiet voice. He said little, and answered as if his mind wandered—it sounded almost as if his mood were like her own, she thought—she felt strangely drowsy, yet safe and content now that all the day's chances were safely over.

It was like waking to come out of the woods on to the green slopes under the Martestokke hills. The sun was gone down, and the town and the bay lay below them in a clear, pale light—above the Aker ridges there was a light-yellow strip edging the pale-blue sky. In the evening hush, sounds were borne to them from far off, as they came out of the cool depths of the wood—a cart-wheel creaked somewhere upon a road, dogs on the farms bayed at each other across the valley. And from the woods behind them birds trilled and sang full-throated, now the sun was down.

Smoke was in the air from the fires on lands under clearance, and out in a field there was the red flare of a bonfire; against the great ruddy flame the clearness of the night seemed a kind of darkness.

They were riding between the fences of the convent-fields when the stranger spoke to her again. He asked her what she thought best; should he go with her to the gate and ask for speech of the Lady Groa, so that he might tell her how this thing had come about. But Ingebjörg would have it that they should steal in through the church; then maybe they might slip into the convent without any one knowing they had been away so much too long—it might be her kinsfolks' visit had made Sister Potentia forget them.

The open place before the west door of the church was empty and still, and it came not into Kristin's thoughts to wonder at this, though there was wont to be much life there of an evening, with folks from the neighborhood who came to the nuns' church, and from the houses round

about wherein lay-servants and commoners dwelt. They said farewell to Erlend here. Kristin stood and stroked his horse; it was black, and had a comely head and soft eyes—she thought it like Morvin, whom she had been wont to ride at home when she was a child.

"What is your horse's name, sir?" she asked, as it turned its head from her and snuffed at its master's breast.

"Bayard," said he, looking at her over the horse's neck. "You ask my horse's name, but not mine?"

"I would be fain to know your name, sir," she replied, and bent her head a little.

"I am called Erlend Nikulaussön," said he.

"Then, Erlend Nikulaussön, have thanks for your good service this night," said Kristin, and proffered him her hand. Of a sudden she flushed red, and half withdrew her hand from his.

"Lady Aashild Gautesdatter of Dovre, is she your kinswoman?" she asked.

To her wonder she saw that he, too, blushed—he dropped her hand suddenly, and answered:

"She is my mother's sister. And I am Erlend Nikulaussön of Husaby." He looked at her so strangely that she became still more abashed, but she mastered herself, and said:

" 'Tis true I should have thanked you with better words, Erlend Nikulaussön; but I know not what I can say to you."

He bowed before her, and she felt that now she must bid him goodbye, though she would fain have spoken more with him. In the church door she turned, and as she saw that Erlend still stood beside his horse, she waved her hand to him in farewell.

The convent was in a hubbub, and all within in great dismay. Haakon had sent word home by a horseman, while he, himself, went seeking the maids in the town; and folks had been sent from the convent to help him. The nuns had heard the wild beasts had killed and eaten up two children down in the town. This, to be sure, was a lie, and the pard—there was only one—had been caught before vespers by some men from the King's palace.

Kristin stood with bent head and kept silence, while the Abbess and Sister Potentia poured out their wrath upon the two maidens. She felt as though something were asleep within her. Ingebjörg wept and began to make excuse—they had gone out with Sister Potentia's leave, with fitting attendance, and, sure, they were not to blame for what had happened after.

But Lady Groa said they might now stay in the church till the hour of midnight struck, that they might strive to turn their thoughts to the things of the spirit, and might thank God who had saved their lives and honor. "God hath now manifested clearly to you the truth about the world," said she; "wild beasts and the servants of the devil threaten his children there at every footstep, and there is no salvation except ye hold fast to Him with prayer and supplication."

She gave them each a lighted candle and bade them go with Sister Cecilia Baardsdatter, who was often alone in the church praying the whole night long.

Kristin put her candle upon St. Lawrence's altar and knelt on the praying-stool. She fixed her gaze on the flame while she said over the Paternoster and the Ave Maria softly. The sheen of the candle seemed little by little to enfold her and to shut out all that was outside her and the light. She felt her heart open and overflow with thankfulness and praise and love of God and His gentle Mother—they came so near to her. She had always known they saw her, but tonight she *felt* that it was so. She saw the world

as in a vision; a great dark room whereinto fell a sunbeam; the motes were dancing in and out between the darkness and the light, and she felt that now she had at last slipped into the sunbeam.

She felt she would gladly have stayed for ever in this dark, still church—with the few small spots of light like golden stars in the night, the sweet stale scent of incense, and the warm smell of the burning wax. And she at rest within her own star.

It was as if some great joy were at an end, when Sister Cecilia came gliding to her and touched her shoulder. Bending before the altars, the three women went out of the little south door into the convent close.

Ingebjörg was so sleepy that she went to bed without a word. Kristin was glad—she had been loth to have her good thoughts broken in on. And she was glad, too, that they must keep on their shifts at night—Ingebjörg was so fat and had been so over-hot.

She lay awake long, but the deep flood of sweetness that she had felt lifting her up as she knelt in the church would not come again. Yet she felt the warmth of it within her still; she thanked God with all her heart, and thought she felt her spirit strengthened while she prayed for her father and mother and sisters, and for Arne Gyrdsön's soul.

Father, she thought—she longed so much for him, for all they had been to one another before Simon Darre came into their lives. There welled up in her a new tenderness for him—there was, as it were, a foretaste of mother's love and care in her love for her father this night; dimly she felt that there was so much in life that he had missed. She called to mind the old, black wooden church at Gerdarud—she had seen there this last Easter the graves of her three little brothers and of her grandmother, her father's own mother, Kristin Sigurdsdatter, who died when she brought him into the world.

What could Erlend Nikulaussön have to do at Gerdarud—she could not think.

She had no knowledge that she had thought much of him that evening, but the whole time the thought of his dark, narrow face and his quiet voice had hung somewhere in the dusk outside the glow of light that enfolded her spirit.

When she awoke the next morning, the sun was shining into the dormitory, and Ingebjörg told her how Lady Groa herself had bidden the lay-sisters not to wake them for matins. She had said that when they woke, they might go over to the kitchen-house and get some food. Kristin grew warm with gladness at the Abbess' kindness—it seemed as if the whole world had been good to her.

3

The farmers' guild of Aker had St. Margaret for their patroness, and they began their festival each year on the twentieth of July, the day of St. Margaret's Mass. On that day the guild brothers and sisters, with their children, their guests and their serving-folk, gathered at Aker's church and heard mass at St. Margaret's altar there; after that they wended their way to the hall of the guild, which lay near the Hofvin Hospital—there they were wont to hold a drinking-feast lasting five days.

But since both Aker's church and the Hofvin spital belonged to Nonneseter, and as, besides, many of the Aker farmers were tenants of the convent, it had come to be the custom that the Abbess and some of the elder Sisters should honor the guild by coming to the feasting on the first day. And those of the young maids who were at the convent only to learn, and were not to take the veil, had

leave to go with them and to dance in the evening; therefore at this feast they wore their own clothes and not the convent habit.

And so there was great stir and bustle in the novices' sleeping rooms on the eve of St. Margaret's Mass; the maids who were to go to the guild feast ransacking their chests and making ready their finery, while the others, less fortunate, went about something moodily and looked on. Some had set small pots in the fireplace and were boiling water to make their skin white and soft; others were making a brew to be smeared on their hair—then they parted the hair into strands and twisted them tightly round strips of leather, and this gave them curling, wavy tresses.

Ingebjörg brought out all the finery she had, but could not think what she should wear—come what might, not her best, leaf-green velvet dress; that was too good and too costly for such a peasant rout. But a little, thin sister who was not to go with them—Helga was her name; she had been vowed to the convent by her father and mother while still a child —took Kristin aside and whispered: she was sure Ingebjörg would wear the green dress and her pink silk shift too.

"You have ever been kind to me, Kristin," said Helga. "It beseems me little to meddle in such doings—but I will tell you none the less. The knight who brought you home that evening in the spring—I have seen and heard Ingebjörg talking with him since—they spoke together in the church, and he has tarried for her up in the hollow when she hath gone to Ingunn at the commoners' house. But 'tis you he asks for, and Ingebjörg has promised him to bring you there along with her. But I wager you have not heard aught of this before!"

"True it is that Ingebjörg has said naught of this," said Kristin. She pursed up her mouth that the other might not see the smile that would come out. So this was Ingebjörg's way. " 'Tis like she knows I am not of such as run to trysts with strange men round house-corners and behind fences," said she proudly.

"Then I might have spared myself the pains of bringing you tidings whereof 'twould have been but seemly I should say no word," said Helga, wounded, and they parted.

But the whole evening Kristin was put to it not to smile when anyone was looking at her.

Next morning, Ingebjörg went dallying about in her shift, till Kristin saw she meant not to dress before she herself was ready.

Kristin said naught, but laughed as she went to her chest and took out her golden-yellow silken shift. She had never worn it before, and it felt so soft and cool as it slipped down over her body. It was broidered with goodly work, in silver and blue and brown silk, about the neck and down upon the breast, as much as should be seen above the low-cut gown. There were sleeves to match, too. She drew on her linen hose, and laced up the small, purple-blue shoes which Haakon, by good luck, had saved that day of commotion. Ingebjörg gazed at her— then Kristin said laughing:

"My father ever taught me never to show disdain of those beneath us—but 'tis like you are too grand to deck yourself in your best for poor tenants and peasant-folk—"

Red as a berry, Ingebjörg slipped her woolen smock down over her white hips and hurried on the pink silk shift. Kristin threw over her own head her best velvet gown—it was violet-blue, deeply cut out at the bosom, with long slashed sleeves flowing well-nigh to the ground. She fastened the gilt belt about her waist, and hung her gray squirrel cape over her shoulders. Then she spread her masses of yellow hair out over her shoulders and back, and fitted the golden fillet, chased with small roses, upon her brow.

She saw that Helga stood watching them. Then she took from her chest a great silver clasp. It was that she had on her cloak the night Bentein met her on the highway, and she had never cared to wear it since. She went to Helga, and said in a low voice:

"I know 'twas your wish to show me goodwill last night; think me not unthankful—" and with that she gave her the clasp.

Ingebjörg was a fine sight, too, when she stood fully decked in her green gown, with a red silk cloak over her shoulders and her fair, curly hair waving behind her. They had ended by striving to out-dress each other, thought Kristin, and she laughed.

The morning was cool and fresh with dew as the procession went forth from Nonneseter and wound its way westward toward Frysja. The hay-making was near at an end here on the lowlands, but along the fences grew blue-bells and yellow crowsfoot in clumps; in the fields the barley was in ear, and bent its heads in pale silvery waves just tinged with pink. Here and there, where the path was narrow and led through the fields, the corn all but met about folks' knees.

Haakon walked at the head, bearing the convent's banner with the Virgin Mary's picture upon the blue silken cloth. After him walked the servants and the commoners, and then came the Lady Groa and four old Sisters on horseback, while behind these came the young maidens on foot; their many-hued holiday attire flaunted and shone in the sunlight. Some of the commoners' womenfolk and a few armed serving-men closed the train.

They sang as they went over the bright fields, and the folk they met at the byways stood aside and gave them reverent greeting. All round, out on the fields, they could see small groups of men coming walking and riding, for folks were drawing toward the church from every house and every farm. Soon they heard behind them the sound of hymns chanted in men's deep voices, and the banner of the Hovedö monastery rose above a hillock—the red silk shone in the sun, swaying and bending to the step of the bearer.

The mighty, metal voice of the bells rang out above the neighing and screaming of stallions as the procession climbed the last slope to the church. Kristin had never seen so many horses at one time—a heaving, restless sea of horses' backs round about the green before the church door. Upon the sward stood and sat lay folk dressed in all their best—but all rose in reverence as the Virgin's flag from Nonneseter was borne in among them, and all bowed deeply before the Lady Groa.

It seemed as though more folk had come than the church could hold, but for those from the convent room had been kept in front near the altar. Straightway after them the Cistercian monks from Hovedö marched in and went up into the choir—and forthwith song burst from the throats of men and boys and filled the church.

Soon after the mass had begun, when the service brought all to their feet, Kristin caught sight of Erlend Nikulaussön. He was tall, and his head rose above those about him—she saw his face from the side. He had a high, steep, and narrow forehead, and a large, straight nose —it jutted, triangle-like, from his face, and was strangely thin about the fine, quivering nostrils—something about it reminded Kristin of a restless, highstrung stallion. His face was not as comely as she had thought it—the long-drawn lines running down to his small, weak, yet well-formed mouth gave it as

'twere a touch of joylessness—ay, but yet he *was* comely.

He turned his head and saw her. She knew not how long they stood thus, looking into each other's eyes. From that time she thought of naught but the end of the mass; she waited, intent on what would then befall.

There was some pressing and thronging as the folks made their way out from the overcrowded church. Ingebjörg held Kristin back till they were at the rear of the throng; she gained her point—they were quite cut off from the nuns, who went out first—the two girls were among the last in coming to the offertory-box and out of the church.

Erlend stood without, just by the door, beside the priest from Gerdarud and a stoutish, red-faced man, splendid in blue velvet. Erlend himself was clad in silk, but of a sober hue—a long coat of brown, figured with black, and a black cloak with a pattern of small yellow hawks inwoven.

They greeted each other and crossed the green together to where the men's horses stood tethered. While they spoke of the fine weather, the goodly mass and the great crowd of folk that were mustered, the fat, ruddy knight—he bore golden spurs and was named Sir Munan Baardsön—took Ingebjörg by the hand; 'twas plain he was mightily taken with the maid. Erlend and Kristin fell behind —they were silent as they walked.

There was a great to-do upon the church-green as folk began to ride away —horses jostled one another, people shouted—some angry, others laughing. Many sat in pairs upon the horses; men had their wives behind them, or their children in front upon the saddle; youths swung themselves up beside a friend. They could see the church banners, the nuns and the priests far down the hill already.

Sir Munan rode by; Ingebjörg sat in

front of him, his arm about her. Both of them called out and waved. Then Erlend said:

"My serving-men are both with me—they could ride one horse and you have Haftor's—if you would rather have it so?"

Kristin flushed as she replied: "We are so far behind the others already—I see not your serving-men hereabouts, and—" Then she broke into a laugh, and Erlend smiled.

He sprang to the saddle and helped her to a seat behind him. At home Kristin had often sat thus sidewise behind her father, after she had grown too big to ride astride the horse. Still, she felt a little bashful and none too safe as she laid a hand upon Erlend's shoulder; the other she put on the horse's back to steady herself. They rode slowly down towards the bridge.

In a while Kristin thought she must speak, since he was silent, so she said: "We looked not, sir, to meet you here today."

"Looked you not to meet me?" asked Erlend, turning his head. "Did not Ingebjörg Filippusdatter bear you my greeting, then?"

"No," said Kristin. "I heard naught of any greeting—she hath not named you once since you came to our help last May," said she guilefully. She was not sorry that Ingebjörg's falseness should come to light.

Erlend did not look back again, but she could hear by his voice that he was smiling when he asked again:

"But the little dark one—the novice—I mind not her name—her I even fee'd to bear you my greeting."

Kristin blushed, but she had to laugh too: "Ay, 'tis but Helga's due I should say that she earned her fee," she said.

Erlend moved his head a little—his neck almost touched her hand. Kristin shifted her hand at once farther out on his shoulder. Somewhat uneasily she thought, maybe she had been more bold than was fitting, seeing she had come to this feast after a man had, in a manner, made tryst with her there.

Soon after Erlend asked:

"Will you dance with me tonight, Kristin?"

"I know not, sir," answered the maid.

"You think, mayhap, 'tis not seemly?" he asked, and, as she did not answer, he said again: "It may well be it is not so. But I thought now maybe you might deem you would be none the worse if you took my hand in the dance tonight. But, indeed, 'tis eight years since I stood up to dance."

"How may that be, sir?" asked Kristin. "Mayhap you are wedded?" But then it came into her head that had he been a wedded man, to have made tryst with her thus would have been no fair deed of him. On that she tried to mend her speech, saying: "Maybe you have lost your betrothed maid or your wife?"

Erlend turned quickly and looked on her with strange eyes.

"Hath not Lady Aashild . . . ? Why grew you so red when you heard who I was that evening?" he asked a little after.

Kristin flushed red once more, but did not answer; then Erlend asked again:

"I would fain know what my mother's sister said to you of me."

"Naught else," said Kristin quickly, "but in your praise. She said you were so comely and so great of kin that—she said that beside such as you and her kin we were of no such great account—my folk and I—"

"Doth she still talk thus, living the life she lives," said Erlend, and laughed bitterly. "Ay, ay—if it comfort her. . . . Said she naught else of me?"

"What should she have said?" asked Kristin; she knew not why she was grown so strangely heavy-hearted.

"Oh, she might have said—" he spoke

in a low tone, looking down, "she might have said that I had been under the Church's ban, and had to pay dear for peace and atonement——"

Kristin was silent a long time. Then she said softly:

"There is many a man who is not master of his own fortunes—so have I heard said. 'Tis little I have seen of the world—but I will never believe of you, Erlend, that 'twas for any—dishonorable —deed."

"May God reward you for those words, Kristin," said Erlend, and bent his head and kissed her wrist so vehemently that the horse gave a bound beneath them. When Erlend had it in hand again, he said earnestly: "Dance with me to-night then, Kristin. Afterward I will tell how things are with me—will tell you all—but tonight we will be happy to-gether?"

Kristin answered: "Ay," and they rode a while in silence.

But ere long Erlend began to ask of Lady Aashild, and Kristin told all she knew of her; she praised her much.

"Then all doors are not barred against Björn and Aashild?" asked Erlend.

Kristin said they were thought much of, and that her father and many with him deemed that most of the tales about these two were untrue.

"How liked you my kinsman, Munan Baardsön?" asked Erlend, laughing slyly.

"I looked not much upon him," said Kristin, "and methought, too, he was not much to look on."

"Knew you not," asked Erlend, "that he is her son?"

"Son to Lady Aashild!" said Kristin, in great wonder.

"Ay, her children could not take their mother's fair looks, though they took all else," said Erlend.

"I have never known her first hus-band's name," said Kristin.

"They were two brothers who wedded two sisters," said Erlend. "Baard and Nikulaus Munansön. My father was the elder, my mother was his second wife, but he had no children by his first. Baard, whom Aashild wedded, was not young either, nor, I trow, did they ever live happily together—ay, I was a little child when all this befell, they hid from me as much as they could. . . . But she fled the land with Sir Björn and married him against the will of her kin—when Baard was dead. Then folk would have had the wedding set aside—they made out that Björn had sought her bed while her first husband was still living, and that they had plotted together to put away my father's brother. 'Tis clear they could not bring this home to them, since they had to leave them together in wedlock. But to make amends, they had to forfeit all their estate—Björn had killed their sister's son, too—my mother's and Aashild's, I mean—"

Kristin's heart beat hard. At home her father and mother had kept strict watch that no unclean talk should come to the ears of their children or of young folk— but still, things had happened in their own parish and Kristin had heard of them—a man had lived in adultery with a wedded woman. That was whoredom, one of the worst of sins; 'twas said they plotted the husband's death, and that brought with it outlawry and the Church's ban. Lavrans had said no woman was bound to stay with her hus-band, if he had had to do with another's wife; the state of a child gotten in adultery could never be mended, not even though its father and mother were free to wed afterward. A man might bring into his family and make his heir his child by any wanton or strolling beg-garwoman, but not the child of his adultery—not if its mother came to be a knight's lady. She thought of the mis-liking she had ever felt for Sir Björn, with his bleached face and fat, yet shrunken body. She could not think how Lady Aashild could be so good and yielding at all times to the man who had led her away into such shame; how such a gracious woman could have let herself be beguiled by him. He was not even good to her; he let her toil and moil with all the farm-work; Björn did naught but drink beer. Yet Aashild was ever mild and gentle when she spoke with her husband. Kristin wondered if her father could know all this, since he had asked Sir Björn to their home. Now she came to think, too, it seemed strange Erlend should think fit to tell such tales of his near kin. But like enough he deemed she knew of it already.

"I would like well," said Erlend in a while, "to visit her, Moster* Aashild, some day—when I journey northwards. Is he comely still, Björn, my kinsman?"

"No," said Kristin. "He looks like hay that has lain the winter through upon the fields."

"Ay, ay, it tells upon a man, I trow," said Erlend, with the same bitter smile. "Never have I seen so fair a man—'tis twenty years since, I was but a lad then —but his like have I never seen—"

A little after they came to the hospital. It was an exceeding great and fine place, with many houses both of stone and of wood—houses for the sick, almshouses, hostels for travelers, a chapel and a house for the priest. There was great bustle in the courtyard, for food was being made ready in the kitchen of the hospital for the guild feast, and the poor and sick too, that were dwelling in the place, were to be feasted on the best this day.

The hall of the guild was beyond the garden of the hospital, and folks took their way thither through the herb-garden, for this was of great renown. Lady Groa had had brought hither plants

_____

* Moster = mother's sister.

that no one had heard of in Norway before, and, moreover, all plants that else folks were used to grow in gardens, throve better in her herbaries, both flowers and pot-herbs and healing herbs. She was a most learned woman in all such matters, and had herself put into the Norse tongue the herbals of the Salernitan school. . . . Lady Groa had been more than ever kind to Kristin since she had marked that the maid knew somewhat of herb-lore, and was fain to know yet more of it.

So Kristin named for Erlend what grew in the beds on either side the grassy path they walked on. In the midday sun there was a warm and spicy scent of dill and celery, garlic and roses, southernwood and wallflower. Beyond the shadeless, baking herb-garden, the fruit orchards looked cool and enticing—red cherries gleamed amid the dark leafy tops, and the apple trees drooped their branches heavy with green fruit.

About the garden was a hedge of sweet briar. There were some flowers on it still—they looked the same as other briar roses, but in the sun the leaves smelled of wine and apples. Folk plucked sprays to deck themselves as they went past. Kristin, too, took some roses and hung them on her temples, fixed under her golden fillet. One she kept in her hand. . . . After a time Erlend took it, saying no word. A while he bore it in his hand as they walked, then fastened it with the brooch upon his breast—he looked awkward and bashful as he did it, and was so clumsy that he pricked his fingers till they bled.

Broad tables were spread in the loft-room of the guild's hall—two by the main walls, for the men and the women; and two smaller boards out on the floor, where children and young folk sat side by side.

At the women's board Lady Groa was in the high-seat, the nuns and the chief of the married women sat on the inner bench along the wall, and the unwedded women on the outer benches, the maids from Nonneseter at the upper end. Kristin knew that Erlend was watching her, but she durst not turn her head even once, either when they rose or when they sat down. Only when they got up at last to hear the priest read the names of the dead guildbrothers and sisters, she stole a hasty glance at the men's table—she caught a glimpse of him where he stood by the wall, behind the candles burning on the board. He was looking at her.

The meal lasted long, with all the toasts in honor of God, the Virgin Mary, and St. Margaret and St. Olav and St. Halvard, and prayers and song between.

Kristin saw through the open door that the sun was gone; sounds of fiddling and song came in from the green without, and all the young folks had left the tables already when Lady Groa said to the convent maidens that they might go now and play themselves for a time if they listed.

Three red bonfires were burning upon the green; around them moved the many-colored chains of dancers. The fiddlers sat aloft on heaped-up chests and scraped their fiddles—they played and sang a different tune in every ring; there were too many folk for *one* dance. It was nearly dark already—northward the wooded ridge stood out coal-black against the yellow-green sky.

Under the loft-balcony folk were sitting drinking. Some men sprang forward, as soon as the six maids from Nonneseter came down the steps. Munan Baardsön flew to meet Ingebjörg and went off with her, and Kristin was caught by the wrist —Erlend, she knew his hand already. He pressed her hand in his so that their rings grated on one another and bruised the flesh.

He drew her with him to the outermost bonfire. Many children were dancing there; Kristin gave her other hand to a twelve-year-old lad, and Erlend had a little, half-grown maid on his other side.

No one was singing in the ring just then—they were swaying in and out to the tune of the fiddle as they moved round. Then someone shouted that Sivord the Dane should sing them a new dance. A tall, fair-haired man with huge fists stepped out in front of the chain and struck up his ballad:

> Fair goes the dance at Munkolm
>   On silver sand.
> There danceth Ivar Sir Alfsön—
>   Holds the Queen's own hand.
> *Know ye not Ivar Sir Alfsön?*

The fiddlers knew not the tune, they thrummed their strings a little, and the Dane sang alone—he had a strong, tuneful voice:

> "Mind you, Queen of the Danemen,
>   That summer fair,
> They led you out of Sweden,
>   To Denmark here?
>
> They led you out of Sweden,
>   To Denmark here,
> All with a crown of the red gold
>   And many a tear.
>
> All with a crown of the red gold
>   And tear-filled eyne—
> —Mind you, Queen of the Danemen
>   You first were mine?"

The fiddles struck in again, the dancers hummed the new-learned tune and joined in the burden:

> "And are you, Ivar Sir Alfsön,
>   Sworn man to me,
> Then shall you hang tomorrow
>   On the gallows tree!"
>
> But 'twas Ivar Alfsön,
>   All unafraid
> He leaped into the gold-bark
>   In harness clad.
>
> "God send you, oh Dane-Queen,
>   So many a good night,
> As in the high heavens
>   Are stars alight.

> God send you, oh Dane-King,
>   So many ill years
> As be leaves on the linden—
>   Or the hind hath hairs."
> *Know ye not Ivar Sir Alfsön?*

It was far on in the night, and the fires were but heaps of embers growing more and more black. Kristin and Erlend stood hand in hand under the trees by the garden fence. Behind them the noise of the revelers was hushed—a few young lads were hopping round the glowing mounds singing softly, but the fiddlers had sought their resting-places, and most of the people were gone. One or two wives went round seeking their husbands, who were lying somewhere out of doors overcome by the beer.

"Where think you I can have laid my cloak?" whispered Kristin. Erlend put his arm about her waist and drew his mantle round them both. Close pressed to one another they went into the herb-garden.

A lingering breath of the day's warm spicy scents, deadened and damp with the chill of the dew, met them in there. The night was very dark, the sky overcast, with murky gray clouds close down upon the tree-tops. But they could tell that there were other folks in the garden. Once Erlend pressed the maiden close to him and asked in a whisper:

"Are you not afraid, Kristin?"

In her mind she caught a faint glimpse of the world outside this night—and knew that this was madness. But a blessed strengthlessness was upon her. She only leaned closer to the man and whispered softly—she herself knew not what.

They came to the end of the path; a stone wall divided them from the woods. Erlend helped her up. As she jumped down on the other side, he caught her and held her lifted in his arms a moment before he set her on the grass.

She stood with upturned face to take his kiss. He held her head between his hands—it was so sweet to her to feel his fingers sink into her hair—she felt she must repay him, and so she clasped his head and sought to kiss him, as he had kissed her.

When he put his hands upon her breast, she felt as though he drew her heart from out her bosom; he parted the folds of silk ever so little and laid a kiss betwixt them—it sent a glow into her inmost soul.

"You I could never harm," whispered Erlend. "You should never shed a tear through fault of mine. Never had I dreamed a maid might be so good as you, my Kristin—"

He drew her down into the grass beneath the bushes; they sat with their backs against the wall. Kristin said naught, but when he ceased from caressing her, she put up her hand and touched his face.

In a while Erlend asked: "Are you not weary, my dear one?" And when Kristin nestled in to his breast, he folded his arms around her, and whispered: "Sleep, sleep, Kristin, here in my arms—"

She slipped deeper and deeper into darkness and warmth and happiness upon his breast.

When she came to herself again, she was lying outstretched in the grass with her cheek upon the soft brown silk above his knees. Erlend was sitting as before with his back to the stone wall, his face looked gray in the gray twilight, but his wide opened eyes were marvelously clear and fair. She saw he had wrapped his cloak all about her—her feet were so warm and snug with the fur lining around them.

"Now have you slept in my lap," said he, smiling faintly. "May God bless you, Kristin—you slept as safe as a child in its mother's arms—"

"Have *you* not slept, Sir Erlend?"

asked Kristin; and he smiled down into her fresh opened eyes:

"Maybe the night will come when you and I may lie down to sleep together—I know not what you will think when you have weighed all things. I have watched by you tonight—there is still so much betwixt us two that 'tis more than if there had lain a naked sword between you and me. Tell me if you will hold me dear, when this night is past?"

"I will hold you dear, Sir Erlend," said Kristin. "I will hold you dear, so long as you will—and thereafter I will love none other."

"Then," said Erlend slowly, "may God forsake me if any maid or woman come to my arms ere I may make you mine in law and honor. Say you this, too," he prayed. Kristin said:

"May God forsake me if I take any other man to my arms so long as I live on earth."

"We must go now," said Erlend, a little after, "before folk waken."

They passed along without the wall among the bushes.

"Have you bethought you," asked Erlend, "what further must be done in this?"

" 'Tis for you to say what we must do, Erlend," answered Kristin.

"Your father," he asked in a little, "they say at Gerdarud he is a mild and a righteous man. Think you he will be so exceeding loth to go back from what he hath agreed with Andres Darre?"

"Father has said so often, he would never force us, his daughters," said Kristin. "The chief thing is that our lands and Simon's lie so fitly together. But I trow father would not that I should miss all my gladness in this world for the sake of that." A fear stirred within her that so simple as this perhaps it might not prove to be—but she fought it down.

"Then maybe 'twill be less hard than I deemed in the night," said Erlend. "God help me, Kristin—methinks I *cannot* lose you now—unless I win you now, never can I be glad again."

They parted among the trees, and in the dawning light Kristin found her way to the guest-chamber where the women from Nonneseter were to lie. All the beds were full, but she threw a cloak upon some straw on the floor and laid her down in all her clothes.

When she awoke, it was far on in the day. Ingebjörg Filippusdatter was sitting on a bench near by, stitching down an edge of fur that had been torn loose on her cloak. She was full of talk as ever.

"Were you with Erlend Nikulaussön the whole night?" she asked. " 'Twere well you went warily with that lad, Kristin—how think you Simon Andressön would like it if you came to be dear friends with him?"

Kristin found a hand-basin and began to wash herself.

"And your betrothed—think you he would like that you danced with Dumpy Munan last night? Surely we must dance with him who chooses us out on such a night of merry-making—and Lady Groa had given us leave."

Ingebjörg pshawed:

"Einar Einarssön and Sir Munan are friends—and, besides, he is wedded and old. Ugly he is to boot for that matter—but likeable and hath becoming ways—see what he gave me for a remembrance of last night," and she held forth a gold clasp which Kristin had seen in Sir Munan's hat the day before. "But this Erlend —'tis true he was freed of the ban at Easter last year, but they say Eline Ormsdatter has been with him at Husaby since —Sir Munan says Erlend hath fled to Sira Jon at Gerdarud, and he deems 'tis because he cannot trust himself not to fall back into sin, if he meet her again—"

Kristin crossed over to the other—her face was white.

"Knew you not this?" said Ingebjörg. "That he lured a woman from her husband somewhere in Haalogaland in the North—and held her with him at his manor in despite of the King's command and the Archbishop's ban—they had two children together—and he was driven to fly to Sweden, and hath been forced to pay in forfeit so much of his lands and goods, Sir Munan says he will be a poor man in the end unless he mends his ways the sooner."

"Think not but that I know all this," said Kristin, with a set face. "But 'tis known the matter is ended now."

"Ay, but as to that Sir Munan said there had been an end between them so many times before," said Ingebjörg pensively. "But all these things can be nothing to you—you that are to wed Simon Darre. But a comely man is Erlend Nikulaussön, sure enough."

The company from Nonneseter was to set out for home that same day after nones. Kristin had promised Erlend to meet him by the wall where they had sat the night before, if she could but find a way to come.

He was lying face downwards in the grass with his head upon his hands. As soon as he saw her, he sprang to his feet and held out both his hands, as she was about jumping from the wall.

Kristin took them, and the two stood a little, hand in hand. Then said Kristin:

"Why told you me that of Sir Björn and Lady Aashild yesterday?"

"I can see you know it all," said Erlend, and let go her hands suddenly. "What think you of me now, Kristin?

"I was eighteen then," he went on vehemently, " 'tis ten years since that the King, my kinsman, sent me with the mission to Vargöyhus, and we stayed the winter at Steigen. . . . She was wife to the Lagmand, Sigurd Saksulvsön. . . . I thought pity of her, for he was old and ugly beyond belief. I know not how it came to pass—ay, but I loved her too. I bade Sigurd crave what amends he would; I would fain have done right by him—he is a good and doughty man in many ways—but he would have it that all must go by law; he took the matter to the Thing—I was to be branded for whoredom with the wife of him whose guest I had been, you understand . . .

"Then it came to my father's ears, and then to King Haakon's . . . he—he drove me from his court. And if you must know the whole—there is naught more now betwixt Eline and me save the children, and she cares not much for them. They are in Österdal, upon a farm I owned there; I have given it to Orm, the boy—but she will not stay with them. Doubtless she reckons that Sigurd cannot live forever—but I know not what she would be at.

"Sigurd took her back again—but she says she fared like a dog and a bondwoman in his house—so she set a tryst with me at Nidaros. 'Twas little better for me at Husaby with my father. I sold all I could lay hands on, and fled with her to Holland—Count Jacob stood my friend. Could I do aught else?—she was great with my child. I knew many a man had lived even so with another's wife and had got off cheap enough—if he were rich, that is. But so it is with King Haakon, he is hardest upon his own kin. We were away from one another for a year, but then my father died and then she came back. Then there were other troubles. My tenants denied me rent and would have no speech with my bailiffs because I lay under ban—I, on my side, dealt harshly with them, and so they brought suit against me for robbery; but I had not the money to pay my household withal; and you can see I was too young to meet these troubles wisely, and my kinsfolk would not help me—save Munan—he did all his wife would let him. . . .

"Ay, now you know it, Kristin: I have

lost much both of lands and goods and of honor. True it is; you would be better served if you held fast to Simon Andressön."

Kristin put her arms about his neck.

"We will abide by what we swore to each other yesternight, Erlend—if so be you think as I do."

Erlend drew her close to him, kissed her and said:

"You will see too, trust me, that all things will be changed with me now—for none in the world has power on me now but you. Oh, my thoughts were many last night, as you slept upon my lap, my fairest one. So much power the devil cannot have over a man that I should ever work you care and woe—you, my dearest life. . . ."

4

At the time he dwelt at Skog, Lavrans Björgulfsön had made gifts of land to Gerdarud church, that masses for the souls of his father and mother might be said on their death-days. Björgulf Ketilsön's day was the thirteenth of August, and Lavrans had settled with his brother that this year Aasmund should bring Kristin out to Skog that she might be at the mass.

She went in fear that something should come in the way, so that her uncle would not keep his promise—she thought she had marked that Aasmund did not care overmuch about her. But the day before the mass was to be, Aasmund Björgulfsön came to the convent to fetch his brother's daughter. Kristin was told to clothe herself in lay garb, but simply and in dark garments. There had been some carping at the Sisters of Nonneseter for going about too much without the convent walls; therefore the Bishop had given order that the maidens who were

not to take the veil must wear naught like to the habit of the order when they went visiting their kinsfolk—so that laymen could not mistake them for novices or nuns.

Kristin's heart was full of gladness as she rode along the highway with her uncle, and Aasmund grew more friendly and merry with her when he saw the maid was not so tongue-tied after all with folk. Otherwise Aasmund was somewhat moody and downcast; he said it looked as though there would be a call to arms in the autumn, and that the King would lead an army into Sweden to avenge the slaying of his son-in-law and the husband of his niece. Kristin had heard of the murder of the Swedish Dukes, and thought it a most foul deed—yet all these questions of state seemed far away from her. No one spoke much of such things at home in the Dale; she remembered, too, that her father had been to the war against Duke Eirik at Ragnhildarholm and Konungahella. Then Aasmund told her of all that had come and gone between the King and the Dukes. Kristin understood but little of this, but she gave careful heed to all her uncle told of the making and breaking of the betrothals of the King's daughters. It gave her comfort to think 'twas not everywhere as it was at home in her countryside, that a betrothal once fixed by word of mouth was held to bind nigh as fast as a wedding. Then she took courage to tell of her adventure on the evening before Halvards-wake, and asked her uncle if he knew Erlend of Husaby. Aasmund spoke well of Erlend —said he had guided his affairs unwisely, but his father and the King were most to blame; they had borne themselves as though the young lad were a very limb of the devil only because he had fallen into this misfortune. The King was over-pious in such matters, and Sir Nikulaus was angry because Erlend had lost much good land, so they had thundered about whoredom and hell fire—"and there must be a bit of the dare-devil in every likely lad," said Aasmund Björgulfsön. "And the woman was most fair. But you have no call now to look Erlend's way, so trouble yourself no more about his doings."

Erlend came not to the mass, as he had promised Kristin he would, and she thought about this more than of God's word. She felt no sorrow that this was so—she had only that strange new feeling that she was cut off from all the ties that she had felt binding on her before.

She tried to take comfort—like enough Erlend deemed it wisest that no one in whose charge she was should come to know of their friendship at this time. She could understand herself that 'twas wise. But her heart had longed so for him, and she wept when she had gone to rest in the loft-room where she was to sleep with Aasmund's little daughters.

The day after, she went up into the wood with the youngest of her uncle's children, a little maid of six years. When they were come to the pastures among the woods a little way off, Erlend came running after them. Kristin knew it was he before she had seen who was coming.

"I have sat up here on the hill spying down into the courtyard the whole day," said he. "I thought surely you would find a chance to come out—"

"Think you I came out to meet you then?" said Kristin, laughing. "And are you not afraid to beat about my uncle's woods with dogs and bow?"

"Your uncle gave me leave to take my pastime hunting here," said Erlend. "And the dogs are Aasmund's—they found me out this morning." He patted them and lifted the little girl up in his arms.

"*You* know me, Ragndid? But say not you have spoken with me, and you can have this"—and he took out a bunch of raisins and gave them to the child. "I had

brought them for you," he said to Kristin. "Think you this child can hold her tongue?"

They talked fast and laughed together. Erlend was dressed in a short close-fitting brown jacket and had a small red silk cap pulled down over his black hair—he looked so young; he laughed and played with the child; but sometimes he would take Kristin's hand, and press it till it hurt her.

He spoke of the rumors of war and was glad: " 'Twill be easier for me to win back the King's friendship," said he, "and then will all things be easy," he said vehemently.

At last they sat down in a meadow up among the woods. Erlend had the child on his lap; Kristin sat by his side; under cover of the grass he played with her fingers. He pressed into her hand three gold rings bound together by a cord:

"By and by," he whispered, "you shall have as many as will go on your fingers. . . .

"I shall wait for you here on this field each day about this time, as long as you are at Skog," he said, as they parted. "And you must come if you can."

The next day Aasmund Björgulfsön set out with his wife and children to the manor of Gyrid's kin in Hadeland. They had been scared by the talk of war; the folk about Oslo still went in terror since Duke Eirik's harrying of that countryside some years before. Aasmund's old mother was so fearful, she was minded to seek shelter in Nonneseter—besides, she was too weak to travel with the others. So Kristin was to stay at Skog with the old woman—as she called her grandmother —till Aasmund came back from Hadeland.

About the midday hour, when the folk on the farm were resting, Kristin went to the loft-room where she slept. She had brought some clothes with her in a sheepskin bag, and now she changed her garments, humming to herself the while.

Her father had given her a dress of thick cotton stuff from the East, sky-blue with a close pattern of red flowers; this she put on. She brushed and combed out her hair and bound it back from her face with a red silk ribbon, wound a red silk belt tightly about her waist, and put Erlend's rings upon her fingers; all the time she wondered if he would think her fair.

The two dogs that had been with Erlend in the forest had slept in the loft-room overnight—she called them to go with her now. She stole out round the houses and took the same path as the day before up through the hill-pastures.

The field amid the forest lay lonely and silent in the burning midday sun; the pine woods that shut it in on all sides gave out a hot, strong scent. The sun stung, and the blue sky seemed strangely near and close down upon the tree-tops.

Kristin sat down in the shade in the borders of the wood. She was not vexed that Erlend was not there; she was sure he would come, and it gave her an odd gladness to sit there alone a little and to be the first.

She listened to the low hum of tiny life above the yellow, scorched grass, pulled a few dry, spicy-scented flowers that she could reach without moving more than her hand, and rolled them between her fingers and smelled them—she sat with wide-open eyes sunk in a kind of drowse.

She did not move when she heard a horse in the woods. The dogs growled, and the hair on their necks bristled— then they bounded up over the meadow, barking and wagging their tails. Erlend sprang from his horse at the edge of the forest, let it go with a clap on its flank, and ran down towards her with the dogs jumping about him. He caught their muzzles in his hands and came to her leading the two elk-gray, wolf-like beasts.

Kristin smiled and held out her hand without getting up.

Once, while she was looking at the dark head that lay in her lap, between her hands, something bygone flashed on her mind. It stood out, clear yet distant, as a homestead far away on a mountain slope may start to sight of a sudden, from out dark clouds, when a sunbeam strikes it on a stormy day. And it was as though there welled up in her heart all the tenderness Arne Gyrdsön had once begged for, while, as yet, she did not understand his words. With timid passion, she drew the man up to her and laid his head upon her breast, kissing him as if afraid he should be taken from her. And when she saw his head upon her arm, she felt as though she clasped a child—she hid his eyes with one of her hands, and showered little kisses upon his mouth and cheek.

The sunshine had gone from the meadow—the leaden color above the tree-tops had thickened to dark-blue, and spread over the whole sky; little, coppery flashes like fire-tinged smoke flickered within the clouds. Bayard came down to them, neighed loudly once, and then stood stock-still, staring before him. Soon after came the first flash of lightning, and the thunder followed close, not far away.

Erlend got up and took hold of the horse. An old barn stood at the lowest end of the meadow; they went thither, and he tied Bayard to some woodwork just inside the door. At the back of the barn lay some hay; Erlend spread his cloak out, and they seated themselves with the dogs at their feet.

And now the rain came down like a sheet before the doorway. It hissed in the trees and lashed the ground—soon they had to move farther in, away from the drips from the roof. Each time it lightened and thundered, Erlend whispered:

"Are you not afraid, Kristin—?"

"A little—" she whispered back, and drew closer to him.

They knew not how long they had sat—the storm had soon passed over—it thundered far away, but the sun shone on the wet grass outside the door, and the sparkling drops fell more and more rarely from the roof. The sweet smell of the hay in the barn grew stronger.

"Now must I go," said Kristin; and Erlend answered: "Ay, 'tis like you must." He took her foot in his hand: "You will be wet—you must ride and I must walk—out of the woods . . ." and he looked at her so strangely.

Kristin shook—it must be because her heart beat so, she thought—her hands were cold and clammy. As he kissed her vehemently she weakly tried to push him from her. Erlend lifted his face a moment—she thought of a man who had been given food at the convent one day —he had kissed the bread they gave him. She sank back upon the hay. . . .

She sat upright when Erlend lifted his head from her arms. He raised himself suddenly upon his elbow:

"Look not so—Kristin!"

His voice sent a new, wild pang into Kristin's soul—he was not glad—*he* was unhappy too—!

"Kristin, Kristin! Think you I lured you out here to me in the woods meaning this—to make you mine by force—?" he asked in a little.

She stroked his hair and did not look at him.

" 'Twas not force, I trow—you had let me go as I came, had I begged you—" said she, in a low voice.

"I know not," he answered, and hid his face in her lap. . . .

"Think you that I would betray you?" asked he vehemently. "Kristin—I swear to you by my Christian faith—may God forsake me in my last hour, if I keep not faith with you till the day of my death—"

She could say naught, she only stroked his hair again and again.

" 'Tis time I went home, is it not?" she asked at length, and she seemed to wait in deadly terror for his answer.

"Maybe so," he answered dully. He got up quickly, went to the horse, and began to loosen the reins.

Then she, too, got up. Slowly, wearily, and with crushing pain it came home to her—she knew not what she had hoped he might do—set her upon his horse, maybe, and carry her off with him so she might be spared from going back among other people. It was as though her whole body ached with wonder—that this ill thing was what was sung in all the songs. And since Erlend had wrought her this, she felt herself grown so wholly his, she knew not how she should live away from him any more. She was to go from him now, but she could not understand that it should be so.

Down through the woods he went on foot, leading the horse. He held her hand in his, but they found no words to say.

When they were come so far that they could see the houses at Skog, he bade her farewell.

"Kristin—be not so sorrowful—the day will come or ever you know it, when you will be my wedded wife—"

But her heart sank as he spoke.

"Must you go away, then?" she asked, dismayed.

"As soon as you are gone from Skog," said he, and his voice already rang more bright. "If there be no war, I will speak to Munan—he has long urged me that I should wed—he will go with me and speak for me to your father."

Kristin bent her head—at each word he said, she felt the time that lay before grow longer and more hard to think of— the convent, Jörundgaard—she seemed to float upon a stream which bore her far from it all.

"Sleep you alone in the loft-room, now your kinsfolk are gone?" asked Erlend. "Then will I come and speak with you tonight—will you let me in?"

"Ay," said Kristin low. And so they parted.

The rest of the day she sat with her father's mother, and after supper she took the old lady to her bed. Then she went up to the loft-room, where she was to lie. There was a little window in the room; Kristin sat herself down on the chest that stood below it—she had no mind to go to bed.

She had long to wait. It was quite dark without when she heard the soft steps upon the balcony. He knocked upon the door with his cloak about his knuckles, and Kristin got up, drew the bolt, and let Erlend in.

She marked how glad he was, when she flung her arms about his neck and clung to him.

"I have been fearing you would be angry with me," he said.

"You must not grieve for our sin," he said, sometime after. " 'Tis not a deadly sin. God's law is not like to the law of the land in this. . . . Gunnulv, my brother, once made this matter plain to me—if two vow to have and hold each other fast for all time, and thereafter lie together, then they are wedded before God and may not break their troths without great sin. I can give you the words in Latin when they come to my mind—I knew them once. . . ."

Kristin wondered a little why Erlend's brother should have said this—but she thrust from her the hateful fear that it might have been said of Erlend and another—and sought to find comfort in his words.

They sat together on the chest, he with his arm about her, and now Kristin felt that 'twas well with her once more and she was safe—beside him was the only

spot now where she could feel safe and sheltered.

At times Erlend spoke much and cheerfully—then he would be silent for long, while he sat caressing her. Without knowing it, Kristin gathered up out of all he said each little thing that could make him fairer and dearer to her, and lessen his blame in all she knew of him that was not good.

Erlend's father, Sir Nikulaus, had been so old before he had children, he had not patience enough nor strength enough left to rear them up himself; both the sons had grown up in the house of Sir Baard Petersön at Hestnæs. Erlend had no sisters and no brother save Gunnulv; he was one year younger and was a priest at Christ's Church in Nidaros. "He is dearest to me of all mankind, save only you."

Kristin asked if Gunnulv were like him, but Erlend laughed and said they were much unlike, both in mind and body. Now Gunnulv was in foreign lands studying—he had been away these three years, but had sent letters home twice, the last a year ago, when he thought to go from St. Geneviève's in Paris and make his way to Rome. "He will be glad, Gunnulv, when he comes home and finds me wed," said Erlend.

Then he spoke of the great heritage he had had from his father and mother—Kristin saw he scarce knew himself how things stood with him now. She knew somewhat of her father's dealings in lands. . . . Erlend had dealt in his the other way about, sold and scattered and wasted and pawned, worst of all in the last years, when he had been striving to free him of his paramour, thinking that, this done, his sinful life might in time be forgotten and his kin stand by him once more; he had thought he might some day come to be Warden of half the Orkdöla country, as his father had been before him.

"But now do I scarce know what the

end will be," said he. "Maybe I shall sit at last on a mountain croft like Björn Gunnarsön, and bear out the dung on my back as did the thralls of old, because I have no horse."

"God help you," said Kristin, laughing. "Then I must come to you for sure—I trow I know more of farm-work and country ways than you."

"I can scarce think you have borne out the dung-basket," said he, laughing too.

"No; but I have seen how they spread the dung out—and sown corn have I, well-nigh every year at home. 'Twas my father's wont to plow himself the fields nearest the farm, and he let me sow the first piece that I might bring good fortune." The thought sent a pang through her heart, so she said quickly: "And a woman you must have to bake, and brew the small beer, and wash your one shirt, and milk—and you must hire a cow or two from the rich farmer near by—"

"Oh, God be thanked that I hear you laugh a little once more!" said Erlend and caught her up so that she lay on his arms like a child.

Each of the six nights which passed ere Aasmund Björgulfsön came home, Erlend was in the loft-room with Kristin.

The last night he seemed as unhappy as she; he said many times they must not be parted from one another a day longer than needful. At last he said very low:

"Now should things go so ill that I cannot come back hither to Oslo before winter—and if it so falls out you need help of friends—fear not to turn to Sira Jon here at Gerdarud; we are friends from childhood up; and Munan Baardsön, too, you may safely trust."

Kristin could only nod. She knew he spoke of what she had thought on each single day; but Erlend said no more of it. So she, too, said naught, and would not show how heavy of heart she was.

On the other nights he had gone from

her when the night grew late, but this last evening he begged hard that he might lie and sleep by her an hour. Kristin was fearful, but Erlend said haughtily, "Be sure that were I found here in your bower, I am well able to answer for myself." She herself, too, was fain to keep him by her yet a little while, and she had not strength enough to deny him aught.

But she feared that they might sleep too long. So most of the night she sat leaning against the head of the bed, dozing a little at times, and scarce knowing herself when he caressed her and when she only dreamed it. Her one hand she held upon his breast, where she could feel the beating of his heart beneath, and her face was turned to the window that she might see the dawn without.

At length she had to wake him. She threw on some clothes and went out with him upon the balcony. He clambered over the railing on the side that faced on to another house near by. Now he was gone from her sight—the corner hid him. Kristin went in again and crept into her bed; and now she quite gave way and fell to weeping for the first time since Erlend had made her all his own.

5

At Nonneseter the days went by as before. Kristin's time was passed between the dormitory and the church, the weaving-room, the book-hall and the refectory. The nuns and the convent-folk gathered in the pot-herbs and the fruits from the herb-garden and the orchard; Holycross Day came in the autumn with its procession, then there was the fast before Michaelmas. Kristin wondered— none seemed to mark any change in her. But she had ever been quiet when among strangers, and Ingebjörg Filippusdatter, who was by her night and day, was well able to chatter for them both.

Thus no one marked that her thoughts were far away from all around her. Erlend's paramour—she said to herself, she was Erlend's paramour now. It seemed now as though she had dreamed it all—the eve of St. Margaret's Mass, that hour in the barn, the nights in her bower at Skog—either she had dreamed it, or else all about her now was a dream. But one day she must waken, one day it must all come out. Not for a moment did she think aught else than that she bore Erlend's child within her.

But what would happen to her when this came to light, she could not well think. Would she be put into the black hole, or be sent home? She saw dim pictures of her father and mother far away. Then she shut her eyes, dizzy and sick, bowed in fancy beneath the coming storm and tried to harden herself to bear it, since she thought it must end by sweeping her forever into Erlend's arms —the only place where now she felt she had a home.

Thus was there in this strained waiting as much of hope as terror, as much of sweetness as of torment. She was unhappy—but she felt her love for Erlend as it were a flower planted within her— and, spite of her unhappiness, it put forth fresher and richer blooms each day. That last night when he had slept by her side she had felt, as a faint and fleeting bliss, that there awaited her a joy and happiness in his arms such as she had not yet known—she thrilled now at the thought of it; it came to her like warm, spicy breaths from sun-heated gardens. Wayside brat—Inga had flung the word at her—she opened her arms to it and pressed it to her bosom. Wayside brat was the name they gave to the child begotten in secret in woods or fields. She felt the sunshine, and the smell of the pines in the forest pasture. Each new,

creeping tremor, each sudden pulse-beat in her body she took as a reminder from the unborn babe that now she was come out into new paths—and were they never so hard to follow to the end, she was sure they must lead to Erlend at the last.

She sat betwixt Ingebjörg and Sister Astrid and sewed at the great tapestry of knights and birds amid leafy tendrils. And as she sewed she thought of how she should fly when the time was come, and it could no longer be hidden. She saw herself walking along the highways, clothed like a poor woman; all she owned of gold and silver she bore within a bundle in her hand. She bought herself shelter on a farm somewhere in a faraway countryside—she went as a servingwench, bore the water-carrier's yoke upon her neck, worked in the byres, baked and washed, and was cursed because she would not tell who was the child's father. Then Erlend came and found her.

Sometimes she dreamed that he came too late. She lay snow-white and fair in the poor peasant's bed. Erlend stooped as he came in at the door; he had on the long black cloak he had used to wear when he came to her by night at Skog. The woman led him forward to where she lay, he sank down and took her cold hands, his eyes were sad as death— Dost thou lie here, my one delight . . . ? Bent with sorrow he went out with his tender son clasped to his breast, in the folds of his cloak—nay, she thought not in good sooth that it would so fall out; she had no mind to die, Erlend should have no such sorrow. . . . But her heart was so heavy it did her good to dream these dreams. . . .

Then for a moment it stood out cold and clear as ice before her—the child, that was no dream, that must be faced; she must answer one day for what she had done—and it seemed as if her heart stood still with terror.

But after a little time had gone by, she came to think 'twas not so sure after all she was with child. She understood not herself why she was not glad—it was as though she had lain and wept beneath a warm covering, and now must get up in the cold. A month went by—then two; now she was sure that she had been spared this ill-hap—and, empty and chill of soul, she felt yet unhappier than before. In her heart there dawned a little bitterness toward Erlend. Advent drew near, and she had heard neither from or of him; she knew not where he was.

And now she felt she could not bear this fear and doubt—it was as though a bond betwixt them had snapped; now she was afraid indeed—might it not so befall that she should never see him more? All she had been safely linked to once, she was parted from now—and the new tie that bound her to her lover was such a frail one. She never thought that he would mean to play her false—but there was so much that might happen. . . . She knew not how she could go on any longer day after day, suffering the tormenting doubt of this time of waiting.

Now and then she thought of her father and mother and sisters—she longed for them, but as for something she had lost forever.

And sometimes in church, and elsewhere too, she would feel a great yearning to take part in all that this meant, the communion of mankind with God. It had ever been a part of her life; now she stood outside with her unconfessed sin.

She told herself that this cutting adrift from home and kin and Church was but for a time. Erlend must take her by the hand and lead her back into it all. When her father had given consent to their love, she could go to him as of yore; when she and Erlend were wed, they could confess and do penance for their transgression.

She began to seek for tokens that other folk were not without sin any more than they. She hearkened more to tale-bearing, and marked all the little things about her which showed that not even the Sisters in the convent here were altogether godly and unworldly. These were only little things—under Lady Groa's rule Nonneseter to the world was a pattern of what a godly sisterhood should be. Zealous in their devotions, diligent, full of care for the poor and sick, were the nuns. Their aloofness from the world was not so strict but that the Sisters both had visits from their friends and kin in the parlor, and themselves were given leave to visit these in the town when aught was afoot; but no nun had brought shame upon the house by her life all the years of Lady Groa's rule.

But Kristin had now an ear alive to all the little jars within the convent walls—little wranglings and spites and vanities. Save in the nursing of the sick, none of the Sisters would help with the rough housework—all were minded to be women of learning or skilled in some craft; the one strove to outdo the other, and the Sisters who had no turn for learning or the nobler crafts, lost heart and mooned through the hours as though but half awake.

Lady Groa herself was wise as well as learned; she kept a wakeful eye on her spiritual daughters' way of life and their diligence, but she troubled herself little about their souls' health. She had been kind and friendly to Kristin at all times—she seemed to like her better than the other young girls, but that was because Kristin was apt at books and needlework, diligent and sparing of words. Lady Groa never looked for an answer from any of the Sisters; but, on the other hand, she was ever glad to speak with men. They came and went in her parlor—tenant farmers and bailiffs of the convent. Preaching Friars from the Bishop, stewards of estates on Hovedö with whom she was at law. She had her hands full with the oversight of the convent's great estates, with the keeping of accounts, sending out church vestments, and taking in books to be copied and sending them away again. Not the most evil-minded of men could find aught unseemly in Lady Groa's way of life. But she liked only to talk of such things as women seldom know about.

The prior, who dwelled in a house by himself, northward of the church, seemed to have no more will of his own than the Abbess's writing-reed or her scourge. Sister Potentia looked after most things within the house; and she thought most of keeping such order as she had seen in the far-famed German convent where she had passed her noviciate. She had been called Sigrid Ragnvaldsdatter before, but had taken a new name when she took the habit of the order, for this was much the use in other lands; it was she, too, who had thought of making the maidens, who were at Nonneseter as pupils, and for a time only, wear novice's dress.

Sister Cecilia Baardsdatter was not as the other nuns. She went about quietly, with downcast eyes, answered always gently and humbly, was serving-maid to all, did for choice all the roughest work, fasted much more than she need—as much as Lady Groa would let her—and knelt by the hour in the church after evensong or went thither before matins.

But one evening, after she had been all day at the beck with two lay-sisters washing clothes, she suddenly burst into a loud sobbing at the supper-table. She cast herself upon the stone floor, crept among the Sisters on hands and knees, beat her breast, and with burning cheeks and streaming tears begged them all to forgive her. She was the worst sinner of them all—she had been hard as stone with pride all her days; pride, and not meekness or thankfulness for Jesus's re-

deeming death, had held her up, when she had been tempted in the world; she had fled thither not because she loved a man's soul, but because she loved her own vainglory. She had served her sisters out of pride, vanity had she drunken from her water-cup, self-righteousness had she spread thick upon her dry bread, while the other Sisters were drinking their beer and eating their bread-slices with butter.

Of all this Kristin understood no more than that not even Cecilia Baardsdatter was truly godly at heart. An unlit tallow candle that has hung from the roof and grown foul with soot and cobweb—to this she herself likened her unloving chastity.

Lady Groa went herself and lifted up the sobbing woman. Sternly she said, that for this disorder Cecilia should as a punishment move from the Sisters' dormitory into the Abbess's own bed, and lie there till she was free of this fever.

"And thereafter, Sister Cecilia, shall you sit in my seat for the space of a week; we will seek counsel of you in spiritual things and give you such honor for your godly life, that you may have your fill of the homage of sinful mankind. Thus may you judge if it be worth so much striving, and thereafter choose whether you will live by the rules, as do we others, or keep on in exercises that no one demands of you. Then can you ponder whether you will do for love of God, that He may look down upon you in His mercy, all those things which you say you have done that we should look up to you."

And so it was done. Sister Cecilia lay in the Abbess's room for fourteen days; she had a high fever, and Lady Groa herself tended her. When she got up again, she had to sit for a week at the side of the Abbess in the high-seat, both in the church and in the convent, and all waited on her—she wept all the time as though she were being beaten with whips. But afterwards she was much calmer and happier. She lived much as before, but she blushed like a bride if anyone looked at her, whether she was sweeping the floor or going alone to the church.

None the less did this matter of Sister Cecilia awake in Kristin a great longing for peace and atonement with all wherefrom she had come to feel herself cast out. She thought of Brother Edvin, and one day she took courage and begged leave of Lady Groa to go out to the barefoot friars and visit a friend she knew there.

She marked that Lady Groa disliked this—there was scant friendship between the Minorites and the other cloisters in the bishopric. And the Abbess was no better pleased when she heard who was Kristin's friend. She said this Brother Edvin was an unstable man of God—he was ever wandering about the country and seeking leave to pay begging visits to strange bishoprics. The common folk in many places held him to be a holy man, but he did not seem to understand that a Franciscan's first duty was obedience to those set over him. He had shriven freebooters and outlaws, baptized their children and chanted them to their graves, without asking leave—yet, doubtless, he had sinned as much through ignorance as in despite, and he had borne meekly the penances laid upon him on account of these things. He was borne with, too, because he was skilled in his handicraft —but even in working at this, he had fallen out with his craft-fellows; the master-limners of the Bishop of Bergen would not suffer him to come and work in the bishopric there.

Kristin made bold to ask where he had come from, this monk with the un-Norse name. Lady Groa was in the mood for talking; she told how he had been born here in Oslo, but his father was an Eng-

lishman, Rikard Platemaster, who had wedded a farmer's daughter from the Skogheim Hundred, and had taken up his abode in the town—two of Edvin's brothers were armorers of good repute in Oslo. But this eldest of the Platemaster's sons had been a restless spirit all his days. 'Twas true he had felt a call to the life of the cloister from childhood up; he had joined the Cistercians at Hovedö as soon as he was old enough. They sent him to a monastery in France to be trained—for his gifts were good; while still there he had managed to get leave to pass from the Cistercian into the Minorite Order. And at the time the unruly friars began building their church eastward in the fields in despite of the Bishop's command, Brother Edvin had been one of the worst and most stiff-necked of them all—nay, he had half killed with his hammer one of the men the Bishop sent to stop the work.

It was a long time now since any one had spoken so much with Kristin at one time, so when Lady Groa said that now she might go, the young girl bent and kissed the Abbess's hand, fervently and reverently; and as she did so, tears came into her eyes. And Lady Groa, who saw she was weeping, thought it was from sorrow—and so she said: maybe she might, after all, let her go out one day to see Brother Edvin.

And a few days later she was told some of the convent folk had an errand to the King's palace, and they could take her out along with them to the Brothers in the fields.

Brother Edvin was at home. Kristin had not thought she could have been so glad to see any one, except it had been Erlend. The old man sat and stroked her hand while they talked together, in thanks for her coming. No, he had not been in her part of the country since the night he lay at Jörundgaard, but he had heard she was to wed, and he wished her all good fortune. Then Kristin begged that he would go over to the church with her.

They had to go out of the monastery and round to the main door; Brother Edvin durst not take her through the courtyard. He seemed altogether exceeding downcast, and fearful of doing aught that might offend. He had grown very old, thought Kristin.

And when she had laid upon the altar her offering for the officiant monk who was in the church, and afterward asked Edvin if he would confess her, he grew very frightened. He dared not, he said; he had been strictly forbidden to hear confession.

"Ay, maybe you have heard of it," said he. "So it was that I felt I could not deny to those poor unfortunates the gifts which God had given me of His free grace. But, 'tis true, I should have enjoined on them to seek forgiveness in the right place—ay, ay. . . . And you, Kristin, you are in duty bound to confess to your own prior."

"Nay, but this is a thing I cannot confess to the prior of the convent," said Kristin.

"Think you it can profit you aught to confess to me what you would hide from your true father confessor?" said the monk more severely.

"If so be you cannot confess me," said Kristin, "at least you can let me speak with you and ask your counsel about what lies upon my soul."

The monk looked about him. The church was empty at the moment. Then he sat himself down on a chest which stood in a corner: "You must remember that I cannot absolve you, but I will counsel you, and keep silence as though you had told me in confession."

Kristin stood up before him, and said:

"It is this: I cannot be Simon Darre's wife."

"Therein you know well that I can counsel no otherwise than would your own prior," said Brother Edvin. "To undutiful children God gives no happiness, and your father has looked only to your welfare—that you know full well."

"I know not what your counsel will be, when you have heard me to the end," answered Kristin. "Thus stands it now with us: Simon is too good to gnaw the bare branch from which another man has broken the blossom."

She looked the monk straight in the face. But when she met his eyes and marked how the dry, wrinkled old face changed, grew full of sorrow and dismay—something seemed to snap within her, tears started to her eyes, and she would have cast herself upon her knees. But Edvin stopped her hurriedly:

"Nay, nay, sit here upon the chest by me—confess you I cannot." He drew aside and made room for her.

She went on weeping; he stroked her hand, and said gently:

"Mind you that morning, Kristin, I first saw you there on the stairway in the Hamar church . . . ? I heard a tale once, when I was in foreign lands, of a monk who could not believe that God loved all us wretched sinners. . . . Then came an angel and touched his eyes, and he beheld a stone in the bottom of the sea, and under the stone there lived a blind, white, naked creature; and he gazed at it until he came to love it, for it was so frail and weak. When I saw you sitting there, so little and so frail, within the great stone house, methought it was but reason that God should love such as you. Fair and pure you were, and yet did you need a helper and a protector. Methought I saw the whole church, with you in it, lying in the hollow of God's hand."

Kristin said low:

"We have bound ourselves one to the other with the dearest oaths—and I have heard that, in the eyes of God, such a pact hallows our coming together as much as if our fathers and mothers had given us one to the other."

The monk answered sadly:

"I see well, Kristin, some one who knew it not to the full has spoken to you of the canonical law. You could not bind yourself by oath to this man without sinning against your father and mother: them had God set over you before you met him. And is it not a sorrow and a shame for his kin, too, if they learn that he has lured astray the daughter of a man who has borne his shield with honor at all seasons—betrothed, too, to another? I hear by your words, you deem you have not sinned so greatly—yet dare you not confess this thing to your appointed priest. And if so be you think you are as good as wed to this man, wherefore set you not on your head the linen coif of wedlock, but go still with flowing hair amid the young maids with whom you can have no great fellowship any more—for now must the chief of your thoughts be with other things than they have in mind?"

"I know not what they have in their minds," said Kristin wearily. "True it is that all my thoughts are with the man I long for. Were it not for my father and mother, I would gladly bind up my hair this day—little would I care if I were called wanton, if only I might be called his."

"Know you if this man means so to deal toward you, that you may be called his with honor some day?" asked Brother Edvin.

Then Kristin told of all that had passed between Erlend Nikulaussön and herself. And while she spoke, she seemed not even to call to mind that she had ever doubted the outcome of it all.

"See you not, Brother Edvin," she began again, "we could not help ourselves. God help me, if I were to meet him without here, when I go from you, and

should he pray me to go with him, I would go. I wot well, too, I have seen now there be other folk who have sinned as well as we. . . . When I was a girl at home 'twas past my understanding how aught could win such power over the souls of men that they could forget the fear of sin; but so much have I learned now: if the wrongs men do through lust and anger cannot be atoned for, then must heaven be an empty place. They tell of you, even, that you, too, once struck a man in wrath—"

" 'Tis true," said the monk. "God's mercy alone have I to thank that I am not called manslayer. 'Tis many years agone—I was a young man then, and methought I could not endure the wrong the Bishop would have put upon us poor friars. King Haakon—he was Duke then —had given us the ground for our house, but we were so poor we had to work upon our church ourselves—with some few workmen who gave their help more for heavenly reward than for what we could pay them. Maybe 'twas sinful pride in us beggar-monks to wish to build our church so fair and goodly—but we were happy as children in the fields, and sang songs of praise while we hewed and built and toiled. Brother Ranulv—God rest his soul—was master-builder—he was a right skillful stonecutter; nay, I trow the man had been granted skill in all knowledge and all arts by God Himself. I was a carver of stone panels in those days; I had but just finished one of St. Clara, whom the angels were bearing to the church of St. Francis in the dawn of Christmas Day—a most fair panel it had proved, and all of us joyed in it greatly— then the hellish miscreants tore down the walls, and a stone fell and crushed my panels—I struck at a man with my hammer, I could not contain me. . . .

"Ay, now you smile, my Kristin. But see you not that 'tis not well with you now, since you would rather hear such tales of other folks' frailties than of the life and deeds of good men, who might serve you as a pattern . . . ?

" 'Tis no easy matter to give you counsel," he said, when it was time for her to go. "For were you to do what were most right, you would bring sorrow to your father and mother and shame to all your kin. But you must see to it that you free yourself from the troth you plighted to Simon Andressön—and then must you wait in patience for the lot God may send you, make in your heart what amends you can—and let not this Erlend tempt you to sin again, but pray him lovingly to seek atonement with your kin and with God.

"From your sin I cannot free you," said Brother Edvin, as they parted, "but pray for you I will with all my might . . ."

He laid his thin, old hands upon her head and prayed, in farewell, that God might bless her and give her peace.

6

Afterward, there was much in what Brother Edvin had said to her that Kristin could not call to mind. But she left him with a mind strangely clear and peaceful.

Hitherto she had striven with a dull, secret fear and tried to brave it out; telling herself she had not sinned so deeply. Now she felt Edvin had shown her plainly and clearly that she had sinned indeed; such and such was her sin, and she must take it upon her and try to bear it meekly and well. She strove to think of Erlend without impatience—either because he did not send word of himself, or because she must want his caresses. She would only be faithful and full of love for him.

She thought of her father and mother, and vowed to herself that she would require them for all their love, once they had got over the sorrow she must bring upon them by breaking with the Dyfrin folk. And well-nigh most of all, she thought of Brother Edvin's words of how she must not seek comfort in looking on others' faults; she felt she grew humble and kind, and now she saw at once how easy it was for her to win folks' friendship. Then was she comforted by the thought that after all 'twas not so hard to come to a good understanding with people—and so it seemed to her it surely could not be so hard for her and Erlend either.

Until the day she gave her word to Erlend, she had always striven earnestly to do what was right and good—but she had done all at the bidding of others. Now she felt she had grown from maid to woman. 'Twas not only by reason of the fervent secret caresses she had taken and given, not only that she had passed from her father's ward and was now under Erlend's will. For Edvin had laid upon her the burden of answering for her own life, ay, and for Erlend's too. And she was willing to bear it well and bravely. Thus she went about among the nuns at Yuletide; and throughout the goodly rites and the joy and peace of the holy time, though she felt herself unworthy, yet she took comfort in thinking that the time would soon come when she could set herself right again.

But the second day of the new year, Sir Andres Darre with his wife and all five children came, all unlooked for, to the convent. They were come to keep the last days of Yuletide with their friends and kindred in the town, and they asked that Kristin might have leave to be with them in their lodging for a short space.

"For methought, my daughter," said Lady Angerd, "you would scarce be loth to see a few new faces for a time."

The Dyfrin folk dwelled in a goodly house that stood in a dwelling-place near the Bishop's palace—Sir Andres' cousin owned it. There was a great hall where the serving-folk slept, and a fine loft-room with a fireplace of masonry and three good beds; in the one Sir Andres and Lady Angerd slept with their youngest son, Gudmund, who was yet a child; in another slept Kristin and their two daughters, Astrid and Sigrid, and in the third Simon and his eldest brother Gyrd Andressön.

All Sir Andres' children were comely; Simon the least so, yet he too was reckoned to be well-favored. And Kristin marked still more than when she was at Dyfrin the year before, that both his father and mother and his four brothers and sisters hearkened most to Simon, and did all he would have them. They all loved each other dearly, but all agreed, without grudging or envy, in setting Simon foremost among them.

Here these good folk lived a merry, care-free life. They visited the churches and made their offerings every day, came together with their friends and drank in their company each evening, while the young folk had full leave to play and dance. All showed Kristin the greatest kindness, and none seemed to mark how little glad she was.

Of an evening, when the light had been put out in the loft-room, and all had sought their beds, Simon was wont to get up and go to where the maidens lay. He would sit a while on the edge of the bed; his talk was mostly to his sisters, but in the dark he would let his hand rest on Kristin's bosom—while she lay there hot with wrath.

Now that her sense of such things was keener, she understood well that there were many things Simon was both too proud and too shy to say to her, since he saw she had no mind to such talk from him. And she felt strangely bitter and angry with him, for it seemed to her as though he would fain be a better man than he who had made her his own— even though Simon knew not there was such a one.

But one night, when they had been dancing at another house, Astrid and Sigrid were left behind there to sleep with a playmate. When, late at night, the Dyfrin folk had gone to rest in their loft-room, Simon came to Kristin's bed and climbed up into it; he laid himself down above the fur cover.

Kristin pulled the coverlid up to her chin and crossed her arms firmly upon her breast. In a little Simon tried to put his hand upon her bosom. She felt the silken broidery on his wristband, and knew he had not taken off any of his clothes.

"You are just as bashful in the dark as in the light, Kristin," said Simon, laughing a little. "Surely you can at least let me have one hand to hold," he said, and Kristin gave him the tips of her fingers.

"Think you not we should have somewhat to talk of, when it so falls out that we can be alone a little while?" said he; and Kristin thought, now was the time for her to speak. So she answered "Yes." But after that she could not utter a word.

"May I come under the fur?" he begged again. " 'Tis cold in the room now—" And he slipped in between the fur coverlid and the woolen blanket she had next her. He bent one arm round the bed head, but so that he did not touch her. Thus they lay awhile.

"You are not over-easy to woo, i' faith," said Simon soon after, with a resigned laugh. "Now I pledge you my word, I will not so much as kiss you, if you would not I should. But surely you can speak to me at least?"

Kristin wet her lips with the tip of her tongue, but still she was silent.

"Nay, if you are not lying there trembling!" went on Simon. "Surely it cannot be that you have aught against me, Kristin?"

She felt she could not lie to Simon, so she said "No,"—but nothing more.

Simon lay a while longer; he tried to get her into talk with him. But at last he laughed again, and said:

"I see well you think I should be content with hearing that you have naught against me—for tonight—and be glad to boot. 'Tis a parlous thing, so proud as you are—yet one kiss must you give me; then will I go my way and not plague you any more—"

He took the kiss, then sat up and put his feet to the floor. Kristin thought, now must she say to him what she had to say—but he was away already by his own bed, and she heard him undress.

The day after Lady Angerd was not so friendly to Kristin as was her wont. The girl saw that the lady must have heard somewhat the night before, and that she deemed her son's betrothed had not borne her toward him as she held was fitting.

Late that afternoon Simon spoke of a friend's horse he was minded to take in barter for one of his own. He asked Kristin if she would go with him to look at it. She was nothing loth; and they went out into the town together.

The weather was fresh and fair. It had snowed a little overnight, but now the sun was shining, and it was freezing so that the snow crackled under their feet. Kristin felt 'twas good to be out and walk in the cold air, and when Simon brought out the horse to show her, she talked of it with him gaily enough; she knew something of horses, she had been so much with her father. And this was a comely beast—a mouse-gray stallion with a black stripe down the back and a clipped mane, well-shapen and lively, but something small and slightly built.

"He would scarce hold out under a full-armed man for long," said Kristin.

"Indeed, no; nor did I mean him for such a rider," said Simon.

He led the horse out into the home-field behind the house, made it trot and walk, mounted to try its paces, and would have Kristin ride it too. Thus they stayed together a good while out on the snowy field.

At last, as Kristin stood giving the horse bread out of her hand, while Simon leaned with his arm over its back, he said all at once:

"Methinks, Kristin, you and my mother are none too loving one with another."

"I have not meant to be unloving to your mother," said she, "but I find not much to say to Lady Angerd."

"Nor seems it you find much to say to me either," said Simon. "I would not force myself upon you, Kristin, before the time comes—but things cannot go on as now, when I can never come to speech with you."

"I have never been one for much speaking," said Kristin. "I know it myself; and I look not you should think it so great a loss, if what is betwixt us two should come to naught."

"You know well what my thoughts are in that matter," said Simon, looking at her.

Kristin flushed red as blood. And it gave her a pang that she could not dislike the fashion of Simon Darre's wooing. After a while he said:

"Is it Arne Gyrdsön, Kristin, you feel you cannot forget?" Kristin but gazed at him; Simon went on, and his voice was gentle and kind: "Never would I blame you for that—you had grown up like brother and sister, and scarce a year is gone by. But be well assured, for your comfort, that I have your good at heart—"

Kristin's face had grown deathly white. Neither of them spoke again as they went back through the town in the twilight. At the end of the street, in the blue-green sky, rode the new moon's sickle with a bright star within its horn.

A year, thought Kristin; and she could not think when she had last given a thought to Arne. She grew afraid—maybe she was a wanton, wicked woman —but one year since she had seen him on his bier in the wake-room, and had thought she should never be glad again in this life—she moaned within herself for terror of her own heart's inconstancy, and of the fleeting changefulness of all things. Erlend! Erlend!—could he forget her—and yet it seemed to her 'twould be worse, if at any time she should forget him.

Sir Andres went with his children to the great Yuletide feast at the King's palace. Kristin saw all the pomp and show of the festival—they came, too, into the hall where sat King Haakon and the Lady Isabel Bruce, King Eirik's widow. Sir Andres went forward and did homage to the King, while his children and Kristin stood somewhat behind. She thought of all Lady Aashild had told her; she called to mind that the King was near of kin to Erlend, their fathers' mothers were sisters—and she was Erlend's light-o'-love, she had no right to stand here, least of all amid these good and worthy folk, Sir Andres' children.

Then all at once she saw Erlend Niku-laussön—he had stepped forward in front of Queen Isabel, and stood with bowed head, and with his hand upon his breast, while she spoke a few words to him; he had on the brown silk clothes that he had worn at the guild feast. Kristin stepped behind Sir Andres' daughters.

When, some time after, Lady Angerd led her daughters up before the Queen, Kristin could not see him anywhere, but indeed she dared not lift her eyes from the floor. She wondered whether he was standing somewhere in the hall, she thought she could feel his eyes upon her—but she thought, too, that all folks looked at her as though they must know she was a liar, standing there with the golden garland on her outspread hair.

He was not in the hall where the young folk were feasted, and where they danced when the tables had been taken away; this evening it was Simon with whom Kristin must dance.

Along one of the longer walls stood a fixed table, and thither the King's men bore ale and mead and wine the whole night long. Once when Simon drew her thither and drank to her, she saw Erlend standing near, behind Simon's back. He looked at her, and Kristin's hand shook when she took the beaker from Simon's hand and set it to her lips. Erlend whispered vehemently to the man who was with him—a tall, comely man, well on in years and somewhat stout, who shook his head impatiently and looked as he were vexed. Soon after Simon led her back to the dance.

She knew not how long this dancing lasted—the music seemed as though 'twould never end, and each moment was long and evil to her with longing and unrest. At last it was over, and Simon drew her to the drinking-board again.

A friend came forward to speak to him, and led him away a few steps, to a group of young men. And Erlend stood before her.

"I have so much I would fain say to you," he whispered. "I know not what to say first—in Jesus' name, Kristin, what ails you?" he asked quickly, for he saw her face grow white as chalk.

She could not see him clearly; it

seemed as though there were running water between their two faces. He took a goblet from the table, drank from it and handed it to her. Kristin felt as though 'twas all too heavy for her, or as though her arm had been cut off at the shoulder; do as she would, she could not lift the cup to her mouth.

"Is it so, then, that you will drink with your betrothed, but not with me?" asked Erlend softly; but Kristin dropped the goblet from her hand and sank forward into his arms.

When she awoke she was lying on a bench with her head in a strange maiden's lap—some one was standing by her side, striking the palms of her hands, and she had water on her face.

She sat up. Somewhere in the ring about her she saw Erlend's face, white and drawn. Her own body felt weak, as though all her bones had melted away, and her head seemed as it were large and hollow; but somewhere within it shone one clear, desperate thought—she must speak with Erlend.

She said to Simon Darre—he stood near by:

" 'Twas too hot for me, I trow—so many tapers are burning here—and I am little used to drink so much wine—"

"Are you well again now?" asked Simon. "You frightened folks. Mayhap you would have me take you home now?"

"We must wait, surely, till your father and mother go," said Kristin calmly. "But sit down here—I can dance no more." She touched the cushion at her side—then she held out her other hand to Erlend:

"Sit you here, Erlend Nikulaussön; I had no time to speak my greetings to an end. 'Twas but of late Ingebjörg said she deemed you had clean forgotten her."

She saw it was far harder for him to keep calm than for her—and it was all she could do to keep back the little tender smile, which would gather round her lips.

"You must bear the maid my thanks for thinking of me still," he stammered. "Almost I was afraid she had forgotten me."

Kristin paused a little. She knew not what she should say, which might seem to come from the flighty Ingebjörg and yet might tell Erlend her meaning. Then there welled up in her the bitterness of all these months of helpless waiting, and she said:

"Dear Erlend, can you think that we maidens could forget the man who defended our honor so gallantly—"

She saw his face change as though she had struck him—and at once she was sorry; then Simon asked what this was they spoke of. Kristin told him of Ingebjörg's and her adventure in the Eikaberg woods. She marked that Simon liked the tale but little. Then she begged him to go and ask of Lady Angerd, whether they should not soon go home; 'twas true that she was weary. When he was gone, she looked at Erlend.

" 'Tis strange," said he in a low voice, "you are so quick-witted—I had scarce believed it of you."

"Think you not I have had to learn to hide and be secret?" said she gloomily.

Erlend's breath came heavily; he was still very pale.

" 'Tis so then?" he whispered. "Yet did you promise me to turn to my friends if this should come to pass. God knows, I have thought of you each day, in dread that the worst might have befallen—"

"I know well what you mean by the worst," said Kristin shortly. "*That* you have no need to fear. To me what seemed the worst was that you would not send me one word of greeting—can you not understand that I am living there among the nuns—like a stranger bird—?" She

stopped—for she felt that the tears were coming.

"Is it therefore you are with the Dyfrin folk now?" he asked. Then such grief came upon her that she could make no answer.

She saw Lady Angerd and Simon come through the doorway. Erlend's hand lay upon his knee, near her, and she could not take it.

"I must have speech with you," said he eagerly, "we have not said a word to one another we should have said—"

"Come to mass in the Maria Church at Epiphany," said Kristin quickly, as she rose and went to meet the others.

Lady Angerd showed herself most loving and careful of Kristin on the way home, and herself helped her to bed. With Simon she had no talk until the day after. Then he said:

"How comes it that you bear messages betwixt this Erlend and Ingebjörg Filippusdatter? 'Tis not fit you should meddle in the matter, if there be hidden dealings between them!"

"Most like there is naught in it," said Kristin. "She is but a chatterer."

"Methinks too," said Simon, "you should have taken warning by what's past, and not trusted yourself out in the wild-wood paths alone with that magpie." But Kristin reminded him hotly, that it was not their fault they had strayed and lost themselves. Simon said no more.

The next day the Dyfrin folks took her back to the convent, before they themselves left for home.

Erlend came to evensong in the convent church every evening for a week without Kristin getting a chance to change a word with him. She felt as she thought a hawk must feel sitting chained to its perch with its hood over its eyes. Every word that had passed between them at their last meeting made her unhappy too—it should never have been like that. It was of no use to say to herself: it had come upon them so suddenly, they had hardly known what they said.

But one afternoon in the twilight there came to the parlor a comely woman, who looked like a townsman's wife. She asked for Kristin Lavransdatter, and said she was the wife of a mercer and her husband had come from Denmark of late with some fine cloaks; Aasmund Björgulfsön had a mind to give one to his brother's daughter, and the maid was to go with her and choose for herself.

Kristin was given leave to go with the woman. She thought it was unlike her uncle to wish to give her a costly gift, and strange that he should send an unknown woman to fetch her. The woman was sparing of her words at first, and said little in answer to Kristin's questions, but when they were come down to the town, she said of a sudden:

"I will not play you false, fair child that you are—I will tell you all this thing as it is, and you must do as you deem best. 'Twas not your uncle who sent me, but a man—maybe you can guess his name, and if you cannot, then you shall not come with me. I have no husband—I make a living for myself and mine by keeping a house of call and selling beer; for such a one it boots not to be too much afraid either of sin or of the watchmen—but I will not lend my house for you to be betrayed inside my doors."

Kristin stood still, flushing red. She was strangely sore and ashamed for Erlend's sake. The woman said:

"I will go back with you to the convent, Kristin; but you must give me somewhat for my trouble—the knight promised me a great reward; but I, too, was fair once, and I, too, was betrayed. And 'twould not be amiss if you should name me in your prayers tonight—they call me Brynhild Fluga."

Kristin drew a ring off her finger and gave it to the woman:

" 'Tis fairly done of you, Brynhild— but if the man be my kinsman Erlend Nikaulaussön, then have I naught to fear; he would have me make peace betwixt him and my uncle. You may set your mind at ease; but I thank you none the less that you would have warned me."

Brynhild Fluga turned away to hide a smile.

She led Kristin by the alleys behind St. Clement's Church, northward towards the river. Here a few small dwelling-places stood by themselves along the river-bank. They went towards one of them, along a path between fences, and here Erlend came to meet them. He looked about him on all sides, then took off his cloak, wrapped it about Kristin, and pulled the hood over her face.

"What think you of this device?" he asked, quickly and low. "Think you 'tis a great wrong I do?—yet needs must I speak with you."

"It boots but little now, I trow, to think what is right and what is wrong," said Kristin.

"Speak not so," begged Erlend. "I bear the blame. . . . Kristin, every day and every night have I longed for you," he whispered close to her.

A shudder passed through her as she met his eyes for a moment. She felt it as guilt in her, when he looked so at her, that she had thought of anything but her love for him.

Brynhild Fluga had gone on before. Erlend asked, when they were come into the courtyard:

"Would you that we should go into the living-room, or shall we talk up in the loft-room?"

"As you will," answered Kristin; and they mounted to the loft-room.

The moment he had barred the door behind them she was in his arms. . . .

She knew not how long she had lain folded thus in his arms, when Erlend said:

"Now must we say what has to be said, my Kristin—I scarce dare let you stay here longer."

"I dare stay here all night long if you would have me stay," whispered she.

Erlend pressed his cheeks to hers.

"Then were I not your friend. 'Tis bad enough as it is, but you shall not lose your good name for my sake."

Kristin did not answer—but a soreness stirred within her; how could he speak thus—he who had lured her here to Brynhild Fluga's house; she knew not why, but she felt it was no honest place. And he had looked that all should go as it had gone, of that she was sure.

"I have thought at times," said Erlend again, "that if there be no other way, I must bear you off by force—into Sweden. Lady Ingebjörg welcomed me kindly in the autumn and was mindful of our kinship. But now do I suffer for my sins—I have fled the land before, as you know—and I would not they should name you as the like of that other."

"Take me home with you to Husaby," said Kristin low. "I cannot bear to be parted from you, and to live on among the maids at the convent. Both your kin and mine would surely hearken to reason, and let us come together and be reconciled with them—"

Erlend clasped her to him, and groaned:

"I cannot bring you to Husaby, Kristin."

"Why can you not?" she asked softly.

"Eline came thither in the autumn," said he after a moment. "I cannot move her to leave the place," he went on hotly, "not unless I bear her to the sledge by force and drive away with her. And that methought I could not do—she has brought both our children home with her."

Kristin felt herself sinking, sinking. In a voice breaking with fear, she said:

"I deemed you were parted from her."

"So deemed I, too," answered Erlend shortly. "But she must have heard in Österdal, where she was, that I had thoughts of marriage. You saw the man with me at the Yuletide feast—'twas my foster-father, Baard Peterson of Hestnæs. I went to him when I came from Sweden; I went to my kinsman, Heming Alvsön in Saltviken, too; I talked with both about my wish to wed, and begged their help. Eline must have come to hear of it. . . .

"I bade her ask what she would for herself and the children—but Sigurd, her husband—they look not that he should live the winter out—and then none could deny us if we would live together. . . .

"I lay in the stable with Haftor and Ulv, and Eline lay in the hall in my bed. I trow my men had a rare jest to laugh at behind my back."

Kristin could not say a word. A little after, Erlend spoke again:

"See you, the day we pledge each other at our espousals, she must understand that all is over between her and me—she has no power over me any more. . . .

"But 'tis hard for the children. I had not seen them for a year—they are fair children—and little can I do to give them a happy lot. 'Twould not have helped them greatly had I been able to wed their mother."

Tears began to roll down over Kristin's cheeks. Then Erlend said:

"Heard you what I said but now, that I had talked with my kinsfolk? Ay, they were glad enough that I was minded to wed. Then I said 'twas you I would have and none other."

"And they liked not that?" asked Kristin at length, forlornly.

"See you not," said Erlend gloomily, "they could say but one thing—they cannot and they will not ride with me to your father, until this bargain 'twixt you and Simon Andressön is undone again. It has made it none the easier for us, Kristin, that you have spent your Yuletide with the Dyfrin folk."

Kristin gave way altogether and wept noiselessly. She had felt ever that there was something of wrong and dishonor in her love, and now she knew the fault was hers.

She shook with the cold when she got up soon after, and Erlend wrapped her in both the cloaks. It was quite dark now without, and Erlend went with her as far as St. Clement's Church; then Brynhild brought her the rest of the way to Nonneseter.

7

A week later Brynhild Fluga came with word that the cloak was ready, and Kristin went with her and met Erlend in the loft-room as before.

When they parted, he gave her a cloak: "So that you may have something to show in the convent," said he. It was a blue velvet with red silk inwoven, and Erlend bade her mark that 'twas of the same hues as the dress she had worn that day in the woods. Kristin wondered it should make her so glad that he said this—she thought he had never given her greater happiness than when he said these words.

But now they could no longer make use of this way of meeting, and it was not easy to find a new one. But Erlend came often to vespers at the convent church, and sometimes Kristin would make herself an errand after the service, up to the commoners' houses; and then they would snatch a few words together by stealth up by the fences in the murk of the winter evening.

Then Kristin thought of asking leave

of Sister Potentia to visit some old, crippled women, alms-folk of the convent, who dwelled in a cottage standing in one of the fields. Behind the cottage was an outhouse where the women kept a cow; Kristin offered to tend it for them; and while she was there Erlend would join her and she would let him in.

She wondered a little to mark that, glad as Erlend was to be with her, it seemed to rankle in his mind that she could devise such a plan.

" 'Twas no good day for you when you came to know me," said he one evening. "Now have you learned to follow the ways of deceit."

"*You* ought not to blame me," answered Kristin sadly.

" 'Tis not you I blame," said Erlend quickly, with a shamed look.

"I had not thought myself," went on Kristin, "that 'twould come so easy to me to lie. But one *can* do what one *must* do."

"Nay, 'tis not so at all times," said Erlend as before. "Mind you not last winter, when you could not bring yourself to tell your betrothed that you would not have him?"

To this Kristin answered naught, but only stroked his face.

She never felt so strongly how dear Erlend was to her, as when he said things like this, that made her grieve or wonder. She was glad when she could take upon herself the blame for all that was shameful and wrong in their love. Had she found courage to speak to Simon as she should have done, they might have been a long way now on the road to have all put in order. Erlend had done all he could when he had spoken of their wedding to his kinsmen. She said this to herself, when the days in the convent grew long and evil—Erlend had wished to make all things right and good again. With little tender smiles she thought of him as he drew a picture of their wed-

ding for her—she should ride to church in silks and velvet, she should be led to the bridal-bed with the high golden crown on her flowing hair—your lovely, lovely hair, he said, drawing her plaits through her hand.

"Yet can it not be the same to you as though I had never been yours," said Kristin musingly, once when he talked thus.

Then he clasped her to him wildly:

"Can I call to mind the first time I drank in Yuletide, think you, or the first time I saw the hills at home turn green when winter was gone? Ay, well do I mind the first time you were mine, and each time since—but to have you for my own is like keeping Yule and hunting birds on green hillsides forever—"

Happily she nestled to him. Not that she ever thought for a moment it would turn out as Erlend was so sure it would —Kristin felt that before long a day of judgment must come upon them. It could not be that things should go well for them in the end. . . . But she was not so much afraid—she was much more afraid Erlend might have to go northward before it all came to light, and she be left behind, parted from him. He was over at the castle at Akersnes now; Munan Baardsön was posted there while the bodyguard was at Tunsberg, where the King lay grievously sick. But sometime Erlend must go home and see to his possessions. That she was afraid of his going home to Husaby because Eline sat there waiting for him, she would not own even to herself; and neither would she own that she was less afraid to be taken in sin along with Erlend, than of standing forth alone and telling Simon and her father what was in her heart.

Almost she could have wished for punishment to come upon her, and that soon. For now she had no other thought than of Erlend; she longed for him in the day and dreamed of him at night; she could not feel remorse, but she took comfort in thinking the day would come when she would have to pay dear for all they had snatched by stealth. And in the short evening hours she could be with Erlend in the alms-women's cowshed, she threw herself into his arms with as much passion as if she knew she had paid with her soul already that she might be his.

But time went on, and it seemed as though Erlend might have the good fortune he had counted on. Kristin never marked that any in the convent mistrusted her. Ingebjörg, indeed, had found out that she met Erlend, but Kristin saw the other never dreamed 'twas aught else than a little passing sport. That a maid of good kindred, promised in marriage, should dare wish to break the bargain her kinsfolk had made, such a thought would never come to Ingebjörg, Kristin saw. And once more a pang of terror shot through her—it might be 'twas a quite unheard-of thing, this she had taken in hand. And at this thought she wished again that discovery might come, and all be at an end.

Easter came. Kristin knew not how the winter had gone; every day she had not seen Erlend had been long as an evil year, and the long evil days had linked themselves together into weeks without end; but now it was spring and Easter was come, she felt 'twas no time since the Yuletide feast. She begged Erlend not to seek her till the Holy Week was gone by; and he yielded to her in this, as he did to all her wishes, thought Kristin. It was as much her own blame as his that they had sinned together in not keeping the Lenten fast. But Easter she was resolved they should keep. Yet it was misery not to see him. Maybe he would have to go soon; he had said naught of it, but she knew that now the King lay dying, and mayhap this might bring some turn in Erlend's fortunes, she thought.

Thus things stood with her, when one of the first days after Easter word was brought her to go down to the parlor to her betrothed.

As soon as he came toward her and held out his hand, she felt there was somewhat amiss—his face was not as it was wont to be; his small, gray eyes did not laugh, they did not smile when he smiled. And Kristin could not help seeing it became him well to be a little less merry. He looked well, too, in a kind of traveling dress—a long blue, close-fitting outer-garment men called *kothardi*, and a brown shoulder-cape with a hood, which was thrown back now; the cold air had given his light-brown hair a yet stronger curl.

They sat and talked for a while. Simon had been at Formo through Lent, and had gone over to Jörungaard almost daily. They were well there; Ulvhild as well as they dared look that she should be; Ramborg was at home now, she was a fair child and lively.

"'Twill be over one of these days—the year you were to be here at Nonneseter," said Simon. "By this time the folks at your home will have begun to make ready for our betrothal-feast—yours and mine."

Kristin said naught, and Simon went on:

"I said to Lavrans, I would ride hither to Oslo and speak to you of this."

Kristin looked down and said low:

"I, too, would fain speak with you of that matter, Simon—alone."

"I saw well myself that we must speak of it alone," answered Simon; "and I was about to ask even now that you would pray Lady Groa to let us go together into the garden for a little."

Kristin rose quickly and slipped from the room without a sound. Soon after she came back followed by one of the nuns with a key.

There was a door leading from the parlor out into an herb-garden that lay behind the most westerly of the convent buildings. The nun unlocked the door and they stepped out into a mist so thick they could see but a few paces in among the trees. The nearest stems were coal-black; the moisture stood in beads on every twig and bough. A little fresh snow lay melting upon the wet mould, but under the bushes some white and yellow lily plants were blooming already, and a fresh, cool smell rose from the violet leaves.

Simon led her to the nearest bench. He sat a little bent forward, with his elbows resting upon his knees. Then he looked up at her with a strange little smile:

"Almost I think I know what you would say to me," said he. "There is another man, who is more to you than I—"

"It is so," answered Kristin faintly.

"Methinks I know his name, too," said Simon, in a harder tone. "It is Erlend Nikulaussön of Husaby?"

After a while Kristin asked in a low voice:

"It has come to your ears, then?"

Simon was a little slow in answering:

"You can scarce think I could be so dull as not to see somewhat when we were together at Yule? I could say naught then, for my father and mother were with us. But this it is that has brought me hither alone this time. I know not whether it be wise of me to touch upon it—but methought we must talk of these things before we are given to one another.

". . . But so it is now, that when I came hither yesterday—I met my kinsman, Master Öistein. And he spoke of you. He said you two had passed across the churchyard of St. Clement's one evening, and with you was a woman they call Brynhild Fluga. I swore a great oath that he must have been amiss! And if you say it is untrue, I shall believe your word."

"The priest saw aright," answered Kristin defiantly. "You forswore yourself, Simon."

He sat still a little ere he asked:

"Know you who this Brynhild Fluga is, Kristin?" As she shook her head, he said: "Munan Baardsön set her up in a house here in the town, when he wedded—she carries on unlawful dealings in wine—and other things—"

"You know her?" asked Kristin mockingly.

"I was never meant to be a monk or a priest," said Simon, reddening. "But I can say at least that I have wronged no maid and no man's wedded wife. See you not yourself that 'tis no honorable man's deed to bring you out to go about at night in such company—?"

"Erlend did not draw me on," said Kristin, red with anger, "nor has he promised me aught. I set my heart on him without his doing aught to tempt me—from the first time I saw him, he was dearer to me than all other men."

Simon sat playing with his dagger, throwing it from one hand to the other.

"These are strange words to hear from a man's betrothed maiden," said he. "Things promise well for us two now, Kristin?"

Kristin drew a deep breath:

"You would be ill served should you take me for your wife now, Simon."

"Ay, God Almighty knows that so it seems indeed," said Simon Andressön.

"Then I dare hope," said Kristin meekly and timidly, "that you will uphold me, so that Sir Andres and my father may let this bargain about us be undone."

"Do you so?" said Simon. He was silent for a little. "God knows whether you rightly understand what you say."

"That do I," said Kristin. "I know the law is such that none may force a maid to marriage against her will; else can she take her plea before the Thing—"

"I trow 'tis before the Bishop," said

Simon, with something of a grim smile. "True it is, I have had no cause to search out how the law stands in such things. And I wot well you believe not either that 'twill come to that pass. You know well enough that I will not hold you to your word, if your heart is too much set against it. But can you not understand— 'tis two years now since our marriage was agreed, and you have said no word against it till now, when all is ready for the betrothal and the wedding. Have you thought what it will mean, if you come forth now and seek to break the bond, Kristin?"

"But you want not me either," said Kristin.

"Ay, but I do," answered Simon curtly. "If you think otherwise, you must even think better of it—"

"Erlend Nikulaussön and I have vowed to each other by our Christian faith," said she, trembling, "that if we cannot come together in wedlock, then neither of us will have wife or husband all our days—"

Simon was silent a good while. Then he said with effort:

"Then I know not, Kristin, what you meant when you said Erlend had neither drawn you on nor promised you aught— he has lured you to set yourself against the counsel of all your kin. Have you thought what kind of husband you will get, if you wed a man who took another's wife to be his paramour—and now would take for wife another man's betrothed maiden—?"

Kristin gulped down her tears; she whispered thickly:

"This you say but to hurt me."

"Think you I would wish to hurt you?" asked Simon, in a low voice.

" 'Tis not as it would have been, had you . . ." said Kristin falteringly. "You were not asked either, Simon—'twas your father and my father who made the pact. It had been otherwise had you chosen me yourself—"

Simon struck his dagger into the bench so that it stood upright. A little after he drew it out again, and tried to slip it back into its sheath, but it would not go down, the point was bent. Then he sat passing it from hand to hand as before.

"You know yourself," said he, in a low tone and with a shaking voice, "you know that you lie, if you would have it that I did not—. You know well enough what I would have spoken of with you— many times—when you met me so that I had not been a man, had I been able to say it—after that—not if they had tried to drag it out of me with red-hot pincers. . . .

"First I thought 'twas yonder dead lad. I thought I must leave you in peace awhile—you knew me not—I deemed 'twould have been a wrong to trouble you so soon after. Now I see you did not need so long a time to forget—now— now—now—"

"No," said Kristin quietly. "I know it, Simon. Now I cannot look that you should be my friend any longer."

"Friend . . . !" Simon gave a short strange laugh. "Do you need my friendship now, then?"

Kristin grew red.

"You are a man," said she softly. "And old enough now—you can choose yourself whom you will wed."

Simon looked at her sharply. Then he laughed as before.

"I understand. You would have me say 'tis I who—. I am to take the blame for the breaking of our bond?

"If so be that your mind is fixed—if you have the will and the boldness to try to carry through your purpose—then I will do it," he said low. "At home, with all my own folks, and before all your kin—save one. To your father you must tell the truth, even as it is. If you would have it so, I will bear your message to him, and spare you, in giving it, in so far as I can—but Lavrans Björgulfsön shall know that never, with my will, would I go back from one word that I have spoken to him."

Kristin clutched the edge of the bench with both hands; this was harder for her to bear than all else that Simon Darre had said. Pale and fearful, she stole a glance at him.

Simon rose.

"Now must we go in," said he. "Methinks we are nigh frozen, both of us, and the sister is sitting waiting with the key. I will give you a week to think upon the matter—I have business in the town here. I shall come hither and speak with you when I am ready to go, but you will scarce care to see aught of me meanwhile."

8

Kristin said to herself: now that, at least, is over. But she felt broken with weariness and sick for Erlend's arms.

She lay awake most of the night, and she resolved to do what she had never dared think of before—send word to Erlend. It was not easy to find anyone who could go such an errand for her. The lay-sisters never went out alone, nor did she know of any of them she thought would be willing; the men who did the farm-work were elder folk and but seldom came near the dwellings of the nuns, save to speak with the Abbess herself. There was only Olav. He was a half-grown lad who worked in the gardens; he had been Lady Groa's foster-son from the time when he was found, a new-born babe, upon the church steps one morning. Folk said one of the lay-sisters was his mother; she was to have been a nun; but after she had been kept in the dark cell for six months—for

grave disobedience, as 'twas said—and it was about that time the child was found —she had been given the lay-sisters' habit and had worked in the farmyard ever since. Kristin had often thought of Sister Ingrid's fate throughout these months, but she had had few chances to speak with her. It was venturesome to trust to Olav—he was but a child, and Lady Groa and all the nuns were wont to chat and jest with him, when they saw the boy. But Kristin deemed it mattered little what risks she took now. And a day or two later, when Olav was for the town one morning, Kristin sent word by him to Akersnes, that Erlend must find some way whereby they might meet alone.

That same afternoon Erlend's own man, Ulf, came to the grille. He said he was Aasmund Björgulfsön's man, and was to pray, on his master's behalf, that his brother's daughter might go down to the town for a little, for Aasmund had not time to come to Nonneseter. Kristin thought this device must surely fail—but when Sister Potentia asked if she knew the bearer of the message, she said, "Yes." So she went with Ulf to Brynhild Fluga's house.

Erlend awaited her in the loft-room— he was uneasy and anxious, and she knew at once, 'twas that he was afraid again of what he seemed to fear the most.

Always it cut her to the soul he should feel such a haunting dread that she might be with child—when yet they could not keep apart. Harassed as she was this evening, she said this to him—hotly enough. Erlend's face flushed darkly, and he laid his head down upon her shoulder.

"You are right," said he. "I must try to let you be, Kristin—not to put your happiness in such jeopardy. If you will—"

She threw her arms around him and laughed, but he caught her round the waist, forced her down upon a bench, and seated himself on the farther side of the board. When she stretched her hand over to him, he covered the palm with vehement kisses.

"I have tried more than you," said he with passion. "You know not how much I deem it means for both of us, that we should be wed with all honor."

"Then you should not have made me yours," said Kristin.

Erlend hid his face in his hands.

"Ay, would to God I had not done you that wrong," he said.

"Neither you nor I wish that," said Kristin, laughing boldly. "And if I may but be forgiven and make my peace at last with my kindred and with God, then shall I not sorrow overmuch though I must wear the woman's hood when I am wed. Ay, and often it seems to me, I could do without peace even, if only I may be with you."

"You shall bring honor with you into my house once more," said Erlend, "not I drag *you* down into dishonor."

Kristin shook her head. Then she said:

" 'Tis like you will be glad then, when you hear that I have talked with Simon Andressön—and he will not hold me to the pact that was made for us by our fathers before I met you."

At once Erlend was wild with joy, and Kristin was made to tell him all. Yet she told not of the scornful words Simon had spoken of Erlend, though she said that before Lavrans he would not take the blame upon himself.

" 'Tis but reason," said Erlend shortly. "They like each other well, your father and he? Ay, me he will like less, I trow— Lavrans."

Kristin took these words as a sign that Erlend felt with her she had still a hard road to travel ere yet they reached their journey's end; and she was thankful to him for it. But he did not come back to this matter; he was glad above measure, saying he had feared so that she would not have courage to speak with Simon.

"You like him after a fashion, I mark well," said he.

"Can it be aught to you," asked Kristin, ". . . after all that has come and gone between you and me, that I can see that Simon is an honest man and a stout?"

"Had you never met me," said Erlend, "you might well have had good days with him, Kristin. Why laugh you?"

"Oh, I did but call to mind somewhat Lady Aashild said once," answered Kristin. "I was but a child then—but 'twas somewhat about good days falling to wise folk, but the best days of all to those who dare be unwise."

"God bless my kinswoman, if she taught you that," said Erlend, and took her upon his knee. " 'Tis strange, Kristin, never have I marked that you were afraid."

"Have you never marked it?" she asked, as she nestled close to him.

He seated her on the bedside and drew off her shoes, but then drew her back again to the table.

"Oh, my Kristin—now at last it looks as if bright days might come for us two. Methinks I had never dealt with you as I have done," he said, stroking and stroking her hair, "had it not been that each time I saw you, I thought ever 'twas not reason that they should give so fine and fair a wife to *me*. . . . Sit you down here and drink to me," he begged.

A moment after came a knock on the door—it sounded like the stroke of a sword hilt.

"Open, Erlend Nikulaussön, if you are within!"

" 'Tis Simon Darre," said Kristin, in a low voice.

"Open, man, in the devil's name—if you be a man!" shouted Simon, and beat on the door again.

Erlend went to the bed and took his sword down from the peg in the wall. He looked round, at a loss what to do:

"There is nowhere here you can hide—"

" 'Twould scarce make things better if I hid," said Kristin. She had risen to her feet; she spoke very quietly, but Erlend saw that she was trembling. "You must open," she said, in the same tone. Simon hammered on the door again.

Erlend went and drew the bolt. Simon stepped in; he had a drawn sword in his hand, but he thrust it back into its sheath at once.

For a while the three stood in silence. Kristin trembled; but yet, in this first moment, she felt a strange, sweet thrill— from deep within her something rose, scenting the combat between two men— she drew a deep breath; here was an end to these endless months of dumb waiting and longing and dread. She looked from one to the other, pale and with shining eyes—then the strain within her broke in a chill, unfathomable despair. There was more of cold scorn than of rage or jealousy in Simon Darre's eyes, and she saw that Erlend, behind his defiant bearing, burned with shame. It dawned upon her, how other men would think of him, who had let her come to him in such a place, and she saw 'twas as though he had had to suffer a blow in the face; she knew he burned to draw his sword and fall upon Simon.

"Why have you come hither, Simon?" she cried aloud in dread.

Both men turned towards her.

"To fetch you home," said Simon. "Here you cannot be—"

" 'Tis not for you, any more, to lay commands on Kristin Lavransdatter," said Erlend fiercely, "she is mine now—"

"I doubt not she is," said Simon savagely, "and a fair bridal bower have you brought her to—" He stood a little, panting; then he mastered his voice and spoke quietly: "But so it is that I am her betrothed still—till her father can come for her. And for so long I mean to guard with edge and point so much of her

honor as can be saved—in others' eyes—"

"What need of *you* to guard her; I can—" he flushed red as blood under Simon's eyes. Then, flying out: "Think you I will suffer threats from a boy like you," he cried, laying his hand on his sword-hilt.

Simon clapped both hands behind him.

"I am not such a coward as to be afraid you should deem me afraid," said he as before. "I will fight you, Erlend Nikulaussön, you may stake your soul upon that, if, within due time, you have not made suit for Kristin to her father—"

"That will I never do at your bidding, Simon Andressön," said Erlend angrily; the blood rushed into his face again.

"Nay—do you it to set right the wrong you have done so young a maid," answered Simon, unmoved, " 'twill be better so for Kristin."

Kristin gave a loud cry, in pain at Erlend's pain. She stamped upon the floor:

"Go, then, Simon, go—what have you to do with our affairs?"

"I told you but now," said Simon. "You must bear with me till your father has loosed you and me from each other."

Kristin broke down utterly.

"Go, go, I will follow straightway. . . . Jesus! why do you torture me so, Simon? . . . you know you deem not yourself I am worthy that you should trouble about me—"

" 'Tis not for your sake I do it," answered Simon. "Erlend—will you not tell her to go with me?"

Erlend's face quivered. He touched her on the shoulder:

"You must go, Kristin. Simon Darre and I will speak of this at another time—"

Kristin got up obediently, and fastened her cloak about her. Her shoes stood by the bedside. . . . She remembered them, but she could not put them on under Simon's eyes.

Outside, the fog had come down again. Kristin flew along, with head bent and hands clutched tight in the folds of her cloak. Her throat was bursting with tears —wildly she longed for some place where she could be alone, and sob and sob. The worst, the worst was still before her; but she had proved a new thing this evening, and she writhed under it—she had proved how it felt to see the man to whom she had given herself humbled.

Simon was at her elbow as she hurried through the lanes, over the common lands and across the open places, where the houses had vanished and there was naught but fog to be seen. Once when she stumbled over something, he caught her arm and kept her from falling.

"No need to run so fast," said he. "Folk are staring after us. . . . How you are trembling!" he said more gently. Kristin held her peace and walked on.

She slipped in the mud of the street, her feet were wet through and icy cold— the hose she had on were of leather, but they were thin; she felt they were giving way, and the mud was oozing through to her naked feet.

They came to the bridge over the convent beck, and went more slowly up the slopes on the other side.

"Kristin," said Simon of a sudden, "your father must never come to know of this."

"How knew you that I was—there?" asked Kristin.

"I came to speak with you," answered Simon shortly. "Then they told me of this man of your uncle's coming. I knew Aasmund was in Hadeland. You two are not over cunning at making up tales.— Heard you what I said but now?"

"Ay," said Kristin. "It was I who sent word to Erlend that we should meet at Fluga's house; I knew the woman—"

"Then shame upon you! But, oh, you could not know what she is—and he. . . . Do you hear," said Simon harshly,

"if so be it *can* be hidden, you must hide from Lavrans what you have thrown away. And if you cannot hide it, then you must strive to spare him the worst of the shame."

"You are ever so marvelous careful for my father," said Kristin, trembling. She strove to speak defiantly, but her voice was ready to break with sobs.

Simon walked on a little. Then he stopped—she caught a glimpse of his face, as they stood there alone together in the midst of the fog. He had never looked like this before.

"I have seen it well, each time I was at your home," said he, "how little you understood, you his womenfolk, what a man Lavrans is. Knows not how to rule you, says yonder Trond Gjesling—and 'twere like he should trouble himself with such work—he who was born to rule over *men*. He was made for a leader, ay, and one whom men would have followed —gladly. These are no times for such men as he—my father knew him at Baaghaus. . . . But, as things are, he has lived his life up there in the Dale, as he were little else but a farmer. . . . He was married off all too young—and your mother, with her heavy mood, was not the one to make it lighter for him to live that life. So it is that he has many friends —but think you there is *one* who is his fellow? His sons were taken from him— 'twas you, his daughters, who were to build up his race after him—must he live now to see the day when one is without health and the other without honor—?"

Kristin pressed her hands tightly over her heart—she felt she must hold it in to make herself as hard as she had need to be.

"Why say you this?" she whispered after a time. "It cannot be that you would ever wish to wed me now—"

"That—would I—not," said Simon unsteadily. "God help me, Kristin—I think of you that evening in the loft-room at Finnsbrekken.—But may the foul fiend fly away with me living the day I trust a maiden's eyes again!

". . . Promise me, that you will not see Erlend before your father comes," said he, when they stood at the gate.

"That will I not promise," answered Kristin.

"Then *he* shall promise," said Simon.

"I will not see him," said Kristin quickly.

"The little dog I sent you once," said Simon before they parted, "him you can let your sisters have—they are grown so fond of him—if you mislike not too much to see him in the house.

". . . I ride north tomorrow early," said he, and then he took her hand in farewell, while the sister who kept the door looked on.

Simon Darre walked downward towards the town. He flung out a clenched fist as he strode along, talked half aloud, and swore out into the fog. He swore to himself that he grieved not over *her*. Kristin—'twas as though he had deemed a thing pure gold—and when he saw it close at hand, it was naught but brass and tin. White as a snowflake had she knelt and thrust her hand into the flame—that was last year; this year she was drinking wine with an outcast ribald in Fluga's loft-room. The devil, no! 'Twas for Lavrans Björgulfsön he grieved, sitting up there on Jörundgaard believing—full surely never had it come into Lavrans' mind that he could be so betrayed by his own. And now he himself was to bear the tidings, and help to lie to *that* man—it was for this that his heart burned with sorrow and wrath.

Kristin had not meant to keep her promise to Simon Darre, but, as it befell, she spoke but a few words with Erlend—one evening up on the road.

She stood and held his hand, strangely meek, while he spoke of what had befallen in Brynhild's loft-room at their last meeting. With Simon Andressön he would talk another time. "Had we fought there, 'twould have been all over the town," said Erlend hotly. "And that he too knew full well—this Simon."

Kristin saw how this thing had galled him. She, too, had thought of it unceasingly ever since—there was no hiding the truth, Erlend came out of this business with even less honor than she herself. And she felt that now indeed they were one flesh—that she must answer for all he did, even though she might mislike his deeds, and that she would feel it in her own flesh when so much as Erlend's skin was scratched.

Three weeks later Lavrans Björgulfsön came to Oslo to fetch his daughter.

Kristin was afraid, and she was sore of heart as she went to the parlor to meet her father. What first struck her, when she saw him standing there speaking to Sister Potentia, was that he did not look as she remembered him. Maybe he was but little changed since they parted a year ago—but she had seen him all her years at home as the young, lusty, comely man she had been so proud to have for father when she was little. Each winter, and each summer that passed over their heads up there at home, had doubtless marked him with the marks of growing age, as they had unfolded her into a full-grown young woman—but she had not seen it. She had not seen that his hair was fading here and there and had taken on a tinge of rusty red near the temples—as yellow hair does when 'tis turning gray. His cheeks had shrunken and grown longer so that the muscles ran in harder lines down to the mouth; his youthful white and red had faded to one weather-beaten shade. His back was not bowed—but yet his shoulder-blades had an unaccustomed curve beneath his cloak. His step was light and firm, as he came toward her with outstretched hand, but yet 'twas not the old brisk and supple motion. Doubtless, all these things had been there last year, only she had not seen them. Perhaps there had been added a little touch—of sadness—which made her see them now. She burst into weeping.

Lavrans put his arm about her shoulder and laid his hand against her cheek.

"Come, come, be still now, child," he said gently.

"Are you angry with me, father?" she asked low.

"Surely you must know that I am," he answered—but he went on stroking her cheek. "Yet so much, too, you sure must know, that you have no need to be afraid of me," said he sadly. "Nay, now must you be still, Kristin; are you not ashamed to bear you in such childish wise." For she was weeping so that she had to seat herself upon the bench. "We will not speak of these things here, where folk go out and in," said he, and he sat himself down by her side and took her hand. "Will you not ask after your mother then—and your sisters . . . ?"

"What does my mother say of this?" asked his daughter.

"Oh, that you can have no need to ask—but we will not talk of it now," he said again. "Else she is well—" and he set to telling this and that of the happenings at home on the farm, till Kristin grew quieter little by little.

But it seemed to her that the strain did but grow worse because her father said naught of her breach of troth. He gave her money to deal out among the poor of the convent and to make gifts to her fellow-pupils. He himself gave rich gifts to the cloister and the Sisters; and no one in Nonneseter knew aught else than that Kristin was now to go home for her betrothal and her wedding. They both ate the last meal at Lady Groa's board in the Abbess's room, and the Lady spoke of Kristin with high praise.

But all this came to an end at last. She had said her last farewell to the Sisters and her friends at the convent gate; Lavrans led her to her horse and lifted her into the saddle. 'Twas so strange to ride with her father and the men from Jörundgaard down to the bridge, along this road, down which she had stolen in the dark; wonderful, too, it seemed to ride through the streets of Oslo freely and in honor. She thought of their splendid wedding train, that Erlend had talked of so often—her heart grew heavy; 'twould have been easier had he carried her away with him. There was yet such a long time before her in which she must live one life in secret and another openly before folks. But then her eye fell on her father's grave, ageing face, and she tried to think that, after all, Erlend was right.

There were a few other travelers in the inn. At eventide they all supped together in a little hearth-room, where there were two beds only; Lavrans and Kristin were to sleep there, for they were the first in rank among the guests. Therefore, when the night drew on a little, the others bade them a friendly goodnight as they broke up and went to seek their sleeping-places. Kristin thought how it was she who had stolen to Brynhild Fluga's loft-room to Erlend's arms—sick with sorrow and with fear that she might never more be his, she thought, no, there was no place for her any more among these others.

Her father was sitting on the farther bench looking at her.

"We are not to go to Skog this time?" asked Kristin, to break the silence.

"No," answered Lavrans. "I have had enough for some time with what your mother's brother made me listen to—because I would not constrain you," he added, as she looked up at him questioningly.

"And, truly, I would have made you keep your word," said he a little after, "had it not been that Simon said he would not have an unwilling wife."

"*I* have never given my word to Simon," said Kristin quickly. "You have ever said before, that you would never force me into wedlock—"

" 'Twould not have been force if I had held you to a bargain that had been published long since and was known to all men," answered Lavrans. "These two winters past you two have borne the name of handfasted folk, and you have said naught against it, nor shown yourself unwilling, till now your wedding-day was fixed. If you would plead that the business was put off last year, so that you have not yet given Simon your troth, then that I call not upright dealing."

Kristin stood gazing down into the fire.

"I know not which will seem the worse," went on her father, "that it be said that you have cast off Simon, or that he has cast off you. Sir Andres sent me a word," Lavrans flushed red as he said it, "he was wroth with the lad, and bade me crave such amends as I should think fit. I had to say what was true—I know not if aught else had been better—that, should there be amends to make, 'twas rather for us to make them. We are shamed either way."

"I cannot think there is such great shame," said Kristin low. "Since Simon and I are of one mind."

"Of one mind?" repeated Lavrans. "He did not hide from me that he was unhappy, but he said, after you had spoken together, he deemed naught but misfortune could come of it if he held you to the pact. . . . But now must you tell me how this has come over you."

"Has Simon said naught?" asked Kristin.

"It seemed as though he thought," said her father, "that you have given your love to another man. Now must you tell me how this is, Kristin."

Kristin thought for a little.

"God knows," said she, in a low voice, "I see well, Simon might be good enough for me, and maybe too good. But 'tis true that I came to know another man; and then I knew I would never have one happy hour more in all my life were I to live it out with Simon—not if all the gold in England were his to give—I would rather have the other if he owned no more than a single cow."

"You look not that I should give you to a serving-man, I trow?" said her father.

"He is as well born as I, and better," answered Kristin. "I meant but this—he has enough both of lands and goods, but I would rather sleep with him on the bare straw than with another man in a silken bed—"

Her father was silent a while.

" 'Tis one thing, Kristin, that I will not force you to take a man that likes you not—though God and St. Olav alone know what you can have against the man I had promised you to. But 'tis another thing whether the man you have set your heart upon is such as I can wed you to. You are young yet, and not over-wise—and to cast his eyes upon a maid who is promised to another—'tis not the wont of an upright man—"

"No man can rule himself in that matter," broke in Kristin.

"Ay, but he can. But so much you can understand, I trow: I will not do such offense to the Dyfrin folk as to betroth you to another the moment you have turned your back on Simon—and least of all to a man who might be more high in rank or richer.—You must say who this man is," he said after a little.

Kristin pressed her hands together and breathed deeply. Then she said very slowly:

"I cannot, father. Thus it stands, that should I not get this man, then you can take me back to the convent and never take me from it again. . . . I shall not live long there, I trow. But 'twould not be seemly that I should name his name, ere yet I know he bears as good a will toward me as I have to him. You—you must not force me to say who he is, before—before 'tis seen whether—whether he is minded to make suit for me through his kin."

Lavrans was a long time silent. He could not but be pleased that his daughter took the matter thus; he said at length:

"So be it, then. 'Tis but reason that you would fain keep back his name, if you know not more of his purposes."

"Now must you to bed, Kristin," he said a little after. He came and kissed her.

"You have wrought sorrow and pain to many by this waywardness of yours, my daughter—but this you know, that

your good lies next my heart. . . . God help me, 'twould be so, I fear me, whatever you might do—He and His gentle Mother will surely help us, so that this may be turned to the best. . . . Go now, and see that you sleep well."

After he had lain down, Lavrans thought he heard a little sound of weeping from the bed by the other wall, where his daughter lay. But he made as though he slept. He had not the heart to say to her that he feared the old talk about her and Arne and Bentein would be brought up again now, but it weighed heavily upon him that 'twas but little he could do to save the child's good name from being besmirched behind his back. And the worst was that he must deem much of the mischief had been wrought by her own thoughtlessness.

SIMONSEN

By SIGRID UNDSET

Translated from the Norwegian by Naomi Walford

Simonsen stopped in the gateway and dug out his worn, greasy old wallet, meaning to slip into it the testimonial he had in his hand. But first he unfolded the grimy paper and read it through, although he knew it by heart:

"Storeman Anton Simonsen has been with our firm for three years. During this time he has shown himself to be a sober, hard-working, and willing man.

N. Nielsen
Hercules Engineering Works."

No, indeed; that reference wouldn't do him much good. Damn the fellow, it was a shabby way to treat him. The chief had never minded pitching the tale to customers about delivery dates and things like that—but write the sort of reference that would get a poor devil a job—not likely! "Well, I can't state that you've carried out your work to our satisfaction," he'd said, the so-and-so. But at least he'd had to put "sober." He hadn't at first, but Simonsen had insisted. "Seems to me I've smelled drink on you from time to time, Simonsen." But Simonsen had spoken up. "I do take a nip now and again, sir," he'd said. "And I believe you would too, if you had to spend your days rummaging about in that cold warehouse. But nobody can say Anton Simonsen was ever the worse for drink at his work—no, not even tipsy.

Not once." So then his lordship had to give in and the secretary lady had to write it out again with "sober" in it. And now here it was—such as it was; no great shakes, but he had nothing better to show.

"Look out, blast you—fathead!"

Simonsen jumped aside against the wall as a cartload of clattering iron girders swung into the gateway. Steam rose from the horses' damp backs as they threw themselves into the collar to drag the sleigh over the bare paving-stones under the arch. The driver shouted something else after him, but Simonsen couldn't hear it for the din of the clashing girders.

He put away his testimonial and slipped the wallet into his breast pocket. Then he glanced indignantly after the sleigh. It was standing in the yard in front of the warehouse, under the crane which projected with its chain and pulley from a dark hole above the barred windows in the blackish-red wall. White steam was rising from the horses' backs, and their coats were matted into little wet, frosty tufts. The carter hadn't put their rugs on them; he was talking to another man.

Simonsen buttoned up his winter overcoat, which was fairly new and tidy, straightened himself up, and threw out his stomach. A sense of his dignity as a citizen arose in him; he was, after all, a respectable member of society, and that ruffian of a driver had bawled at him. And with this feeling something else stirred within him at the sight of the two cart horses, which had hauled their load until the muscles of their sweating loins were tense. He stepped back into the yard.

"You ought to cover those horses of yours, you know. Why d'you let 'em stand in the cold like that, in a muck sweat?"

The carter—a tall lout of a fellow—turned and looked down at him.

"Is that any o' your business, fellow?"

"They'd have something to say to you, wouldn't they, if I was to go up to the office and tell 'em how you treat their animals?"

"Just you get out—and quick about it! What the hell's it got to do with you, eh? Shoving your nose in—" and he took a step toward Simonsen.

Simonsen withdrew a little—but of course the fellow would never dare touch him here in the yard. He stuck out his stomach even farther, saying: "Don't forget they can see you from the office windows, that's all—see how you look after the firm's horses."

With that he turned. And at once the feeling of self-confidence ebbed away. For as he was passing through the gateway a man ran down the steps and shot past him, a gentleman, wearing an astrakhan cap and a fur coat, and carrying a black stick with a silver handle—a red-and-white, fair-haired man, the man he had spoken to when he applied for the job.

Dusk was falling. It was nearly four o'clock. Olga would have something to say about it when he arrived back so late for dinner. Well, he'd just have to tell her he'd been kept late at the warehouse.

Simonsen padded quickly along Torv Street. He both shuffled and hopped, and

with his big round belly and little curved arms he looked rather like a rubber ball rolling and bouncing along. He was a little, short-necked man with a pouchy, fat face and watery eyes hidden far in behind their lids, red-veined cheeks, and a rather blue blob of a nose above the bristly, grayish-yellow moustache.

It was a raw Saturday afternoon early in December, and the air was thick with gray frost-fog that smelled and tasted of gas and soot. Out in the street the sleighs swung from side to side over the plowed-up, pot-holed, hard-frozen snow, while on the pavement the stream of people flowed black and heavy past the illuminated, frosted shopwindows. Somebody bumped into Simonsen every moment, and looked back at him angrily as he bumbled along deep in his own thoughts.

Not that many thoughts were stirring in his mind, for he thrust them away. He'd find something, somehow, somewhere. So he needn't tell Olga that he'd been sacked at last, and was to leave on New Year's Day. Heigh-ho—the battle of life.

There was no great hurry. He had nearly a month. But if it came to the pinch, he'd have to write to Sigurd. Sigurd would always be able to find him a job. It wasn't too much to ask of one's own son—when the son was in Sigurd's position. Still, he didn't care for the idea; it would be for the fourth time. The fourth time in eight whole years, though —eight years exactly at the New Year, since Sigurd had got him into the office because his smart new daughter-in-law, the bitch, didn't think he was good enough to live with them in Fredrikstad. It was a pity he'd lost all three jobs—but that wasn't his fault. At the office it was the girls who'd done for him, cheeky little sluts. As if it mattered to them what he was like so long as he did his work properly—and he had. And he'd taken no liberties with them—as if he would, with such stuck-up, white-faced shrews. And then there was the timber yard. In those days he'd been really neat and respectable, for it was then he had moved to Olga's. He wasn't used to that sort of job, of course; but if it hadn't been for the foreman's malice he would never have lost it. And then he was taken on by the engineering works. And what sort of situation was that for a man nearing sixty, having to learn about a whole lot of queer new things he'd never heard of, and dispatching and packing and invoicing and all the rest of it. The chief storeman was a lazy devil; Simonsen was blamed for everything, and they'd always treated him badly—all of them, from the manager and the chief clerk (who kept reminding him that he'd only been taken on temporarily and asking him whether he had anything else in view) to the head storeman and the foreman and the drivers—*and* the cashier: how sour and cross she'd been every time he went up to her to ask for an advance!

All these things went round and round in his head, rolled up in a gray, woolly fog of anxiety and depression: Olga would nag at him when he got home, Sigurd and his wife would make themselves most unpleasant when they heard he'd been dismissed, and he would have to make a fresh start in a new job where he would dither, frightened and uncomprehending and woolly-minded, faced with new work that he knew nothing about and would never learn, in a new warehouse or perhaps a new office full of strange, hostile things, cowering under constant correction and rebuke, dully awaiting a fresh dismissal—just as he had dithered and cowered, heavy and old and stupid, through his previous situations.

But Simonsen had had a certain amount of practice in keeping gloomy thoughts at bay. He had dithered through

his whole life in just the same way; he had cowered and expected dismissal and reprimand and nagging and unpleasantness as something inevitable. So it had been at sea, so it had been on Consul Isachsen's wharf, and so it had been at home while his wife was alive. She had been ill-tempered and sour and strict and cross-grained—and his daughter-in-law was not so very different.

Yes, Sigurd had been paid out for marrying that shabby-genteel daughter of Captain Myhre's. What good times Simonsen had had at home after Laura's death! The boy had come on well: he'd been good to his old dad—paid his way and everything. Not that it had been so bad here in town either, for the first few years, when he'd been a gay bachelor again, going out and about and having fun. And since he'd taken up with Olga he'd really been very comfortable—on the whole. She hadn't been too easy the time she became pregnant, but that was understandable, and she had calmed down the moment he promised to marry her. Sometimes she went on at him to keep his word, and of course he fully intended to marry her sometime; he'd have done it long ago if he hadn't known what trouble he'd have over it with Sigurd and his wife. But one day he'd find a good, easy job that he could keep, and when Olga expanded her dressmaking business, and her boy Henry went into the office—he was errand-boy there now, and shaping well—they would all be happy and comfortable together. He would sit on the sofa with his toddy and his pipe, and Olga would flit in and out seeing to things, and Svanhild would sit beside him and do her homework. For Olga was a decent, steady person, and nobody should have a chance to call Svanhild a bastard when she started school.

Simonsen had reached Ruseløk Road. The fog lay heavy and raw in the narrow street, and was barred with light—yellowish-green light from the frozen panes of the little shopwindows. In all of these, visible where gas jet or lamp had thawed a clear patch, hung a cluster of paper Christmas-tree baskets, whether it was a draper's or a delicatessen store or a tobacco shop. The reddish glow from the big windows of the market hall on the other side of the street flowed oilily out into the fog; the gas lamps on the terrace above could just be glimpsed, but the big private houses up there were invisible; not a gleam of light came from them, though one could sense them like a wall high up in the fog, pressing down upon the street that ran like a ditch at their foot.

Simonsen toddled and trudged along; the pavement was slippery in many places where the sheet-ice had not been chipped away. Children swarmed in and out of the dark gateways, and in the street among carts and sleighs they tried to slide, wherever there was as much as a slippery runner-track through the bumpy, brown layer of hard-frozen snow.

"Svanhild!"

Simonsen called sharply to a little girl in a dirty white hood. She had clambered up on to the piled-up snow along the edge of the pavement, and from there slid down to the roadway on tiny skis that were black with dirty snow and had hardly any curve left in them.

The child stood still in the middle of the street, looking up at Simonsen, who had stepped over the heap of snow to her. Her blue eyes were conscience-stricken, as she brushed her fair hair up under her hood and wiped her nose on her red-mittened hand.

"How many times have you been told not to run out into the street, Svanhild! Why can't you be a good girl and play in the yard?"

Svanhild looked up fearfully.

"I can't ski in the yard; there isn't any slope."

"And suppose a cart came along and ran over you—or a drunken man carried you off—what d'you think Mum and Dad would say then, eh?"

Svanhild, ashamed, was silent. Simonsen helped her on to the pavement, and they tripped along together hand in hand, her little sticks of skis clattering on the snowless path.

"Do you think Dad'll take you for a walk this evening, when you're such a naughty, disobedient girl, and don't do what you're told? Finished dinner, I suppose, have they?"

"Mummy and Henry and me had dinner a long time ago."

"H'm." Simonsen trudged in through the gateway. MRS. OLGA MARTINSEN. DRESSMAKING. CHILDREN'S AND BOYS' CLOTHES. 3rd FLOOR. ENTRANCE IN YARD was the legend on a white enamel plate. Simonsen crossed the courtyard and glanced up at the lighted window, where some fashion magazines were propped up against the panes. Then he took Svanhild's skis under his arm and led the child up the narrow stairs at the back of the yard.

Outside Olga's door some little boys were reading a comic by the light of a kitchen lamp that hung there. Simonsen growled something and let himself in.

It was dark in the hall. At the farther end, light shone through the glass pane in the sitting-room door. Simonsen went into his own room. It was dark in there too, and cold. Damn it, she'd let the stove go out. He lit the lamp.

"Run in to Mummy, Svanhild, and tell her I'm back."

He opened the door into the next room. At the table, which overflowed with half-finished sewing, pieces cut out and scraps left over, Miss Abrahamsen sat bowed over her work. She had fastened a newspaper to one side of the lamp, so that all the light fell upon her yellow little old-maid's face and brown, rat's paw hands. The steel of the two sewing-machines glinted a little, and against the wall Olga's and Svanhild's white-covered beds could just be discerned.

"Hard at it, then, Miss Abrahamsen!"

"Yes, well—you got to be."

"Funny, this Christmas business. You'd think the world was coming to an end."

Svanhild crept into the room.

"Mum says your dinner's in the oven."

"I shall sit here and enjoy your company, Miss Abrahamsen. It's cold in my room."

Miss Abrahamsen silently cleared a corner of the table while Simonsen fetched his meal: white cabbage soup and sausage.

H'm. Good. If only he'd had—Simonsen rose and knocked at the sitting-room door.

"I say, Olga—"

"Why, good evening, Mr. Simonsen! How are you keeping?"

He opened the door and looked in.

"So it's you! Another new dress, Miss Hellum?"

Olga was standing with her mouth full of pins, fitting her customer. She arranged the folds at Miss Hellum's breast, in front of the wall mirror.

"Like that, I thought." Olga took the lamp from the nickel stand beside her and held it up.

"Ye—es. You're sure it's not lopsided at the back, now, Mrs. Martinsen?"

Two girls who were sitting and waiting in the half light over on the plush sofa put down a fashion journal, glanced at each other and smiled, looked at Miss Hellum and smiled at each other again. "Gracious!" one whispered audibly. They were dressed almost exactly alike, in three-quarter-length coats with a little strip of fur at the neck, and respectable felt hats trimmed with a bird's wing. Simonsen paused in the doorway; he was a little shy of them.

"What do you think of it, Mr. Simonsen? Is it going to look nice?"

"How well that color suits you, Miss Hellum! But to beauty all is becoming, as they say."

"Ah, go on with you!" Miss Hellum laughed. Pretty girl, that. Olga was cutting round the neck, and her customer bent her head a little and shivered at the touch of the cold scissors. She had a pretty, plump neck and curly yellow hair growing low on it, and soft round arms.

"I expect this costs a bit," said Simonsen, feeling the silk—and then feeling her arm, as Olga went to fetch the sleeve.

"Shame on you, Mr. Simonsen!" laughed Miss Hellum. Olga looked annoyed; she shoved him aside and pulled on the sleeve.

"What was I going to say? . . . Oh, yes, Olga. Do you think Henry could nip down and borrow a couple of beers?"

"Poor Henry had to go back to the office; there was an estimate to be copied, he said."

"Oh, did he? Too bad. It's the same every Saturday evening nowadays, seems to me. Yes, it's a grind all right. And it was nearly four before I could get away from the warehouse. Oh, to be young and lovely, Miss Hellum!"

Svanhild looked in.

"Come along, Svanhild. Do you remember my name today?"

"Miss Hellum." Svanhild smiled obediently.

"Would you like some sweets again today?" Miss Hellum looked into her handbag and brought out a paper cornet.

"What do you say now, Svanhild? Your right hand, mind, and a pretty curtsy."

Svanhild whispered thank you, gave her right hand, and curtsied. Then she began breaking apart the camphor-drop sweets that had stuck together in the paper bag.

Miss Hellum dressed and talked and laughed.

"I'll be along for the final fitting on Tuesday, then, at the same time. You won't let me down, Mrs. Martinsen, will you? Good-by, then. Good-by, Mr. Simonsen. 'Bye, Svanhild."

Simonsen gallantly opened the door for her, and she swept out with waving feathers, the muskrat stole flung stylishly back over her shoulder.

"Gosh," said one of the young girls on the sofa. "Not bad."

"Hee-hee! No, she's a one, all right."

Simonsen went back to Miss Abrahamsen and his dinner, which had grown cold. Olga came in soon afterwards, fetched the coffee, and poured it out.

"I don't understand you, Anton, playing the fool like that! What can you be thinking of—in front of other people, too."

"Who cares about those little baggages?"

"It was the pastor's daughter from the Terrace and her friend. You make things hard enough for me as it is, without carrying on so silly with Miss Hellum. Yes, that's given them something to talk about—as if they hadn't enough already!"

"Ah, go on—it wasn't as bad as that."

The front doorbell rang. Miss Abrahamsen went to answer it.

"It's Miss Larsen."

Olga put down her cup and laid a tacked-up dress over her arm.

"Never any peace—"

Miss Abrahamsen bent over her sewing again.

Mrs. Martinsen and Miss Abrahamsen sat sewing all that Sunday. They put off dinner until it was too dark to work;

afterwards Olga lit the lamp and they started again.

"That plastron for Miss Olsen's dress, Miss Abrahamsen—you were working on it just now, weren't you?"

Miss Abrahamsen buzzed away at the machine.

"I put it on the table."

Olga searched, and looked about the floor.

"Svanhild, you haven't seen a little piece of white lace, have you?"

"No," said Svanhild from the window. She crept out and began searching too—but first she laid her doll on the upturned stool that was its bed, and covered it up well.

"Astrid's asleep—she's got diphtheria and scarlet fever," Svanhild protested, as her mother hunted through the doll's things. But relentlessly Olga lifted the patient—it was wrapped in white, ruched lace fastened carefully with safety pins.

"Good gracious! The child must be out of her mind! And I do declare you've torn a hole in it with the pins—you naughty, wicked girl—" she smacked her "—oh, what *shall* I do? Miss Olsen's expensive lace . . ."

Svanhild howled.

"Haven't I told you never to take anything that's on the floor? You're a wicked, mischievous little girl!"

Miss Abrahamsen inspected the plastron.

"I can unpick the pleats and press it and pleat it again so's to hide the tear in a fold. I don't think it'll show—"

Svanhild was yelling at the top of her voice. Simonsen opened the door a crack.

"What on earth's the matter, Svanhild —screaming like that when you know Daddy's taking his nap?"

Olga explained, vehemently.

"Oh, what a bad girl, Svanhild, to play such a nasty trick on your mother. You're not my Svanhild any more."

"I think you might take her out for a bit, Anton. It can't be good for you to lie in bed and sleep all day."

Simonsen scolded the child vigorously as he set off with her. But when they got as far as the hall and he helped her into her outdoor things, he comforted her.

"Don't cry any more now—oh, what an ugly noise! We'll go and toboggan in the Palace Park. It was very wrong of you, you know. Blow your nose now—there. You and I will go off and toboggan now—come along, Svanhild love."

Olga was really too strict with the child sometimes. Not that children shouldn't be punished when they did wrong—but Svanhild took things to heart so. There she was, still sobbing on the sled behind him—poor little mite.

The evening sky was dark purple above the towers and spires of the Terrace. The weather had cleared, and only a thin, sooty frost-haze hung in the streets round the lamps when Simonsen trudged uphill dragging his daughter on the sled.

It was so pretty in the park. Thick white hoarfrost lay on all the trees and bushes, so that they sparkled in the lamplight. But what crowds of children everywhere! On every smallest slope they were sledding or skiing; in the big avenue were swarms of big, rough boys, five or six of them on a fish sledge, yelling and shrieking as they whizzed down over the frozen snow with a long, thin rat's tail of sticks behind them. But Simonsen knew of a nice, quiet little slope; he and Svanhild had often tobogganed there in the evenings. It was fun for her there; Daddy stood at the top and gave her a shove, Svanhild shouted: "Way!" till her thin little voice nearly cracked, and Simonsen roared: "Way!" from right down in his stomach, although the only other people there were two little boys in ski-runners' shoes and woolen caps. Simonsen spoke

to them; their names were Alf and Johannes Hauge, and their father was head of a government office and lived in Park Road. Simonsen gave all three children a shove—they were going to see whose sled ran fastest—but he shoved Svanhild hardest so that she won. Then he trotted down after them and helped Svanhild up again, for otherwise her feet broke through the frozen crust of the snow and she got stuck

But presently Svanhild began to whimper.

"Daddy, my feet are so cold."

"Run then, my dear—come along, we'll go up onto the path and run."

Svanhild ran and cried; her toes hurt her so.

"Come now, you must run faster than that—much, much faster, Svanhild. Try and catch me!"

Simonsen bounced along with little tiny steps, like a rubber ball. And Svanhild ran after him as hard as she could and caught him up—again and again until she was warm and cheerful again, and laughing.

But then they couldn't find the sled. Simonsen hunted above the slope and below the slope and in among the bushes, but it was gone. Alf and Johannes had seen it standing over by the big tree near the path a little while before, but that was all they knew. Yes, and some big, rough boys had passed—Simonsen remembered that. It must have been they who took it.

Svanhild cried bitterly. Simonsen thought of Olga—oh, she really ought to be kinder; she was so snappy all day. Nasty, bad boys to steal a poor little girl's sled. How could children be so cruel.

"Don't cry, sweetheart, we'll find it again, you'll see."

Simonsen trotted about from slope to slope asking if anyone had seen a little blue sled. Svanhild went with him, holding his hand and crying; Alf and Johannes came too, clutching their sled ropes as with wide eyes they told Simonsen all the dreadful things they had heard about big, nasty boys who stole sleds and tobogganed into little children and threw lumps of ice in the Palace Park.

There was no sign of the sled. And up in the main avenue they met a grand, angry lady who turned out to be Alf's and Johannes' nanny, and she scolded them for not having come in half an hour before, and promised them they would catch it from Mummy and Daddy. She wasn't a bit interested to hear that the little girl was called Svanhild and that she had lost her sled; she went on scolding and scolding as she shuffled away holding the little boys' hands in a nurse's iron grasp. And Simonsen nearly got a steering-stick in his eye and the tip of a sled on his shin.

"Well, I'm afraid they've taken your sled, Svanhild; I don't think we shall see *that* again." Simonsen sighed dejectedly. "Hush now, don't cry so, my darling. Daddy'll give you a fine new sled for Christmas. There! Come along, we'll go down Karl Johan and look at the shops —they're wonderful tonight—and perhaps we'll see a fine new sled for you there," he said, brightening.

So Svanhild and her daddy went and looked at the shops. And when they came to a window where the crowds had halted and clustered in a big, black, jostling mass, Simonsen lifted her up on his arm and wriggled and shoved until they got right up to the shining window, and there they stood until there wasn't a single thing in it about which they hadn't talked and wondered how much it cost. In some places there were decorated Christmas trees with electric lights on their branches—and Svanhild was going to have a tree too, on Christmas Eve. In one shop there was a Christmas party, with tremendously grand lady dolls—just

like Svanhild would be when she grew up. And in a shop where they sold trunks and suitcases, there was a tiny, tiny crocodile in a tiny, tiny pool; they had to wait a long time—could it be alive? And at last it blinked one eye the teeniest bit. Fancy, it *was* alive! A little crocodile like that would grow up to be so big that it could eat up a whole Svanhild at one gulp—"but this one can't bite, can it?" "No, this one couldn't do you any harm."

Up in Ekertorvet there was a movie camera in the window, among advertisements in photographs. And Svanhild had been to a movie with Daddy—three times—and they had to go over all they had seen there: the two little girls who had been kidnapped by kidnappers in a motor car, and a lot more. The lost sled was quite forgotten—and so was Mummy, sitting with pursed lips at her sewing until she grew tired and cross—everything was forgotten except that Svanhild was Daddy's little girl and that in seventeen days it would be Christmas.

There was a sports shop with sleds in the window, sleds large and small—but the finest of all, the scarlet one with rose-painting[1] on it and a bronzed iron back-rest—that was the one Daddy would give Svanhild on Christmas Eve.

But after all this they needed something hot inside them. Simonsen knew of a snug little temperance café; it was Sunday, so the licensed ones were closed. There were no other customers, and the lady behind the counter was not insensible to Simonsen's gallant conversation while he had his coffee and sandwich and Svanhild a cream cake and a sip from Daddy's cup now and again.

"Not a word to Mummy!" Simonsen said with a wink. But Svanhild knew better than to tell Mummy when she and Daddy popped in here and there on their

---

[1] Rose-painting: a traditional Norwegian style of decoration.

evening walks, and Svanhild had a stick of barley-sugar although Mummy believed it gave little girls worms in their teeth, and Daddy had something to drink which Mummy thought gave him worms in the stomach. But Mummy was always busy and it made her very cross—and Daddy was busy too when he was in the warehouse, and Henry at the office— When people were grown-up they had to work terribly hard. Svanhild knew that.

But after Sunday came Monday and five other gray week-days. Svanhild sat on the floor in the sewing-room and played, for Daddy came back so late in the evenings now that he had no time to take her for a walk. Daddy was cross too, now, she noticed; perhaps because he had so much work to do at the warehouse, or because Mummy had so much work that she hardly had time to get dinner or supper until late. And Henry was cross as well, for ladies had fittings until late at night in the room where he slept, so that he couldn't get to bed. But Svanhild consoled herself with the thought of the wonderful sled she was going to have for Christmas.

On the fifteenth Anton wrote to his son. He was sick of running after jobs in vain. After that he took a calmer view of the future, and had time once more to go out with Svanhild in the evenings and drag her along on her skis in the park; and they talked about the fine sled she was going to have.

But on the morning of the eighteenth, as Simonsen was nailing up a crate of machinery parts, the chief storeman came to tell him that he was wanted on the telephone. It was Sigurd; he was in town. Would his father drop in at the Augustin for coffee—take a couple of hours off that afternoon so that they could have a talk?

"How's Mossa and the children?"

The children were very well. Mossa was in town too; she had a bit of Christmas shopping to do.

"I've just remembered, son—I haven't a chance of getting even an hour off now, with Christmas coming on."

Sigurd said he'd have a word with the manager.

Well, thanks. Love to Mossa.

How like her! Ask him to dinner? Not on your life! Damned if he wouldn't get himself a skinful before he went to that *party*.

"Do you think you must?" Mrs. Carling asked her husband, who was uncorking a bottle of punch.

"Yes, I really think we can stand the old man a glass of punch."

"Well, well, just as you like, dear." Mossa Carling displayed all the double chins at her command. She was not pretty: her eyelids thickened toward the temples, so that her stabbing little gray eyes seemed to creep toward the bridge of her nose; her face was fat and fresh-colored but her mouth small and pinched, with thin lips. Her chest was narrow and cramped, but the lower half of her body was broad and bulky.

She sat in the middle of the plush sofa under the electric chandelier, whose three lights splendidly illuminated the hotel room with its two iron beds, two mahogany washstands, two bedside tables, the wardrobe with the mirror, and the two armchairs in front of the table, on which an ash tray stood on a mat in the middle of the chenille cloth.

There was a timid knock on the door, and Simonsen stepped warily into the room. He shook hands.

"Well, Sigurd, nice to see you again, my boy. How are you, Mossa? Glad to see you again too—young and pretty as ever, I see."

Mossa rang for coffee and poured it out while Sigurd filled the glasses.

While he talked to Sigurd, Simonsen

glanced at his daughter-in-law, who sat mute with a pinched mouth. Slowly and deviously the conversation turned toward the purpose of the meeting.

"We may smoke, mayn't we, my dear? Here, Father, have a cigar. Now, about what you said in your letter. I went up to the office this morning and had a word with your boss. He agreed with me: you don't fit in here in town. The work's too hard for a man of your age. And I can't get you anything else."

Simonsen said nothing. But Mossa took over.

"You must remember that Sigurd's in a subordinate position himself—in a way, that is. The board of directors wouldn't like him to keep bothering their business connections to give you a job. He's done it three times now, and each time you've lost your position. I must tell you that Sigurd was in quite serious trouble after getting you into this last place, which it seems you've now lost—"

"Yes, I was. No, as I say, you don't fit in here, Father. And you're too old to start anything new. So there's only one way I can help you. I can get you a job at the Mensted works up in Øimark—it's nice easy work. Of course, the wages aren't high: sixty crowns to start with, I believe. But, as I say, I can get you that."

Simonsen was silent.

"Yes, well—that's the only way I can help you," said Sigurd Carling.

"Do you want me to get it for you then, Father?" he asked after a while.

His father cleared his throat once or twice.

"Yes. Well, now. There's one thing, Sigurd—I don't know whether you've heard anything about it, but I'm engaged to be married—to the lady I've been lodging with these last six years. So I shall have to talk this over with Olga first and see what she thinks. Her name's Olga," he explained: "Mrs. Olga Martinsen, a widow."

There was a horribly long pause. Simonsen fidgeted with the tassels on the armchair.

"She's a real, good, respectable, decent person in every way, Olga is. And she's got a big, expanding dressmaking business here in town, so it's quite a question whether she'd care much about moving into the wilds. Her boy's got an office job here, too."

"Is that the lady—" Sigurd spoke very slowly, "—who's said to have a child by you?"

"We've got a little girl, yes; her name's Svanhild—she'll be five in April."

"Oh." This was Mossa. "So you have a daughter by the woman you lodge with—the woman who's such a good, respectable, decent person in every way."

"And so she is—decent and respectable. And hard-working too. And kind."

"Then it's odd, father-in-law—" Mrs. Carling's voice was very sweet and smooth "—that you didn't marry this wonderful Mrs. Martinsen long ago. You had every reason."

"Well, I'll tell you, Mossa my dear." Simonsen perked up as he thought of what to say. "I didn't want to see any wife of mine toiling and slaving so hard, so I waited until I could find something better. But marry her I will. I've promised her that all along, and I'll keep my word as sure as my name's Anton Simonsen."

"Ye—es." Mossa grew sweeter and smoother. "Sixty crowns a month isn't much to marry on, and keep wife and child. And Mrs. Martinsen can hardly hope to build up a very extensive connection in Øimark."

"The worst part of it is this child of yours, Father," said Sigurd. "But no doubt Mrs. Martinsen can be brought to understand the situation, so that we can come to some arrangement."

"You must remember this about that little sister o' yours—about Svanhild. I don't want her to suffer for being illegitimate, and I think you're taking on a big responsibility, Sigurd, if you interfere in this."

Mossa snatched the word from him, and now there was no trace of gentleness in her voice.

"Responsibility! For *your* illegitimate child! That comes well from you, I *must* say! Here's Sigurd offering to get you a position—for the fourth time—in Øimark. To find one here in town is out of the question. If you don't think you can leave town because of your private affairs, you're perfectly free to stay. And if you can find a job and marry on it, we certainly shan't interfere. But naturally Sigurd can't help you in any other way. *His* responsibility, first and foremost, is to his own wife and children."

Mrs. Carling had put on her silk petticoat and draped herself in her new set of furs when on the following morning she climbed the stairs to Mrs. Martinsen's dressmaking establishment in the courtyard off Ruseløk Road. She placed a determined first finger on the bell under Simonsen's dirty visiting card.

The woman who opened the door was small, plump, and dark. She had pretty blue eyes in a face that was pale and washed-out from sitting indoors.

"Are you Mrs. Martinsen? I'm Mrs. Carling. I wanted to speak to you."

Rather hesitantly Olga opened the door of the nearest room.

"Please come in. I'm sorry there's no fire in here; we work in the other rooms."

Mrs. Carling sailed in and seated herself in the only armchair. The room was furnished as rooms to let usually are. On the chest of drawers, which was covered with a white cloth, the photographs of the late Mrs. Simonsen, of Sigurd, and of herself were conscientiously arrayed—engagement photographs—and two groups of the grandchildren.

"Well now, Mrs. Martinsen—" Olga was now standing over by the chest of drawers, observing the speaker "—there are one or two things I'd very much like to talk to you about. Won't you sit down?"

"Thank you, but I really haven't much time. What was it you wanted, Mrs. Carling?"

"Quite so. I won't keep you. We understand that Mr. Simonsen, my husband's father, has certain obligations toward you. I don't know whether he has made the present situation clear to you?"

"About the new job in Øimark? Oh, yes."

"Oh. Well, as you know, it's quite a modest position, so that for the time being he won't be able to fulfill his obligations to the child—his and yours. My husband and I have therefore decided to offer you—"

"Thank you very much." Olga spoke quickly and curtly. "We don't want to trouble you with our affairs, Mrs. Carling. We've agreed about it, Anton and I. We've agreed to get married now, right away."

"I see. Mrs. Martinsen, I must point out that Mr. Simonsen cannot expect any assistance from my husband—none whatever. He has a large family himself. And for four people to live on sixty crowns a month—I understand you have another child besides Mr. Simonsen's—"

"My boy will stay here. I have a sister in Trondhjem Road he can live with. Our plan was for us to live in Fredrikstad; I could carry on my dressmaking there, and Anton could come down to us on weekends."

"Yes, well, that *sounds* a very sensible idea. But you see, there are more than enough dressmakers in Fredrikstad already, so it's doubtful whether it would pay you to give up your connection here and start all over again there, *Miss* Martinsen!"

Olga jumped.

"*Mrs.* Martinsen, I beg your pardon. That's what you call yourself, of course. Yes, you see my husband and I have been making a few inquiries. You can't be surprised that we should want to know just what sort of person it was he'd taken up with."

Olga gave a puff of scorn.

"And it's the same thing for me, Mrs. Simonsen—I beg your pardon, Mrs. *Carling,* I mean. But it so happens that Anton thinks none the worse of me because my fiancé ran away to America, leaving me to support myself and my boy the best way I could. And he's told me, Anton has, he's said it over and over again: 'I shan't let you down, Olga.' So it don't seem to me it need concern you at all, Mrs. Carling. We shan't trouble you and come running to you—and as your husband hasn't even kept his father's name—"

"My dear Mrs. Martinsen." Mossa waved her hand and displayed all her double chins. "I beg you not to get so excited. I hadn't the least idea of meddling in your affairs. Quite the contrary —I came here with the very best intentions. I simply wanted to make it quite clear to you—in case you imagined that Mr. Simonsen was any sort of catch— that if you do marry him, I believe all you'll gain will be the pleasure of supporting both him and his child. Just think for a moment. My dear father-in-law has never been exactly a model of efficiency, has he? We have no guarantee that he won't be dismissed again as usual. Yes. . . . Do you think it will be easy for a man of his age—with a family—to keep on finding new situations? I've come here in a perfectly friendly way to bring you an offer from Mr. Carling. Look, my dear Mrs. Martinsen, up to now you've managed very well without a husband. Mr. Carling offers you a sum of money —we thought five hundred crowns—to compensate you for losing your lodger so suddenly. Without conditions. You understand that if later my father-in-law is so placed that he can marry we won't stand in the way. As you very rightly say, it doesn't concern us. And as for your little girl, we're prepared to offer her a home with us—"

"Never!" Olga flashed. "Let Svanhild go? That's one thing you can be certain I'll never do."

"Well, well. That's entirely as you wish, of course. You and my father-in-law will naturally please yourselves. If you like to marry on sixty crowns a month—give up your livelihood here and try to start a dressmaking business in Fredrikstad, which I assure you will never succeed . . . What baffles me is why you should want Mr. Simonsen at all. To *marry* him! In your circles people surely aren't so particular as to whether or not you've had some little affair with your lodger. How you could take up with him in the first place . . . You must forgive my saying this, but it's no recommendation in my eyes. Frankly, he's a nasty old man—"

Olga broke in: "Please say no more, Mrs. Carling. But I'll tell you just why I wanted Anton Simonsen. Maybe there *is* one or two things against him. But it didn't take me long to find out that he's a kind-hearted man—and there's not too many of that sort about. And as soon as he saw I wanted to make things snug and comfortable for him, he took to me and tidied himself up and behaved himself; and he'd a' done it before, *I* say, if he'd had any kindness or comfort where he come from. Kind and grateful always, Anton's been. And so taken up with Svanhild—almost too much of a good thing, it is—he quite spoils her. I'm fond of Anton, let me tell you, Mrs. Carling."

Mossa stood up and put the tips of her gloved fingers between the lace edges of her muff.

"Ah, well. If you *love* Mr. Simonsen, that's another matter."

Sigurd Carling had a high opinion of his wife's cleverness—he'd heard about it so often that he'd come to believe in it. As Miss Mossa Myhre she had pushed him on and made him the man he was today. Nevertheless, he had his doubts of her being the right person to come to an understanding with Mrs. Martinsen. She had very strict views, and this Olga creature had had two children in a rather irregular manner. And Mossa could make herself most unpleasant. So afterward he regretted having let her go: it had been a stupid thing to do. For an arrangement of some sort there must be. If his father were to move to Fredrikstad with a wife and child whom he couldn't support, it was as clear as daylight what would happen: Sigurd and his wife would never be safe from appeals for help, along with all the other kinds of bother his father always caused. And endless trouble with Mossa.

The matter had to be settled, and at once, before the old man had time to play them any tricks. Sigurd went to the Hercules works and ordered two new turbines, and in passing said a word or two about his father. It was arranged that Simonsen should leave for good on Christmas Eve, so that he might go home with them for the holiday.

Afterward, he too went to see Mrs. Martinsen.

Olga was tear-stained when Simonsen came home at dinnertime. Carling had been there. He'd been quite nice; he had asked to see Svanhild and taken her on his lap, and told her she should have something special for Christmas. Afterward he had talked to Olga. It was about her debts: she owed rent, as well as sums here and there among the tradespeople. And she had accepted his money. Besides that, he had promised her fifteen crowns

a month for Svanhild; that meant something steady coming in, and she had Henry too, who wouldn't be able to support himself for a while—fifteen crowns a month, he'd said, for the time being: "until my father has become self-supporting and can marry you." Olga sat on Simonsen's knee and cried; he was in the armchair in that cold room, in front of the chest of drawers with its family photographs. She cried, and he patted her.

"Oh, Anton, I don't know! What else could I a' done? If he won't help you there's nothing else for it. And I could see he wouldn't—not in any other way. If they set themselves against us, we should never make a go of it in Fredrikstad, you see—"

She blew her nose and wiped her eyes. And had another fit of crying.

"We got to accept it—you got to accept a lot of things when you're poor."

But to go home with Sigurd and Mossa for Christmas was one thing Simonsen would not do. They tempted him with a Christmas tree and grandchildren and goose and beer and spirits and pickled brawn, but the old man stood firm: he wanted to spend Christmas with Olga and the children. The most they managed to get from Simonsen was his promise to go down the day after Christmas Day. Sigurd had given him twenty-five crowns, so it was as well to get him out of town rather than let him loaf about there with money in his pocket until the New Year. Far better for the old boy to have his Christmas drinks with them, under supervision.

When Simonsen came home the evening before Christmas Eve, he had the new sled under his arm. Humming away in a deep bass voice he lit the lamp in his own room and unpacked his parcels.

There were drinks—aqua vitae and punch and brandy, and sweet port for Olga; so with a drop of beer they'd do all right. A pipe for Henry—it hadn't cost much; it was really just to show the boy he hadn't forgotten him, and it was a manly sort of thing to have. All the same he was pretty well broke now; the blouse material for Olga cost only 1 crown 45 øre, but then he'd bought her a brooch too, for 3.75, which looked more like ten crowns' worth. Simonsen took it out of its little box; he was sure she'd like it. He wanted to buy some little trifle for Miss Abrahamsen too—just a souvenir. Something quite small—he could afford that.

And then the sled, of course. Simonsen took the cloth off the table, unpacked the sled, and put it on display.

"Come and have a look, Olga love," he called into the sewing-room.

"What is it? I'm busy."

Simonsen moved the lamp over to the table.

"What do you think Svanhild will say to this, eh, Olga?"

"Mind the veneer, Anton!" and she spread newspaper under the sled and the lamp. "Yes, that's lovely—that's a beautiful sled."

"And look!" Simonsen unbuckled the cushion so that Olga could see all the rose-painting. "The cushion was extra."

"H'm. Must have been dear."

"Five crowns and twenty-five øre with the cushion," Simonsen answered briskly.

"Yes, well, that's a lot of money to spend on a thing like that, Anton. For such a little girl—she'd have been just as happy with a plainer one." Olga sighed.

"Oh, but now we got a little ready money handy, it's fun to give nice things. You've settled your debts and that. I bought something for my sweetheart too —" and he nudged her. "Run and fetch a couple of glasses, Olga—I've got some port. You must taste it and see how you like it—I bought it on your account mostly."

Olga glanced at the many bottles on the chest of drawers and sighed a little. Then she fetched the glasses.

It was late on Christmas Eve when work finished at Mrs. Martinsen's. But at last all was done. Henry had gone off to deliver the last of the completed sewing, and Olga and Miss Abrahamsen had cleared away everything else, heaping it on the chairs and table in the sewing-room. Before she left, Miss Abrahamsen was given coffee and pastries and from Simonsen a bottle of eau-de-Cologne.

Then Olga went into the sitting-room. She cleared the magazines off the table, and materials and half-made garments off the chairs, and picked up pins and buttons to drop them into the glass bowls on the console table. And she lit the candles on the Christmas tree, which she had decorated the night before.

Svanhild and Henry and Simonsen came in; the grown-ups sat down on the plush chairs, but Svanhild skipped and danced and rejoiced; she caught sight of the sled and shrieked with delight, then ran back to the tree again, not knowing what to do with herself for joy. Simonsen beamed and Olga smiled, though her eyes were sadly red; Simonsen had glanced at them several times during the afternoon. It would be the limit if she started to cry on this of all evenings, when they were going to have such a nice time.

He fetched his presents, smiling mischievously: she wouldn't think the blouse material was much of a gift. Then he brought out the eau-de-Cologne; for he had yielded to the temptation of doing things in style when he went into the fifty-øre bazaar after something for Miss Abrahamsen. There was also a cup to hold Olga's ball of wool when she knitted, and a little matchbox that looked like silver for Henry. The boy shook hands and laid pipe and box down by the window, where he had been lounging in a chair. But then came the brooch.

"All those was sort of practical things, Olga; you must have a little trifle for pleasure, too."

Olga picked up the brooch and her eyes filled with tears.

"Such a lot of things, Anton!"

Simonsen threw out his hand in a magnificent gesture.

"You must think of me when you wear it, Olga love."

"Oh, I will, Anton."

"And what about that box that came for Svanhild?"

Olga fetched it. On it was written: "To little Miss Svanhild, c/o Mrs. Martinsen's dressmaking establishment." Olga opened it. The card inside bore the inscription: "Merry Christmas!" It was Sigurd Carling's card. With it was a doll —but what a doll!

It had curly yellow hair and eyes that opened and shut. It was dressed in a white coat and white fur cap, and carried a little pair of skates over its arm—that was the most marvelous thing of all. Svanhild was speechless, but Simonsen talked and talked; he and the child were equally enraptured with the doll.

"Mummy must keep it for you—you'd better only play with it on Sundays."

"He's a good fellow, you know, Sigurd is," he said to Olga, who was bringing in the glasses and the jug of hot water. "It's what I always say: Sigurd's all right at heart—it's that damned hag of his who puts him up to things, for he's a good chap."

Simonsen mixed a toddy and Olga had port. Svanhild too was given a little drop of the sweet wine in her own glass as she sat on Daddy's lap.

"Come along, Henry, and mix yourself a toddy. You're a man now, you know."

Henry rose rather reluctantly, not looking at Simonsen. He had hard, pale eyes in a white, freckled face, and he looked thin and slight in his grown-up clothes.

"Well, *skål*, everybody! Isn't this jolly! Eh, Olga love?"

"Yes," she said, and bit her lip. Tears came into her eyes. "If only we knew what next Christmas was going to be like."

Simonsen lit his cigar. He looked troubled.

"Aren't you going to try your pipe, Henry, my boy? You'll find some tobacco on my chest of drawers if you haven't any yourself."

"No, thanks," said Henry.

"Yes, next Christmas," said Olga, fighting with her tears.

"Hard to say when you don't know," Simonsen said. He leaned back in his chair. "Good cigar, this. Drink up, Olga. Yes, well, perhaps we'll all be celebrating Christmas together among the country bumpkins. I hear they have great goings-on at Christmas up in Øimark. I think you'd like the country, Olga. When you want a Christmas tree, all you got to do is walk out of the door and cut one. Not bad! How'd you like that, Svanhild— going out into the woods with your daddy to cut down a Christmas tree— and then drag it home on your sled, eh?"

Svanhild nodded, radiant.

"And Henry would get time off from the office and spend Christmas with us."

Henry smiled slightly—scornfully.

"Wouldn't that be fun, Svanhild— going to the station to meet Henry? Would you like it if you and Daddy and Mummy lived on a big farm with cows and horses and pigs and roosters and hens and all? And then kind Sigurd, who gave you your doll—he's got a little girl about your age, and a boy just a bit bigger, and a tiny, tiny baby; you could go into town and play with them."

"While I have tea with that stuck-up daughter-in-law of yours, I s'pose! That's the idea, eh, Anton?"

"Oh, well—I don't think that would be necessary—"

"How can you go on talking such nonsense!" Olga laughed—and then burst out crying.

"Oh, now Olga, what are you crying for, love? Why do you take it like that?"

"How do you expect me to take it? Am I supposed to be pleased when that woman throws it in my face that Henry's father made a fool of me, and that now you're leaving me too? And me and my children—my by-blows—we're left with the disgrace. Perhaps you think like they do—you think it serves me right to sit here and make clothes for all the girls you have fun and games with. Just as if it was all right for people to treat me as they choose. Yes, yes—good enough for me. I ought to a' known what you was all like; soon's you get your own way with a poor woman it's love you and leave you—thanks and good-by!"

"But Olga, my dear!"

"Ah, it's nothing to you. No, you can move out into the country, you can, and start all over again with your sozzling and your girls—like you was doing when I found you. And my God, a nice fool I was to give in to you."

"Olga, Olga—remember the children!"

"Ho, they hear enough about it, you may be sure, in the yard and on the stairs. So they might just as well hear it from me too."

"It's Christmas Eve, Olga. Remember that, please," Simonsen said solemnly.

Olga wept quietly with her head on the table. Simonsen laid his hand on her shoulder.

"Now Olga, you know very well—you know very well how fond I am of you. And there's Svanhild—d'you really think I'd forget my own, innocent little girl? Trust me, Olga; I won't let you down or deceive you—I'll keep my promise to you."

"Why, you poor man—" Olga sat up and blew her nose. "That's not for you to decide."

"But you must remember one thing, Olga—" Simonsen laid one arm round her neck and held Svanhild with the other, straightened himself, and stuck out his stomach. "There's One Above—one greater than either Sigurd or Mossa—who *does* decide—for us all."

"Now I think we ought to sing a carol," he said a little later. He took a gulp of toddy and cleared his throat. "The Joy of Christmas'—let's have that; Svanhild knows it, I know. Sing out, now, Svanhild love."

Svanhild sang joyfully, and Simonsen growled too, leaving off when the notes went too high, but beginning again with every verse. Presently Olga joined in with a voice hoarse from weeping. Henry alone did not sing.

Then came the last morning. In Olga's room the alarm clock rang, but Simonsen lay dozing on in the darkness—it was so cold getting up. And everything was dreary and comfortless. That he should have to get up in the cold and go away—away from everything.

Never, in any place where he had lived, had he had so comfortable a bed as this, with eiderdown both under and over him.

Olga opened the door, and by the light shining through from her room she set down the tray she was carrying, lit the lamp, and took the tray over to the bed; on it were coffee and rolls.

"You'll have to get moving now, Anton."

"Yes, yes—I s'pose so."

Simonsen sighed. He drew her down on to the edge of the bed and stroked her—stroked her cheek and arm and breast and hips, as he drank the coffee and dunked the rolls in it.

"This is splendid coffee, my love. Won't you have a drop too?"

"No, I'd better go and get a bit of breakfast ready for you."

Simonsen crawled out of bed, dressed, and packed the last of his belongings. Then he locked both his boxes and went into Olga's room.

He stood by the bed where Svanhild lay asleep, looking down at her with his hands in his pockets. "My Svanhild . . ."

He peeped into the sitting-room too; it was pitch-dark and icy cold. Henry had gone off to Nordmarka with some friends on Christmas morning. Simonsen pottered about in there for a while, and in the darkness knocked against Svanhild's Christmas tree, so that the little tinsel balls tinkled together. Who knew—who knew whether he would ever come back here again?

He returned to Olga's room; it was nice and warm in there. Places were laid at the lower end of the long table where Olga and Miss Abrahamsen worked during the day. On the white cloth were brawn and beer and spirits and all the rest, and over it the lamp shone peacefully, humming softly as it burned. A light fell on Svanhild, asleep in her little bed, with her pretty hair spread over the pillow. His little, little girl . . .

There was a sweet, cozy warmth from Olga's bed, which was unmade, the covers thrown back from the hollow where she had lain. How good his life had been here with Olga and Svanhild! His eyes filled with tears; he let them run without drying them, so that Olga should see them. His pouchy, bluish-red cheeks were quite wet when Olga came in with the coffee.

"We'd better have breakfast," she said.

"Yes, we'd better. What about Svanhild? D'you think she'd like to come to the station, just for the sleigh ride?"

"I thought of that, Anton, but it's so dark and cold outside. But I might wake her now, so she can have a cup of coffee with us."

She went over to the bed and gently shook the child.

"Svanhild, would you like to get up now and have coffee with Mummy and Daddy?"

Svanhild blinked, sitting in her nightgown on Simonsen's lap. The coffee had roused her a little, but she was still quiet and subdued because the grownups were.

"Where are you going, Daddy?"

"Why, to Fredrikstad, don't you remember?"

"When are you coming back?"

"Oh, well—I expect you'll be down to see me first."

"In the country, like you talked about?"

"That's it."

"You'll be able to toboggan with me again there, won't you, Daddy?"

"Yes, that's right—I'll be able to toboggan with you again there."

The doorbell rang. Olga looked out: the sleigh had come. The carter's boy took Simonsen's boxes and went.

Simonsen kissed Svanhild, and having got up, he stood for a little with her on his arm.

"Now you must be a good girl, mind, and do as you're told while Daddy's away!"

"Yes, I will," said Svanhild.

Olga went into the kitchen to turn off the stove, as Svanhild was to be alone at home; then came in again and stood with her hand on the lamp screw.

"Well, Anton—"

He gave Svanhild a smacking kiss, laid her down in her bed, and covered her up.

"Bye-bye then, Svanhild love."

Olga put out the lamp, and they left the room. In the hall he put his arms round her and pressed her to him. They kissed.

In the sleigh they sat in silence as they

jolted down through the darkness of early morning. And they still had nothing to say to each other as they wandered together round the cold, bleak station hall. But she followed at his heels when he bought his ticket and despatched his trunk; she stood behind him, a small figure in black, square in her thick outer clothes.

Then they wandered into the waiting-room and sat looking up at the clock.

"We started in good time, didn't we?" said Olga.

"Yes, we did. Best thing when you're going on a journey. Shame you had to get up so early, though, when it's a holiday."

"Oh, well," said Olga. "Perhaps we'd better go along and take a seat for you on the train."

Simonsen put his things into a smoking-compartment. He stood at the window while she remained down on the platform.

"Mind you, write often, Olga, and tell me how you're getting on."

"Yes—and you too, Anton."

Porters began slamming the carriage doors along the train. Olga got up on the step, and they kissed again.

"Thanks for everything, Olga love."

"And thanks to you, Anton. Good journey!"

The engine whistled—a jerk ran through the train, and it began to move. Olga and Simonsen pulled out their handkerchiefs and waved to each other for as long as the handkerchiefs could be seen.

The train swished away in the first pale light of dawn—past the Bekkelag villas, past Nordstrand and Ljan. There were lights in the windows here and there. Below the railway line the fjord could be glimpsed, ice-gray, with black islands on it.

Oh, it was dreary . . . Simonsen was alone in the compartment, smoking his cigar and looking out of the window. Farms and woods came up and swam past—gray-brown fields with strips of snow along their edges—black woods.

By now Olga would be at home again. What would she be doing? Dressing Svanhild, probably. Olga had to work today, so she'd said. Svanhild would sit on the floor by the window, playing with the waste scraps. Now she had no Daddy to go tobogganing with in the Palace Park.

The snug room with its two warm, white beds. And the lamp, and the sewing everywhere, and the scraps on the floor which one waded through. Svanhild over by the window—his own, precious child. He could see her sitting there so quietly with her little affairs. Now and then a Miss Hellum or someone came in and gave her sweets. She'd miss her Daddy, Svanhild would.

It was wrong. It was all wrong.

For a moment the wrongness of it struck a spark inside him and smarted and burned through all that life had left of Anton Simonsen's heart.

"Svanhild love, my own little Svanhild . . ." he whimpered.

But he thrust the thought away.

That innocent little girl, who was so good—so very good. Surely life would turn out well for her?

He wiped his eyes. There must be One Above who decided these things. That must be his consolation: that there was One who decided . . .

THE LIFE AND WORKS OF
SIGRID UNDSET

By A. H. WINSNES

WRITING in 1927, the year before Sigrid Undset was awarded the Nobel Prize, the Swedish critic Fredrik Böök paid this tribute to her: "She belongs to the small number of eminent contemporary authors whom one may venture to call great." Opinions may differ on the general definition of greatness in a work of literature, but greatness in a novel surely depends on the depth and scope of the novelist's vision of life. A great novelist must be not only a storyteller but, as François Mauriac has said, "a knower of the human heart." In her novels, Sigrid Undset drew a complete picture of human life, from the cradle to the grave—indeed, from the embryonic stirrings in a mother's womb to the wasting of the body after death—and from the drives of instinct and passion to man's deepest desires and highest spiritual yearnings.

And she did not write about the men of our time alone: her mind and imagination range with the same sureness over the near and distant past. She described the Oslo of her youth, its unpretentious, middle-class homes, its boarding houses, its tenements and offices; and with equal vividness she conjured up pictures of town and country life in the Norway of the thirteenth and fourteenth centuries, the castles of the ruling lords, the hovels of the peasantry, the monasteries, and the churches. She saw it all with the same sharpness and clarity of outline; she was equally alive to past and present. "If I understand our age so well," she wrote to her friend Nini Roll Anker, "it is probably because I have always had a vanished age to compare it to."

Sigrid Undset was born in Denmark on May 20, 1882, in the picturesque town of Kalundborg on the island of Zealand. Her father, Ingvald Undset, was a well-known Norwegian archaeologist; in his field of research, the prehistory of the Scandinavian peoples, he had established himself as an internationally recognized authority with his study *The Beginnings of the Iron Age in Northern Europe*. Sigrid's mother, Anna Charlotte Gyth, a highly cultivated woman with wide intellectual interests, was Danish in nationality, but came of a Scottish family. Thus, Sigrid Undset was of mixed Norwegian, Danish, and Scottish descent.

In 1884, two years after her birth, the family returned to Norway, where her father took a post in the museum of antiquities attached to the University of Christiania. But a cloud hung over their lives: Ingvald Undset was suffering from an incurable disease. He spent the last years of his life confined to a wheelchair, and died in 1893, not yet forty. Sigrid Undset was then eleven years old.

She revered her father. Many readers have felt that her feelings for him found expression in the filial love of Kristin, the heroine of her most famous novel, *Kristin Lavransdatter* (1920–1922). More important, Ingvald Undset gave a decisive orientation to his daughter's intellectual life; specifically, he aroused her interest in history and thereby stimulated her imagination. In *Eleven Years,* her recollections of her childhood, ending in the year of her father's death, she tells how as a little girl she would sit entranced listening to the conversation between her father and his friends and fellow scholars. She was an especially attentive listener when the talk turned to the Norse tales and the myths of the Eddas, to Runic inscriptions and the Vikings, to the ancient trade routes of the North. Sigrid Undset grew up in a home in which the Scandinavian past was a familiar and living reality; she could rightly say that she had been "nurtured on history."

The headmistress of Sigrid's high school urged her to continue her academic studies at the university, but she never did. Instead, she left the school for a commercial school, and at seventeen went to work as a secretary for a business firm in Christiania. She stayed with the firm for ten years, and though she disliked office work, performed her duties conscientiously. One of the managers of the firm that employed her later recalled that her amazingly retentive memory and her sense of order made her an almost indispensable worker.

These ten years were more than an interlude in her life. Office work and the daily contacts with businessmen and with her fellow clerks, and secretaries, some of whom lived in boarding houses, some in tenements—all this represented a new world for her to explore. Her curiosity was aroused. She was seized, as she later said, with a desire to know "what these people were like inside." And she familiarized herself with the realities of daily life as lived by millions: the stuff of her early novels of contemporary life.

In 1907, Sigrid Undset published her first novel, *Fru Marte Oulie* (Mrs. Martha Oulie), soon to be followed by a whole series of novels and novellas describing the people and the life of her time: *Den lykkelige alder* (The Happy Age, 1908), *Jenny* (1911), *Fattige skjaebner* (Fates of the Poor, 1913), *Våren* (Spring, 1914), *Splinten av troldspeilet* (Images in the Mirror, 1917), and *De kloge jomfruer* (The Wise Virgins, 1918).

There is nothing of the unusual or the exotic in these books. They tell of ordinary people living ordinary lives, and are written in the traditional style of the realistic novel. What is noteworthy in them is the combination of objectivity and compassionate sympathy in her descriptions of her characters. She treats them objectively and logically, but also experimentally, intent on finding out what they are made of and what the values are by which they live. And what is truly remarkable is the vision of humanity that appears in these early writings. These books marked a sharp break with the view of man that had prevailed in Norwegian literature from about 1880 on, and that may be summed up in a single word: naturalism. Man had been delineated purely and simply as a product of nature, fashioned by heredity and environment and driven by blind instincts. In this view he was denied intelligence and free will, nor did he stand in a rational relationship with any objective scheme of things. In contrast, a recurring theme of Sigrid Undset's novels is the self-centered loneliness and estrangement that lies in store for those who fail to establish a viable relationship with a spiritual force greater and higher than themselves.

Charlotte Hedels, a young woman who figures in *The Happy Age,* is keenly alive to the spiritual emptiness of her historical period—its loss of all sense of the absolute, of all perspective ranging beyond the narrow corridor of the present into the wider reaches of time. In one of Charlotte's statements we hear the voice of Sigrid Undset herself: "We have nothing at stake; there is neither loss nor gain to keep our mind in suspense. . . . We are wrapped up in ourselves." Her friend replies: "Just like the figure in history, Narcissus, who fell in love with his own reflection and drowned himself."

Even more significant than *The Happy Age,* however, are two of the early novels of modern life: *Jenny* and *Spring. Jenny* is Sigrid Undset's saddest book, the only one that is truly joyless. For Jenny there is no solution to her problems, and by withdrawing into herself she cuts herself off from life. But with *Spring* the shadows part to disclose the dawn of a new day. In Rose Wegner, the heroine of the novel, something positive buds and grows. She finds her way toward a higher plane than that of self—the community, the social order, the home. All the main characters are depicted in relation to the home from which they have come; they are analyzed, judged, and justified in terms of their ability to cope with the problems and obligations that a home entails, and the home becomes the source and kernel of both social life and the higher cultural life.

A deep current of moral inspiration runs through these early writings of Sigrid Undset, but the moral heroism she champions contains an element of resignation and surrender. Rose Wegner herself does not attain fulfillment, for a part of her spiritual life remains undeveloped.

In 1924, Sigrid Undset was received into the Roman Catholic Church. The step was not the result of a sudden vocation or conversion. The truths of Christianity were gradually revealed to her, like a growing confirmation of all that thought and experience had taught her. Her discovery of Christianity seems to have been very much like that of G. K. Chesterton. In one of his essays, Chesterton set out to describe "the three or four fundamental ideas which I have found for myself," which sum up "my personal philosophy or natural religion" and he added: "Then I shall describe my startling discovery that the whole thing had been discovered before. It had been discovered by Christianity."

When Sigrid Undset wrote her earliest novels, she was indifferent to religious questions. "The truth is that we believed in nothing," she wrote of herself and her contemporaries at the time of World War I. Writing to a friend in 1915, she said: "As for the Church, I think of it rather as a picturesque ruin, somewhere in the background." Obviously the young Sigrid Undset was nothing if not critical and skeptical. But her skepticism did not turn her into a materialist; instead, it brought her back to religion, for it put her on her guard against the evolutionary optimism and restless radicalism that were widespread among young people in the days of her own youth. Her nature was fundamentally religious; she clung to spiritual values and could not be content with crude modern substitutes for religion.

Among the events and experiences that brought her back to Christianity, none was more decisive than World War I. "In times of catastrophe," writes the English historian Arnold Toynbee, "weaker spirits may have the sensation that reality is nothing but chaos. On other minds, dire events have a contrary effect. The sight of external disorder and the precariousness of all material things may sharpen the vision of the eternal, the imperishable, the unity founded on the belief in a world of eternal spirit." So it was for Sigrid Undset. "The Church," she wrote in 1917, ". . . represents the ideals which, momentarily, we thought we could live without, but which in fact we realize that we cannot live without."

She rediscovered Christianity not only as a subjective experience but as an objective reality, a concrete historical fact. Its undying vigor filled her with wonder and admiration. Unshaken by the ever renewed attempts to refute it as an obsolete relic of the past, allegedly superseded by "evolution" and "progress," Christianity taught the basic truth that—in Sigrid Undset's words—"man was created in the image of God and is called upon to do God's work in this world." The decisive personal factor in the story of her conversion to Catholicism cannot, of course, be put into words by anyone who has not shared that experience. She herself summed it up in a single terse sentence: "Only supernatural intervention can save us from ourselves."

Sigrid Undset's major works are two great novels, both set in the Middle Ages: *Kristin Lavransdatter,* which appeared in three volumes between 1920 and 1922, *Krasen (The Garland),* *Husfrue (The Mistress of Husaby),* *Korset (The Cross),* and *Olav Audunssøn i Hestviken (The Master of Hestviken)* and its sequel *Olav Audunssøn og hans børn (Olav Audunssøn and His Children)* (1925–1927). Both books have been translated into many foreign languages; taken together, they established her as a writer of international stature.

From her childhood Unset was attracted by the life of the Middle Ages. She engrossed herself in the study of the period, in Scandinavia and in Europe as a whole, and her knowledge of it steadily extended and deepened. In this study she was inspired largely by the revival of Scandinavian (and particularly Norwegian) medieval studies that took place in the early twentieth century. Thanks to the pioneering work of such scholars as Fredrik Paasche and Harry Fett, a new picture of the Middle Ages in Norway was pieced together and brought into focus. Up to then, Norwegian civilization of the later Middle Ages had been considered in isolation; now it was seen in a wider context as research revealed the extent of medieval Norway's contacts with Europe. The influence of the Church and Christianity had been regarded as a marginal phenomenon; now documentary evidence was adduced to show how powerfully it had impinged on the spiritual and the day-to-day life of the Norwegian people. In Sigrid Undset's view, the great events of Norway's Middle Ages were not the voyages and raids of the Vikings, but the way in which the people created a Christian society and brought it to a high level of culture in the twelfth, thirteenth, and the first half of the fourteenth century. The last two centuries were the setting for her two great novels.

As a young writer, still seeking her way, Sigrid Undset had tried her hand at a novel based on medieval life in Norway. She submitted the manuscript, written while she was still employed as a secretary in Christiania, to a publisher, but it was rejected—no doubt for good reason. At the time, Undset lacked the maturity to meet the demands of so large a subject. She had yet to pass through the trials that beset a restless and aspiring mind in the modern world, to experience the spiritual void of a wholly secularized society. Years later, she was prepared to understand and embrace the faith of the Middle Ages; she could embody both that faith and the insights gained by half a lifetime of historical study in an epic novel of medieval Norway; she could grasp from within the significance of the Gothic Age, its heavenward aspiration and the conception of life from which it sprang. And in expressing all this, she expressed what, to her mind, was man's essential endeavor: his endeavor through all recorded history to counter the inroads of all-devouring time—his thirst for eternity.

The story of the pilgrimage of Kristin and Olav through the magnificent but perilous lands of the North was shaped by Sigrid Undset out of her own intuitive experience. Her historical novels are of a fundamentally different character from the historical novels of, say, Sir Walter Scott. Undset's novels are symbolic works of art, with a message for our time; they confront the modern reader with the abiding power of religious passion, which rises to its highest pitch in *The Master of Hestviken,* a novel closer in spirit to Dostoevsky than to Scott. Dostoevsky used the Russian nihilists of his time as a vehicle for his vision of a godless world, a world without Christianity. Sigrid Undset turned to the Middle Ages to restore Christianity to its place in the modern world. Her novels of medieval life do not feature well-known historical figures. As in her modern novels, the characters are ordinary men and women amid the environments and conflicts of their own time. The basic themes do not differ from the ones she dealt with in her studies of modern life.

She has been reproached for depicting medieval men whose inner life and moral conflicts are those of today. She insisted, however, that the nature of man remains now very much what it was in earlier times. "Manners and morals may change a great deal," she wrote, "but the human heart stays the same." Both her medieval and her modern novels are based on the view set forth by St. Augustine: "Thou hast made us for Thyself, O Lord, and our heart is restless until it rests in Thee." Yet there is an essential difference between the two genres of her work. Her early novels of contemporary life depict a world in which the notion of eternity has become foreign to men's minds; the characters in her medieval novels put their trust in the word of God, even though they sometimes rebel against it. They know that the human spirit is the meeting place of two worlds—the worlds of time and of eternity, of heaven and earth. They know that good and evil have their final reckoning in the conscience of humanity, their only possible field of battle. And most important of all, they know that no circumstance outside themselves is responsible for the misfortunes that befall them.

To an extraordinary degree, Sigrid Undset had the faculty of identifying herself with both men and women and tracing the intricacies of their spiritual lives. She is at her best in depicting the inner struggles of Kristin and Olav, whose conflicts take various forms. Kristin is self-centered, and an obsession with her own misfortune stands in the way of the divine love that tries to take root within her. Olav's struggle has to do with his sense of personal honor; he is more in awe of the judgment of men than the judgment of God. But he knows that he must ultimately come before the tribunal at which each man will be judged for what he is, not for what he seems to be in the eyes of others.

In both novels a key part is played by the sense of guilt, by repentance and atonement. This interplay of feelings is presented with exceptional insight into the characters of both Kristin and Olav. For both, but perhaps more thoroughly for Olav, the analysis is worked out from the Christian point of view. The central chapter of the novel devoted to him is titled "The Happiness of Olav Audunssøn." The implication of the title might seem ironical, for there is little here of what is usually meant by happiness. But no irony is intended; the chapter is, in fact, an expression of Christian optimism. Olav Audunssøn's happiness lies in his ability to experience sin and repentance. It is twofold: first, the knowledge that he has transgressed a sacred law in contriving to make away with his foe-woman, his perifidious mistress; and second, the dawning realization that atonement lies within his power. He sees that he can, if he will, reconcile himself with his Creator. He seems to hear the voice of Our Lord: "Since at last you love Me, I come to find you. Since you long for Me, I pursue you. I follow hard upon you, since you call Me even while you flee from Me."

The historical novels of Sigrid Undset can be read on several levels. The reader is enchanted by the ease and power with which she conjures up the distant past, by the vivid picture of daily life in medieval Norway, by the varied cast of characters moving against this background. His interest is gripped by the unfolding action, the delineation of character, the analysis of motives. But the dominant and essential theme of these novels is the religious life of the Middle Ages and the consciousness of eternity by which it was governed.

After the publication of *Olav Audunssøn and His Children*, in 1927, Sigrid Undset returned to modern themes. Her later series of novels dealing with contemporary life consists of *Gymnadenia* (The Wild Orchid, 1929), *Den braendende busk* (The Burning Bush, 1930), *Ida Elisabeth* (1932), and *Den trofaste hustru* (The Faithful Wife, 1936).

The first two are the most interesting. *The Wild Orchid* and its sequel *The Burning Bush* tell the story of Paul Selmer, a free-thinker and agnostic, whose eyes are gradually opened to the

spiritual reality to which Christ bore witness. The stages of Selmer's evolution from agnosticism to faith reflect the inner experience of Sigrid Undset herself. To some extent, then, these two novels are autobiographical. But there is no analogy in outward events and circumstances, apart from the fact that both the author and her hero belong to the same generation—the generation that came of age in the years just before World War I —and the same social milieu. Her identity with Selmer lies chiefly on the moral and spiritual plane. There is a similarity of intellect and temperament, the same mixture of cold reason, sober realism, and a concern with deeper, sounder values than those offered by an optimistic faith in evolution. Thought and reflection are the guides that lead Paul Selmer on the path toward conversion, but it is not until he learns to see himself as a party to the revolt against God's will that he takes the decisive step.

In *Ida Elisabeth* and *The Faithful Wife* the religious theme is not worked out with the same force as in *The Wild Orchid* and *The Burning Bush,* but it plays an essential part. These two later novels are based on the contrast between two fundamentally different conceptions of life—one naturalistic, the other supernatural—and on the conflict between man's aspiration toward the transcendental, on the one hand, and an earthbound view that sees in man no more than a "citizen of this world," on the others, the clash of these two opposing conceptions of life illuminates a domain of primal importance for Sigrid Undset: the domain of marriage. Confronting the modern romantic, sensual view of marriage with the Christian view, she demonstrates that the latter has deeper roots in the reality of human life, while at the same time "it soars into infinitely vaster spiritual realms."

These later novels of religious conversion are not quite up to the level of the medieval novels or even with the early narratives of contemporary life; they do not seem, to many readers at least, to achieve the same concentration and clarity of focus. But they do reveal a sensitive grasp of mood and atmosphere, and there is no weakening of her power of insight into the moral life of others, and particularly into the moral dilemmas of ordinary people. From the start Sigrid Undset possessed this power, but it had probably never been accompanied by so keen a sense of compassion as when she described the humdrum lives of Lucy Snipper in *The Wild Orchid,* of Ida Elisabeth in the novel of that name, or of Natalia in *The Faithful Wife.*

After the publication of her first novels, Sigrid Undset felt sure enough of her art and vocation to give up her office job and devote herself entirely to writing. In 1909 she left Norway for her first journey abroad. She stayed for several months in Germany, then went on to Italy and Rome. From the moment of her arrival in the Eternal City she felt at home.

It was in Rome that she met the talented Norwegian painter A. C. Svarstad, whom she married in 1912. He had three children by a previous marriage, and she bore him three more, but the marriage was not a happy one. After some years they separated, and the gulf between them was never bridged. When in 1924 Sigrid Undset was received into the Roman Catholic Church her marriage was dissolved *ipso facto,* since her husband's first wife was still alive.

From 1919 until the occupation of Norway by German troops in World War II, she made her home at Lillehammer, an idyllic town on the shore of Lake Mjøsen in southeastern Norway. There she bought and restored an old farmhouse, and entering its snug and rustic rooms a visitor had the impression of stepping back several centuries into the past. She has given a charming description of life at "Bjerkebaek," as she called her house, in *Happy Days in Norway* (1943), a book written in America during the war.

When the Germans invaded Norway in April 1940, Sigrid Undset was urgently requested by the Norwegian military authorities to leave the country before the occupation was complete. It was feared that the Nazis would force her to make propaganda broadcasts and testify to their "correct" behavior in Norway. There was indeed good reason to think that the Germans would single her out and bring pressure to bear on her. During the 1930s she had repeatedly spoken out against Nazism in newspapers and periodicals, most notably in a short, defiant essay published originally in German: *Fortschritt, Rasse, Religion* (Progress, Race, Religion). Her challenge had not gone unheeded. "Her writings must be banned from German journals, German libraries, and German bookshops," said the newspaper *Westdeutscher Beobachter* in the heyday of Nazism.

So she left her home in Lillehammer and after an adventurous expedition through the Gudbrandsdal and over the mountains, partly on skis, she reached Sweden. From there, by way of Russia and the Pacific Ocean, she went on to the United States, where she arrived in August 1940. She set to work at once for the Norwegian information service in America, and carried on a strenuous wartime career as a journalist, defending fundamental Christian moral values that were at stake in the war and demolishing the "Nordic myth" of Nazi propaganda. Her knowledge of the historical background of the Scandinavian peoples enabled her to expose the absurdity of Nazi racial theories. She never ceased to emphasize the immeasurable debt owed by Western civilization to Christian ideas. "Over our sad chaotic times," she wrote, "rise voices calling for a return to religion. There is a feeling here—sometimes clearly expressed, more often vaguely sensed—that when mankind tries to break with its Creator and suffice unto itself, it actually cuts itself off from the source that nourishes and maintains its temporal life."

In August 1945, after five years' exile, Sigrid Undset returned to Norway and her old home at Lillehammer. The war, the strain of overwork and grief over the death of her eldest son, killed in action, had sorely taxed her strength. She resumed her literary activity, and though she did not feel equal to the imaginative demands of writing a novel, she completed a biography of St. Catherine of Siena published posthumously in 1951.

The life of St. Catherine, a great Christian who, in an age beset by crime and violence, wars and epidemics, consorted with the great ones of this world and worked upon them in the interest of peace and justice, seemed to Sigrid Undset peculiarly relevant to our own time. Her Catherine is not an idealized hagiography. It is, on the contrary, scrupulously straightforward and the saint's personality stands out against a background of sober historical fact. The book is, in fact, closely related to Sigrid Undset's medieval novels.

She spent the last years of her life working on a study of Edmund Burke, the English statesman and political writer. He too, it seemed to her, had a message for our time; like Sigrid Undset herself, Burke was deeply conscious of an organic interrelation in the life of peoples. But she did not live to complete this book. After a short illness, she died at Lillehammer on June 10, 1949, at the age of sixty-seven.

A. H. Winsnes is professor of literature at the University of Oslo. Translated by James Emmons.

THE 1928 PRIZE

By KJELL STRÖMBERG

SIGRID UNDSET was only forty-six when she won the Nobel Prize. She was thus the youngest laureate since Rudyard Kipling, who had been honored at the age of forty-two in 1907. Two years later Sinclair Lewis won it at the age of forty-five, thereby relegating the great Norwegian novelist to third place, where she was to remain until 1957, when Albert Camus received this supreme literary distinction when he was only forty-four.

Sigrid Undset was the third woman and the third Norwegian author to win the Nobel Prize for Literature. Two other women who were proposed in the same year were Ricarda Huch, a German poet and essayist, and Concha Espina, a Spanish novelist who was not only enthusiastically endorsed by the most respectable of her compatriots, but had already been honored during her lifetime by a statue of herself in her native town of Santander. There was no lack of deserving Norwegian candidates to compete with Sigrid Undset: the first of these was Olav Duun, the author of *People of Juvik,* a peasant epic in six volumes which he had just completed; and Olaf Bull, a lyric poet of undoubted genius who belonged to the school which Verlaine had described in the past as the school of the *maudits*—the accursed.

In the heart of the Swedish Academy there was no doubt that a Prize would sooner or later go to Sigrid Undset, particularly after the publication of *Kristin Lavransdatter.* This great fresco of life in the Middle Ages in a still primitive Northern country had shown that its author possessed the most powerful, if not the most original, talent to appear since the literary generation which followed Knut Hamsun (the 1920 Prize-winner), Hans E. Kinck, and Arne Garborg in Norway. Even before the publication of the last volume in 1922, Sigrid Undset was proposed for the first time for the Nobel Prize. The first expert who was called upon for his views, Doctor Sven Söderman, brought in an extremely favorable report. It ended with the following words in praise of *Kristin Lavransdatter:* "It is many years since I have read any epic work of comparable stature with such intense interest and such a feeling of ample reward for the effort involved. *Jean-Christophe* [by Romain Rolland] captivates one in a different way, and is more varied, but much of it appeals only to a purely intellectual curiosity. Here, everything is poetry and human truth; contemporary literature can only offer a few works to compare with this one. This book has already taken on the aspect of a monument in the literature of Norway. . . . *Kristin Lavransdatter* is Sigrid Undset's latest work, and a masterpiece which alone would justify her candidacy for the Nobel Prize."

This enthusiastic opinion dates from 1922 and, as we have seen, it applies exclusively to the great historical novel which will always remain Sigrid Undset's most important work. But Doctor Söderman was just as full of respect and praise for her earlier books, which dealt with the problems confronting the young married or unmarried woman wishing to earn her living in modern society at the beginning of this century. These books took the form of short, autobiographical studies, of which the best is perhaps the charming, delectable story called "Spring," which appeared in 1914.

After *Kristin Lavransdatter,* that extremely vivid, lifesize self-portrait, Sigrid Undset published a new medieval novel which was almost as massive, but with a man as the central figure: it was the cycle of Olav Audunssøn, whose first volume appeared in 1925. She was again nominated for the Nobel Prize in 1926, and finally, in 1928, proposed once more by her compatriots. But this time it was Per Hallström, the president of the Nobel Committee of the Swedish Academy, who himself took over the task of expert. He did not hesitate to point out a certain timelag in one or two of Sigrid Undset's novels, between the primitive conditions of outdoor life and the refinements of indoor living which, for modern men and women, are the fruits of centuries of educated feeling. And he recommended a rather more expectant attitude to his colleagues in the Academy.

But the barricades could not hold out any longer and, carried forward on a wave of enthusiasm from all the Scandinavian countries, the author of *Kristin Lavransdatter* succeeded in winning over even the most recalcitrant members of the jury. No other Scandinavian writer apart from Selma Lagerlöf has ever enjoyed such a huge circulation abroad. In spite of (or perhaps because of) this unusual popularity, the Swedish Academy took good care not to mention this book by name in its short report on the reasons for awarding the Prize. It stated simply that the 1928 Prize was awarded to Sigrid Undset "principally for her powerful descriptions of Northern life during the Middle Ages."

Sigrid Undset had been converted to Catholicism after she had finished writing *Kristin Lavransdatter:* She admitted that this had happened under the influence of Jacques Maritain, whom she had met in Paris and admired deeply. She did not conceal from her circle of friends at that time her firm conviction that after this public manifestation she would never be awarded the Nobel Prize by an Academy of whom the Archbishop of Uppsala, Primate of the Swedish Church, was a member, in spite of the ecumenical tendencies of this holder of high office in the Church, which a few years later were to win for him the Nobel Prize for Peace. But Nathan Söderblom, who afterward became a kind of pope of the Protestant churches, was one of the first to congratulate the great novelist who had become a Catholic; and this in spite of their having crossed swords the year before at a very animated debate on the concepts of human nature and divine grace according to St. Thomas and Martin Luther.

Although no one in Sweden took umbrage at Sigrid Undset's religious attitudes, they were surprised by her decision to give the whole of her Prize money to social and charitable organizations. Even before leaving Stockholm, she arranged for half the money to be put into a trust fund: the interest was to be used to help the parents of backward or delinquent children, so that they would not have to be separated from them. One wonders whether this indicated some personal tragedy in her own life. People would have considered it more natural for her to have kept her Prize money for her old age: and indeed she must have badly needed it when the war drove her into exile in 1940, when Hitler's armies overran and destroyed her house at Lillehammer, near the Swedish frontier. It would have seemed equally understandable if, like Bernard Shaw, she had created a fund with a purely literary purpose, or some kind of international movement for cooperation in the field of literature.

Before her death in 1949, Sigrid Undset was the subject of a unique tribute from the old King of Norway, Haakon, who had also recently returned from exile: he awarded her the Grand Cross of his own Order of Saint Olav.

Translated by Camilla Sykes.

William Butler Yeats

1923

"For his always inspired poetry, which

in a highly artistic form gives expression

to the spirit of a whole nation"

Illustrated by ROBIN JACQUES

PRESENTATION ADDRESS

By PER HALLSTRÖM

CHAIRMAN OF THE NOBEL COMMITTEE
OF THE SWEDISH ACADEMY

VERY EARLY, in the first bloom of youth, William Butler Yeats emerged as a poet with an indisputable right to the name; his autobiography shows that the inner promptings of the poet determined his relations to the world even when he was a mere boy. He has developed organically in the direction indicated by his emotional and intellectual life from the very beginning.

He was born in an artistic home—in Dublin—thus beauty naturally became a vital necessity for him. He showed artistic powers, and his education was devoted to the satisfying of this tendency; little effort was made to secure traditional schooling. He was educated for the most part in England, his second fatherland; nonetheless his decisive development was linked to Ireland, chiefly to the comparatively unspoiled Celtic district of Connaught where his family had their summer home. There he inhaled the imaginative mysticism of popular belief and popular stories which is the most distinctive feature of his people, and amidst a primitive nature of mountain and sea he became absorbed in a passionate endeavor to capture its very soul.

The soul of nature was to him no empty phrase, for Celtic pantheism, the belief in the existence of living, personal powers behind the world of phenomena, which most of the people had retained, seized hold of Yeats's imagination and fed his innate and strong religious needs. When he came nearest to the scientific spirit of his time, in zealous observations of the life of nature, he characteristically concentrated on the sequence of various bird notes at daybreak and the flight of moths as the stars of twilight were kindled. The boy got so far in his intimacy with the rhythm of the solar day that he could determine the time quite exactly by such natural signs. From this intimate communion with the sounds of morning and night-time, his poetry later received many of its most captivating traits.

He abandoned his training in the fine arts soon after he had grown up in order to devote himself to poetry, for which his inclination was strongest. But this training is evident throughout his whole career, both in the intensity with which he worships form and personal style and, still more, in the paradoxically audacious solution of problems in which his acute but fragmentary philosophical speculation sought its way to what he needed for his own peculiar nature.

The literary world he entered, when he settled down in London at the end of the eighties, did not offer him much positively, but it at least offered him fellowship in opposition, which to pugnacious youth seems particularly dear. It was filled with weariness and rebellion toward the spirit of the times which had prevailed just before, namely that of dogmatic natural science and naturalistic art. There were few whose hostility was so deeply grounded as that of Yeats, altogether intuitive, visionary, and indomitably spiritualistic as he was.

He was disturbed not only by the cocksureness of natural science and the narrowness of reality-aping art; even more, he was horrified by the dissolution of personality and the frigidity which issued from skepticism, by the desiccation of imagination and emotional life in a world which at best had faith only in a collective and automatic progression to the sacred land of Cockaigne. Events proved him to be terribly right: the "paradise" which could be reached by humanity with such schooling, we have now the dubious advantage of enjoying.

Even more beautiful kinds of social utopianism, represented by the greatly admired poet William Morris, did not captivate such an individualist as young Yeats. Later he found his way to people, and then not as an abstract conception, but as the Irish people, to whom he had been close as a child. What he sought in that people was not the masses stirred by present-day demands, but an historically developed soul which he wished to arouse to more conscious life.

In the intellectual unrest of London, things nationally Irish remained dear to Yeats's heart; this feeling was nurtured by summer visits to his homeland and by comprehensive studies of its folklore and customs. His earlier lyrics are almost exclusively built on his impressions from these. His early poems immediately won high esteem in England because the new material, with its strong appeal to the imagination, received a form which, despite its special characteristics, was nevertheless linked closely with several of the noblest traditions of English poetry. The blending together of Celtic and English, which had never been successfully effected in the political sphere, became a reality here in the world of poetic imagination—a symptom of no small spiritual significance.

However much Yeats had read of English masters, his verse has a new character. The cadence and the colors have changed, as if they had been moved to another air—that of the Celtic twilight by the sea. There is a greater element of song than is usual in modern English poetry. The music is more melancholy, and, under the gentle rhythm, which for all its freedom moves as securely as a sleepwalker, we have a hint of yet another rhythm with the slow breathing of the wind and the eternal pulse of the powers of nature. When this art reaches its highest level it is absolutely magical, but it is seldom easy to grasp. It is indeed often so obscure that an effort is needed to understand it. This obscurity lies partly in the mysticism of the actual subject, but perhaps just as much in the Celtic temperament, which seems to be more distinguished by fire, delicacy, and penetration than by clearness. But no small part may have played by the tendencies of the time: symbolism and *l'art pour l'art,* chiefly absorbed by the task of finding the boldly appropriate word.

Yeats's association with the life of a people saved him from the barrenness which attended so much of the effect for beauty that marked his age. Around him as the central point and leader arose, within a group of his countrymen in the literary world of London, that mighty movement which has been named the Celtic revival and which created a new national literature, an Anglo-Irish literature.

The foremost and most versatile poet of this group was Yeats. His rousing and rallying personality caused the movement to grow and flower very quickly, by giving a common aim to hitherto scattered forces or by encouraging new forces previously unconscious of their existence.

Then, too, the Irish theater came into existence. Yeats's active propaganda created both a stage and a public, and the first performance was given with his drama *The Countess Cathleen* (1892). This work, extraordinarily rich in poetry, was followed by a series of poetic dramas, all on Irish subjects drawn mainly from the old heroic sagas. The most beautiful among these are *Deirdre* (1907), the fateful tragedy of the Irish Helen; *The Green Helmet* (1910), a merrily heroic myth of a peculiarly primitive wildness; and above all *The King's Threshold* (1904), where the simple material has been permeated by thought of a rare grandeur and depth. The quarrel about the place and rank of the bard at the king's court here gives rise to the ever-burning question as to how much spiritual things are to hold good in our world, and whether they are to be received with true or false faith. With the claims on which the hero stakes his life, he defends in the supremacy of poetry all that makes the life of man beautiful and worthy. It would not become all poets to put forward such claims, but Yeats could do so: his idealism has never been dulled, nor has the severity of his art. In these dramatic pieces his verse attains a rare beauty and sureness of style.

Most enchanting, however, is his art in *The Land of Heart's Desire* (1894), which has all the magic of fairy poetry and all the freshness of spring, in its clear but as it were dreamy melody. Dramatically, also, this work is one of his finest; and it might be called the flower of his poetry, had he not also written the little prose drama *Cathleen ni Houlihan* (1902), which is at once his simplest folk play and his most classically perfect work.

Here more powerfully than anywhere else he touches the patriotic string. The subject is Ireland's struggle for liberty throughout the ages, and the chief personage is Ireland herself, impersonated by a wandering beggar woman. But we hear no simple tone of hatred, and the profound pathos of the piece is more restrained than in any other comparable poem. We hear only the purest and highest part of the nation's feeling; the words are few and the action the simplest possible. The whole thing is greatness without a touch of affectation. The subject, having come to Yeats in a dream, has retained its visionary stamp of being a gift from above—a conception not foreign to Yeats's esthetic philosophy.

Much more might be said of Yeats's work, but it must suffice to mention the ways followed by his dramas of recent years. They have often been romantic by virtue of their strange and uncommon material, but they have generally striven after classic simplicity of form. This classicism has been gradually developed into bold archaism; the poet has sought to attain the primitive plasticity found in the beginning of all dramatic art. He has devoted much intensive, acute thought to the task of emancipating himself from the modern stage, with its scenery that disturbs the picture called up by the imagination, with its plays whose features are necessarily exaggerated by the footlights, with its audience's demand for realistic illusion. Yeats wishes to bring out the poem as it was born in the poet's vision; he has given form to this vision following Greek and Japanese models. Thus he has revived the use of masks and has found a great place for the actors' gestures to the accompaniment of simple music.

In the pieces thus simplified and brought to a strict stylistic unity, whose subjects are still taken by preference from the hero legends of Ireland, he has sometimes attained a fascinating effect, even for the mere reader, both in the highly compressed dialogue and in the choruses with their deep lyrical tone. All this, however, is in its period of growth, and it is not yet possible to decide whether the sacrifices made are fully compensated for by what has been gained. These pieces, though in themselves highly noteworthy, will probably find greater difficulty in becoming popular than the earlier ones.

In these plays as well as in his clearest and most beautiful lyrics, Yeats has achieved what few poets have been able to do: he has succeeded in preserving contact with his people while upholding the most aristocratic artistry. His poetical work has arisen in an exclusively artistic milieu which has had many perils; but without abjuring the articles of his esthetic faith, his burning and questing personality, ever aiming at the ideal, has contrived to keep itself free from esthetic emptiness. He has been able to follow the spirit that early appointed him the interpreter of his country, a country that had long waited for someone to bestow on it a voice. It is not too much to call such a life's work great.

ACCEPTANCE SPEECH

By WILLIAM BUTLER YEATS

I HAVE BEEN all my working life indebted to the Scandinavian nation. When I was a very young man, I spent several years writing in collaboration with a friend the first interpretation of the philosophy of the English poet Blake. Blake was first a disciple of your great Swedenborg and then in violent revolt and then half in revolt, half in discipleship. My friend and I were constantly driven to Swedenborg for an interpretation of some obscure passage, for Blake is always in his mystical writings extravagant, paradoxical, obscure. Yet he has had upon the last forty years of English imaginative thought the influence which Coleridge had upon the preceding forty; and he is always in his poetry, often in his theories of painting, the interpreter or the antagonist of Swedenborg. Of recent years I have gone to Swedenborg for his own sake, and when I received your invitation to Stockholm, it was to his biography that I went for information. Nor do I think that our Irish theater could have ever come into existence but for the theater of Ibsen and Bjørnson. And now you have conferred upon me this great honor. Thirty years ago a number of Irish writers met together in societies and began a remorseless criticism of the literature of their country. It was their dream that by freeing it from provincialism they might win for it European recognition. I owe much to those men, still more to those who joined our movement a few years later, and when I return to Ireland these men and women, now growing old like myself, will see in this great honor a fulfillment of that dream. I in my heart know how little I might have deserved it if they had never existed.

PURGATORY

By W. B. YEATS

A Boy

An Old Man

A ruined house and a bare tree in the background.

Boy. Half-door, hall door,
  Hither and thither day and night,
  Hill or hollow, shouldering this pack,
  Hearing you talk.
Old Man.   Study that house.
  I think about its jokes and stories;
  I try to remember what the butler
  Said to a drunken gamekeeper
  In mid-October, but I cannot.
  If I cannot, none living can.
  Where are the jokes and stories of a house,
  Its threshold gone to patch a pig-sty?
Boy. So you have come this path before?
Old Man. The moonlight falls upon the path,
  The shadow of a cloud upon the house,
  And that's symbolical; study that tree,
  What is it like?
Boy.   A silly old man.
Old Man. It's like—no matter what it's like.
  I saw it a year ago stripped bare as now,

So I chose a better trade.
I saw it fifty years ago
Before the thunderbolt had riven it,
Green leaves, ripe leaves, leaves thick as butter,
Fat, greasy life. Stand there and look,
Because there is somebody in that house.

    [*The Boy puts down pack and stands in the doorway.*]

Boy. There's nobody here.

Old Man.   There's somebody there.

Boy. The floor is gone, the windows gone,
  And where there should be roof there's sky,
  And here's a bit of an egg-shell thrown
  Out of a jackdaw's nest.

Old Man.   But there are some
  That do not care what's gone, what's left:
  The souls in Purgatory that come back
  To habitations and familiar spots.

Boy. Your wits are out again.

Old Man.   Re-live
  Their transgressions, and that not once
  But many times; they know at last
  The consequence of those transgressions
  Whether upon others or upon themselves;
  Upon others, others may bring help,
  For when the consequence is at an end
  The dream must end; if upon themselves,
  There is no help but in themselves
  And in the mercy of God.

Boy.   I have had enough!
  Talk to the jackdaws, if talk you must.

Old Man. Stop! Sit there upon that stone.
  That is the house where I was born.

Boy. The big old house that was burnt down?

Old Man. My mother that was your grand-dam owned it,
  This scenery and this countryside.
  Kennel and stable, horse and hound—
  She had a horse at the Curragh, and there met
  My father, a groom in a training stable,

Looked at him and married him.
Her mother never spoke to her again,
And she did right.
Boy. What's right and wrong?
My grand-dad got the girl and the money.
Old Man. Looked at him and married him,
And he squandered everything she had.
She never knew the worst, because
She died in giving birth to me,
But now she knows it all, being dead.
Great people lived and died in this house;
Magistrates, colonels, members of Parliament,
Captains and Governors, and long ago
Men that had fought at Aughrim and the Boyne.
Some that had gone on Government work
To London or to India came home to die,
Or came from London every spring
To look at the may-blossom in the park.
They had loved the trees that he cut down
To pay what he had lost at cards
Or spent on horses, drink, and women;
Had loved the house, had loved all
The intricate passages of the house,
But he killed the house; to kill a house
Where great men grew up, married, died,
I here declare a capital offense.
Boy. My God, but you had luck! Grand clothes,
And maybe a grand horse to ride.
Old Man. That he might keep me upon his level
He never sent me to school, but some
Half-loved me for my half of her:
A gamekeeper's wife taught me to read,
A Catholic curate taught me Latin.
There were old books and books made fine
By eighteenth-century French binding, books
Modern and ancient, books by the ton.
Boy. What education have you given me?
Old Man. I gave the education that befits

A bastard that a pedlar got
Upon a tinker's daughter in a ditch.
When I had come to sixteen years old
My father burned down the house when drunk.

Boy. But that is my age, sixteen years old,
At the Puck Fair.

Old Man.   And everything was burnt;
Books, library, all were burnt.

Boy. Is what I have heard upon the road the truth,
That you killed him in the burning house?

Old Man. There's nobody here but our two selves?

Boy. Nobody, Father.

Old Man.   I stuck him with a knife,
That knife that cuts my dinner now,
And after that I left him in the fire.
They dragged him out, somebody saw
The knife-wound but could not be certain
Because the body was all black and charred.
Then some that were his drunken friends
Swore they would put me upon trial,
Spoke of quarrels, a threat I had made.
The gamekeeper gave me some old clothes,
I ran away, worked here and there
Till I became a pedlar on the roads,
No good trade, but good enough
Because I am my father's son,
Because of what I did or may do.
Listen to the hoof-beats! Listen, Listen!

Boy. I cannot hear a sound.

Old Man.   Beat! Beat!
This night is the anniversary
Of my mother's wedding night,
Or of the night wherein I was begotten.
My father is riding from the public-house,
A whiskey-bottle under his arm.

                    [*A window is lit showing a young girl.*]
Look at the window; she stands there
Listening, the servants are all in bed,

She is alone, he has stayed late
Bragging and drinking in the public-house.
Boy. There's nothing but an empty gap in the wall.
You have made it up. No, you are mad!
You are getting madder every day.
Old Man. It's louder now because he rides
Upon a graveled avenue
All grass today. The hoof-beat stops,
He has gone to the other side of the house,
Gone to the stable, put the horse up.
She has gone down to open the door.
This night she is no better than her man
And does not mind that he is half drunk,
She is mad about him. They mount the stairs.
She brings him into her own chamber.
And that is the marriage-chamber now.
The window is dimly lit again.

Do not let him touch you! It is not true
That drunken men cannot beget,
And if he touch he must beget
And you must bear his murderer.
Deaf! Both deaf! If I should throw
A stick or a stone they would not hear;
And that's a proof my wits are out.
But there's a problem: she must live
Through everything in exact detail,
Driven to it by remorse, and yet
Can she renew the sexual act
And find no pleasure in it, and if not,
If pleasure and remorse must both be there,
Which is the greater?
                    I lack schooling.
Go fetch Tertullian; he and I
Will ravel all that problem out
Whilst those two lie upon the mattress
Begetting me.
                    Come back! Come back!

And so you thought to slip away,
My bag of money between your fingers,
And that I could not talk and see!
You have been rummaging in the pack.

> [*The light in the window has faded out.*]

Boy. You never gave me my right share.
Old Man. And had I given it, young as you are,
You would have spent it upon drink.
Boy. What if I did? I had a right
To get it and spend it as I chose.
Old Man. Give me that bag and no more words.
Boy. I will not.
Old Man.   I will break your fingers.

> [*They struggle for the bag. In the struggle it drops, scattering the money. The Old Man staggers but does not fall. They stand looking at each other. The window is lit up. A man is seen pouring whiskey into a glass.*]

Boy. What if I killed you? You killed my grand-dad,
Because you were young and he was old.
Now I am young and you are old.
Old Man [*staring at window*]. Better-looking, those sixteen
years—
Boy. What are you muttering?
Old Man.   Younger—and yet
She should have known he was not her kind.
Boy. What are you saying? Out with it!

> [*Old Man points to window.*]

My God! The window is lit up
And somebody stands there, although
The floorboards are all burnt away.
Old Man. The window is lit up because my father
Has come to find a glass for his whiskey.
He leans there like some tired beast.
Boy. A dead, living, murdered man!
Old Man. "Then the bride-sleep fell upon Adam":
Where did I read those words?
                          And yet
There's nothing leaning in the window

But the impression upon my mother's mind;
Being dead she is alone in her remorse.
Boy. A body that was a bundle of old bones
Before I was born. Horrible! Horrible!

[*He covers his eyes.*]

Old Man. That beast there would know nothing, being nothing,
If I should kill a man under the window
He would not even turn his head.   [*He stabs the Boy.*]
My father and my son on the same jack-knife!
That finishes—there—there—there—

[*He stabs again and again. The window grows dark.*]

"Hush-a-bye baby, thy father's a knight,
Thy mother a lady, lovely and bright."
No, that is something that I read in a book,
And if I sing it must be to my mother,
And I lack rhyme.

[*The stage has grown dark except where the tree stands
in white light.*]
                              Study that tree.
It stands there like a purified soul,
All cold, sweet, glistening light.
Dear mother, the window is dark again,
But you are in the light because
I finished all that consequence.
I killed that lad because had he grown up
He would have struck a woman's fancy,
Begot, and passed pollution on.
I am a wretched foul old man
And therefore harmless. When I have stuck
This old jack-knife into a sod
And pulled it out all bright again,
And picked up all the money that he dropped,
I'll to a distant place, and there
Tell my old jokes among new men.

[*He cleans the knife and begins to pick up money.*]
Hoof-beats! Dear God,
How quickly it returns—beat—beat—!

Her mind cannot hold up that dream.
Twice a murderer and all for nothing,
And she must animate that dead night
Not once but many times!

                O God,
Release my mother's soul from its dream!
Mankind can do no more. Appease
The misery of the living and the remorse of the dead.

THE WILD SWANS AT COOLE

By W. B. YEATS

THE WILD SWANS AT COOLE

The trees are in their autumn beauty,
The woodland paths are dry,
Under the October twilight the water
Mirrors a still sky;
Upon the brimming water among the stones
Are nine-and-fifty swans.

The nineteenth autumn has come upon me
Since I first made my count;
I saw, before I had well finished,
All suddenly mount
And scatter wheeling in great broken rings
Upon their clamorous wings.

I have looked upon those brilliant creatures,
And now my heart is sore.
All's changed since I, hearing at twilight,
The first time on this shore,
The bell-beat of their wings above my head,
Trod with a lighter tread.

Unwearied still, lover by lover,
They paddle in the cold
Companionable streams or climb the air;
Their hearts have got grown old;
Passion or conquest, wander where they will,
Attend upon them still.

But now they drift on the still water,
Mysterious, beautiful;
Among what rushes will they build,
By what lake's edge or pool
Delight men's eyes when I awake some day
To find they have flown away?

IN MEMORY OF MAJOR ROBERT GREGORY

I

Now that we're almost settled in our house
I'll name the friends that cannot sup with us
Beside a fire of turf in th' ancient tower,
And having talked to some late hour
Climb up the narrow winding stairs to bed:
Discoverers of forgotten truth
Or mere companions of my youth,
All, all are in my thoughts tonight being dead.

II

Always we'd have the new friend meet the old
And we are hurt if either friend seem cold,
And there is salt to lengthen out the smart
In the affections of our heart,
And quarrels are blown up upon that head;
But not a friend that I would bring
This night can set up quarreling,
For all that come into my mind are dead.

III

Lionel Johnson comes the first to mind,
That loved his learning better than mankind,
Though courteous to the worst; much falling he
Brooded upon sanctity

Till all his Greek and Latin learning seemed
A long blast upon the horn that brought
A little nearer to his thought
A measureless consummation that he dreamed.

IV

And that inquiring man John Synge comes next,
That dying chose the living world for text
And never could have rested in the tomb
But that, long traveling, he had come
Towards nightfall upon certain set apart
In a most desolate stony place,
Towards nightfall upon a race
Passionate and simple like his heart.

V

And then I think of old George Pollexfen,
In muscular youth well known to Mayo men
For horsemanship at meets or at racecourses,
That could have shown how pure-bred horses
And solid men, for all their passion, live
But as the outrageous stars incline
By opposition, square and trine;
Having grown sluggish and contemplative.

VI

They were my close companions many a year,
A portion of my mind and life, as it were,
And now their breathless faces seem to look
Out of some old picture-book;
I am accustomed to their lack of breath,
But not that my dear friend's dear son,
Our Sidney and our perfect man,
Could share in that discourtesy of death.

VII

For all things the delighted eye now sees
Were loved by him: the old storm-broken trees

That cast their shadows upon road and bridge;
The tower set on the stream's edge;
The ford where drinking cattle make a stir
Nightly, and startled by that sound
The water-hen must change her ground;
He might have been your heartiest welcomer.

VIII

When with the Galway foxhounds he would ride
From Castle Taylor to the Roxborough side
Or Esserkelly plain, few kept his pace;
At Mooneen he had leaped a place
So perilous that half the astonished meet
Had shut their eyes; and where was it
He rode a race without a bit?
And yet his mind outran the horses' feet.

IX

We dreamed that a great painter had been born
To cold Clare rock and Galway rock and thorn,
To that stern color and that delicate line
That are our secret discipline
Wherein the gazing heart doubles her might.
Soldier, scholar, horseman, he,
And yet he had the intensity
To have published all to be a world's delight.

X

What other could so well have counseled us
In all lovely intricacies of a house
As he that practiced or that understood
All work in metal or in wood,
In molded plaster or in carven stone?
Soldier, scholar, horseman, he,
And all he did done perfectly
As though he had but that one trade alone.

XI

Some burn faggots, others may consume
The entire combustible world in one small room
As though dried straw, and if we turn about
The bare chimney is gone black out
Because the work had finished in that flare.
Soldier, scholar, horseman, he,
As 'twere all life's epitome.
What made us dream that he could comb gray hair?

XII

I had thought, seeing how bitter is that wind
That shakes the shutter, to have brought to mind
All those that manhood tried, or childhood loved
Or boyish intellect approved,
With some appropriate commentary on each;
Until imagination brought
A fitter welcome; but a thought
Of that late death took all my heart for speech.

AN IRISH AIRMAN FORESEES HIS DEATH

I know that I shall meet my fate
Somewhere among the clouds above;
Those that I fight I do not hate,
Those that I guard I do not love;
My country is Kiltartan Cross,
My countrymen Kiltartan's poor,
No likely end could bring them loss
Or leave them happier than before.
Nor law, nor duty bade me fight,
Nor public men, nor cheering crowds,
A lonely impulse of delight
Drove to this tumult in the clouds;

I balanced all, brought all to mind,
The years to come seemed waste of breath,
A waste of breath the years behind
In balance with this life, this death.

MEN IMPROVE WITH THE YEARS

I am worn out with dreams;
A weather-worn, marble triton
Among the streams;
And all day long I look
Upon this lady's beauty
As though I had found in a book
A pictured beauty,
Pleased to have filled the eyes
Or the discerning ears,
Delighted to be but wise,
For men improve with the years;
And yet, and yet,
Is this my dream, or the truth?
O would that we had met
When I had my burning youth!
But I grow old among dreams,
A weather-worn, marble triton
Among the streams.

THE COLLAR-BONE OF A HARE

Would I could cast a sail on the water
Where many a king has gone
And many a king's daughter,
And alight at the comely trees and the lawn,

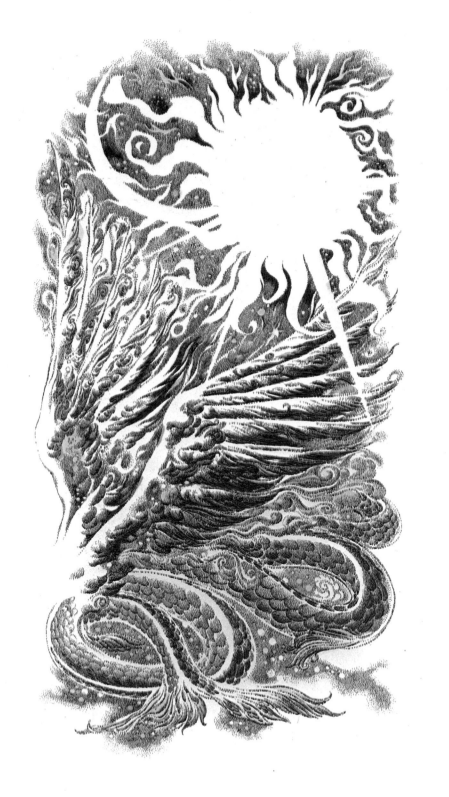

The playing upon pipes and the dancing,
And learn that the best thing is
To change my loves while dancing
And pay but a kiss for a kiss.

I would find by the edge of that water
The collar-bone of a hare
Worn thin by the lapping of water,
And pierce it through with a gimlet, and stare
At the old bitter world where they marry in churches,
And laugh over the untroubled water
At all who marry in churches,
Through the white thin bone of a hare.

UNDER THE ROUND TOWER

'Although I'd lie lapped up in linen
A deal I'd sweat and little earn
If I should live as live the neighbors,'
Cried the beggar, Billy Byrne;
'Stretch bones till the daylight come
On great-grandfather's battered tomb.'

Upon a gray old battered tombstone
In Glendalough beside the stream,
Where the O'Byrnes and Byrnes are buried,
He stretched his bones and fell in a dream
Of sun and moon that a good hour
Bellowed and pranced in the round tower;

Of golden king and silver lady,
Bellowing up and bellowing round,
Till toes mastered a sweet measure,
Mouth mastered a sweet sound,
Prancing round and prancing up
Until they pranced upon the top.

That golden king and that wild lady
Sang till stars began to fade,
Hands gripped in hands, toes close together,
Hair spread on the wind they made;
That lady and that golden king
Could like a brace of blackbirds sing.

'It's certain that my luck is broken,'
That rambling jailbird Billy said;
'Before nightfall I'll pick a pocket
And snug it in a feather bed.
I cannot find the peace of home
On great-grandfather's battered tomb.'

SOLOMON TO SHEBA

Sang Solomon to Sheba,
And kissed her dusky face,
'All day long from mid-day
We have talked in the one place,
All day long from shadowless noon
We have gone round and round
In the narrow theme of love
Like an old horse in a pound.'

To Solomon sang Sheba,
Planted on his knees,
'If you had broached a matter
That might the learned please,
You had before the sun had thrown
Our shadows on the ground
Discovered that my thoughts, not it,
Are but a narrow pound.'

Sang Solomon to Sheba,
And kissed her Arab eyes,
'There's not a man or woman
Born under the skies
Dare match in learning with us two,
And all day long we have found
There's not a thing but love can make
The world a narrow pound.'

THE LIVING BEAUTY

I bade, because the wick and oil are spent
And frozen are the channels of the blood,
My discontented heart to draw content
From beauty that is cast out of a mold
In bronze, or that in dazzling marble appears,
Appears, but when we have gone is gone again,
Being more indifferent to our solitude
Than 'twere an apparition. O heart, we are old;
The living beauty is for younger men:
We cannot pay its tribute of wild tears.

A SONG

I thought no more was needed
Youth to prolong
Than dumb-bell and foil
To keep the body young.
O who could have foretold
That the heart grows old?

[281]

Though I have many words,
What woman's satisfied,
I am no longer faint
Because at her side?
O who could have foretold
That the heart grows old?

I have not lost desire
But the heart that I had;
I thought 'twould burn my body
Laid on the death-bed,
For who could have foretold
That the heart grows old?

TO A YOUNG BEAUTY

Dear fellow-artist, why so free
With every sort of company,
With every Jack and Jill?
Choose your companions from the best;
Who draws a bucket with the rest
Soon topples down the hill.

You, may, that mirror for a school,
Be passionate, not bountiful
As common beauties may,
Who were not born to keep in trim
With old Ezekiel's cherubim
But those of Beauvarlet.

I know what wages beauty gives,
How hard a life her servant lives,
Yet praise the winters gone:
There is not a fool can call me friend,
And I may dine at Journey's end
With Landor and with Donne.

TO A YOUNG GIRL

My dear, my dear, I know
More than another
What makes your heart beat so;
Not even your own mother
Can know it as I know,
Who broke my heart for her
When the wild thought,
That she denies
And has forgot,
Set all her blood astir
And glittered in her eyes.

THE SCHOLARS

Bald heads forgetful of their sins,
Old, learned, respectable bald heads
Edit and annotate the lines
That young men, tossing on their beds,
Rhymed out in love's despair
To flatter beauty's ignorant ear.

All shuffle there; all cough in ink;
All wear the carpet with their shoes;
All think what other people think;
All know the man their neighbor knows.
Lord, what would they say
Did their Catullus walk that way?

[283]

TOM O'ROUGHLEY

'Though logic-choppers rule the town,
And every man and maid and boy
Has marked a distant object down,
An aimless joy is a pure joy,'
Or so did Tom O'Roughley say
That saw the surges running by,
'And wisdom is a butterfly
And not a gloomy bird of prey.

'If little planned is little sinned
But little need the grave distress.
What's dying but a second wind?
How but in zig-zag wantonness
Could trumpeter Michael be so brave?'
Or something of that sort he said,
'And if my dearest friend were dead
I'd dance a measure on his grave.'

SHEPHERD AND GOATHERD

Shepherd. That cry's from the first cuckoo of the year.
    I wished before it ceased.

Goatherd.   Nor bird nor beast
    Could make me wish for anything this day,
    Being old, but that the old alone might die,
    And that would be against God's Providence.
    Let the young wish. But what has brought you here?
    Never until this moment have we met
    Where my goats browse on the scarce grass or leap
    From stone to stone.

Shepherd.   I am looking for strayed sheep;

Something has troubled me and in my trouble
I let them stray. I thought of rhyme alone,
For rhyme can beat a measure out of trouble
And make the daylight sweet once more; but when
I had driven every rhyme into its place
The sheep had gone from theirs.

Goatherd.   I know right well
    What turned so good a shepherd from his charge.

Shepherd. He that was best in every country sport
    And every country craft, and of us all
    Most courteous to slow age and hasty youth,
    Is dead.

Goatherd.   The boy that brings my griddle-cake
    Brought the bare news.

Shepherd.   He had thrown the crook away
    And died in the great war beyond the sea.

Goatherd. He had often played his pipes among my hills,
    And when he played it was their loneliness,
    The exultation of their stone, that cried
    Under his fingers.

Shepherd.   I had it from his mother,
    And his own flock was browsing at the door.

Goatherd. How does she bear her grief? There is not a shepherd
    But grows more gentle when he speaks her name,
    Remembering kindness done, and how can I,
    That found when I had neither goat nor grazing
    New welcome and old wisdom at her fire
    Till winter blasts were gone, but speak of her
    Even before his children and his wife?

Shepherd. She goes about her house erect and calm
    Between the pantry and the linen-chest,
    Or else at meadow or at grazing overlooks
    Her laboring men, as though her darling lived,
    But for her grandson now; there is no change
    But such as I have seen upon her face
    Watching our shepherd sports at harvest-time
    When her son's turn was over.

Goatherd.   Sing your song.
    I too have rhymed my reveries, but youth
    Is hot to show whatever it has found,
    And till that's done can neither work nor wait.
    Old goatherds and old goats, if in all else
    Youth can excel them in accomplishment,
    Are learned in waiting.

Shepherd.   You cannot but have seen
    That he alone had gathered up no gear,
    Set carpenters to work on no wide table,
    On no long bench nor lofty milking-shed
    As others will, when first they take possession,
    But left the house as in his father's time
    As though he knew himself, as it were, a cuckoo,
    No settled man. And now that he is gone
    There's nothing of him left but half a score
    Of sorrowful, austere, sweet, lofty pipe tunes.

Goatherd. You have put the thought in rhyme.

Shepherd.   I worked all day,
    And when 'twas done so little had I done
    That maybe 'I am sorry' in plain prose
    Had sounded better to your mountain fancy.

                                   [*He sings.*]

    'Like the speckled bird that steers
    Thousands of leagues oversea,
    And runs or a while half-flies

On his yellow legs through our meadows,
He stayed for a while; and we
Had scarcely accustomed our ears
To his speech at the break of day,
Had scarcely accustomed our eyes
To his shape at the rinsing-pool
Among the evening shadows,
When he vanished from ears and eyes.
I might have wished on the day
He came, but man is a fool.'

Goatherd. You sing as always of the natural life,
And I that made like music in my youth
Hearing it now have sighed for that young man
And certain lost companions of my own.

Shepherd. They say that on your barren mountain ridge
You have measured out the road that the soul treads
When it has vanished from our natural eyes;
That you have talked with apparitions.

Goatherd.   Indeed
My daily thoughts since the first stupor of youth
Have found the path my goats' feet cannot find.

Shepherd. Sing, for it may be that your thoughts have plucked
Some medicable herb to make our grief
Less bitter.

Goatherd.   They have brought me from that ridge
Seed-pods and flowers that are not all wild poppy.

                                        [*Sings.*]

'He grows younger every second
That were all his birthdays reckoned
Much too solemn seemed;
Because of what he had dreamed,
Or the ambitions that he served,

Much too solemn and reserved.
Jaunting, journeying
To his own dayspring,
He unpacks the loaded pern
Of all 'twas pain or joy to learn,
Of all that he had made.
The outrageous war shall fade;
At some old winding whitethorn root
He'll practice on the shepherd's flute,
Or on the close-cropped grass
Court his shepherd lass,
Or put his heart into some game
Till daytime, playtime seem the same;
Knowledge he shall unwind
Through victories of the mind,
Till, clambering at the cradle-side,
He dreams himself his mother's pride,
All knowledge lost in trance
Of sweeter ignorance.'

Shepherd. When I have shut these ewes and this old ram
   Into the fold, we'll to the woods and there
   Cut out our rhymes on strips of new-torn bark
   But put no name and leave them at her door.
   To know the mountain and the valley have grieved
   May be a quiet thought to wife and mother,
   And children when they spring up shoulder-high.

LINES WRITTEN IN DEJECTION

When have I last looked on
The round green eyes and the long wavering bodies
Of the dark leopards of the moon?
All the wild witches, those most noble ladies,

For all their broom-sticks and their tears,
Their angry tears, are gone.
The holy centaurs of the hills are vanished;
I have nothing but the embittered sun;
Banished heroic mother moon and vanished,
And now that I have come to fifty years
I must endure the timid sun.

THE DAWN

I would be ignorant as the dawn
That has looked down
On that old queen measuring a town
With the pin of a brooch,
Or on the withered men that saw
From their pedantic Babylon
The careless planets in their courses,
The stars fade out where the moon comes,
And took their tablets and did sums;
I would be ignorant as the dawn
That merely stood, rocking the glittering coach
Above the cloudy shoulders of the horses;
I would be—for no knowledge is worth a straw—
Ignorant and wanton as the dawn.

ON WOMAN

May God be praised for woman
That gives up all her mind,
A man may find in no man
A friendship of her kind

That covers all he has brought
As with her flesh and bone,
Nor quarrels with a thought
Because it is not her own.

Though pedantry denies,
It's plain the Bible means
That Solomon grew wise
While talking with his queens,
Yet never could, although
They say he counted grass,
Count all the praises due
When Sheba was his lass,
When she the iron wrought, or
When from the smithy fire
It shuddered in the water:
Harshness of their desire
That made them stretch and yawn,
Pleasure that comes with sleep,
Shudder that made them one.
What else He give or keep
God grant me—no, not here,
For I am not so bold
To hope a thing so dear
Now I am growing old,
But when, if the tale's true,
The Pestle of the moon
That pounds up all anew
Brings me to birth again—
To find what once I had
And know what once I have known,
Until I am driven mad,
Sleep driven from my bed,
By tenderness and care,
Pity, an aching head,
Gnashing of teeth, despair;
And all because of some one

Perverse creature of chance,
And live like Solomon
That Sheba led a dance.

THE FISHERMAN

Although I can see him still,
The freckled man who goes
To a gray place on a hill
In gray Connemara clothes
At dawn to cast his flies,
It's long since I began
To call up to the eyes
This wise and simple man.
All day I'd looked in the face
What I had hoped 'twould be
To write for my own race
And the reality;
The living men that I hate,
The dead man that I loved,
The craven man in his seat,
The insolent unreproved,
And no knave brought to book
Who has won a drunken cheer,
The witty man and his joke
Aimed at the commonest ear,
The clever man who cries
The catch-cries of the clown,
The beating down of the wise
And great Art beaten down.

Maybe a twelvemonth since
Suddenly I began,
In scorn of this audience,
Imagining a man,

And his sun-freckled face,
And gray Connemara cloth,
Climbing up to a place
Where stone is dark under froth,
And the down-turn of his wrist
When the flies drop in the stream;
A man who does not exist,
A man who is but a dream;
And cried, 'Before I am old
I shall have written him one
Poem maybe as cold
And passionate as the dawn.'

THE HAWK

'Call down the hawk from the air;
Let him be hooded or caged
Till the yellow eye has grown mild,
For larder and spit are bare,
The old cook enraged,
The scullion gone wild.'

'I will not be clapped in a hood,
Nor a cage, nor alight upon wrist,
Now I have learnt to be proud
Hovering over the wood
In the broken mist
Or tumbling cloud.'

'What tumbling cloud did you cleave,
Yellow-eyed hawk of the mind,
Last evening? that I, who had sat
Dumbfounded before a knave,
Should give to my friend
A pretense of wit.'

MEMORY

One had a lovely face,
And two or three had charm,
But charm and face were in vain
Because the mountain grass
Cannot but keep the form
Where the mountain hare has lain.

HER PRAISE

She is foremost of those that I would hear praised.
I have gone about the house, gone up and down
As a man does who has published a new book,
Or a young girl dressed out in her new gown,
And though I have turned the talk by hook or crook
Until her praise should be the uppermost theme,
A woman spoke of some new tale she had read,
A man confusedly in a half dream
As though some other name ran in his head.
She is foremost of those that I would hear praised.
I will talk no more of books or the long war
But walk by the dry thorn until I have found
Some beggar sheltering from the wind, and there
Manage the talk until her name come round.
If there be rags enough he will know her name
And be well pleased remembering it, for in the old days,
Though she had young men's praise and old men's blame,
Among the poor both old and young gave her praise.

THE PEOPLE

'What have I earned for all that work,' I said,
'For all that I have done at my own charge?
The daily spite of this unmannerly town,
Where who has served the most is most defamed,
The reputation of his lifetime lost
Between the night and morning. I might have lived,
And you know well how great the longing has been,
Where every day my footfall should have lit
In the green shadow of Ferrara wall;
Or climbed among the images of the past—
The unperturbed and courtly images—
Evening and morning, the steep street of Urbino
To where the Duchess and her people talked
The stately midnight through until they stood
In their great window looking at the dawn;
I might have had no friend that could not mix
Courtesy and passion into one like those
That saw the wicks grow yellow in the dawn;
I might have used the one substantial right
My trade allows: chosen my company,
And chosen what scenery had pleased me best.'
Thereon my phoenix answered in reproof,
'The drunkards, pilferers of public funds,
All the dishonest crowd I had driven away,
When my luck changed and they dared meet my face,
Crawled from obscurity, and set upon me
Those I had served and some that I had fed;
Yet never have I, now nor any time,
Complained of the people.'

                        All I could reply
Was: 'You, that have not lived in thought but deed,
Can have the purity of a natural force,

But I, whose virtues are the definitions
Of the analytic mind, can neither close
The eye of the mind nor keep my tongue from speech.'
And yet, because my heart leaped at her words,
I was abashed, and now they come to mind
After nine years, I sink my head abashed.

HIS PHOENIX

There is a queen in China, or maybe it's in Spain,
And birthdays and holidays such praises can be heard
Of her unblemished lineaments, a whiteness with no stain,
That she might be that sprightly girl trodden by a bird;
And there's a score of duchesses, surpassing womankind,
Or who have found a painter to make them so for pay
And smooth out stain and blemish with the elegance of his mind:
I knew a phoenix in my youth, so let them have their day.

The young men every night applaud their Gaby's laughing eye,
And Ruth St. Denis had more charm although she had poor luck;
From nineteen hundred nine or ten, Pavlova's had the cry,
And there's player in the States who gathers up her cloak
And flings herself out of the room when Juliet would be bride
With all a woman's passion, a child's imperious way,
And there are—but no matter if there are scores beside:
I knew a phoenix in my youth, so let them have their day.

There's Margaret and Marjorie and Dorothy and Nan,
A Daphne and a Mary who live in privacy;
One's had her fill of lovers, another's had but one,
Another boasts, 'I pick and choose and have but two or three.'
If head and limb have beauty and the instep's high and light
They can spread out what sail they please for all I have to say,
Be but the breakers of men's hearts or engines of delight:
I knew a phoenix in my youth, so let them have their day.

There'll be that crowd, that barbarous crowd, through all the centuries,
And who can say but some young belle may walk and talk men wild
Who is my beauty's equal, though that my heart denies,
But not the exact likeness, the simplicity of a child,
And that proud look as though she had gazed into the burning sun,
And all the shapely body no tittle gone astray.
I mourn for that most lonely thing; and yet God's will be done:
I knew a phoenix in my youth, so let them have their day.

A THOUGHT FROM PROPERTIUS

She might, so noble from head
To great shapely knees
The long flowing line,
Have walked to the altar
Through the holy images
At Pallas Athene's side,
Or been fit spoil for a centaur
Drunk with the unmixed wine.

BROKEN DREAMS

There is gray in your hair.
Young men no longer suddenly catch their breath
When you are passing;
But maybe some old gaffer mutters a blessing
Because it was your prayer
Recovered him upon the bed of death.
For your sole sake—that all heart's ache have known,
And given to others all heart's ache,

From meager girlhood's putting on
Burdensome beauty—for your sole sake
Heaven has put away the stroke of her doom,
So great her portion in that peace you make
By merely walking in a room.

Your beauty can but leave among us
Vague memories, nothing but memories.
A young man when the old men are done talking
Will say to an old man, 'Tell me of that lady
The poet stubborn with his passion sang us
When age might well have chilled his blood.'

Vague memories, nothing but memories,
But in the grave all, all, shall be renewed.
The certainty that I shall see that lady
Leaning or standing or walking
In the first loveliness of womanhood,
And with the fervor of my youthful eyes,
Has set me muttering like a fool.

You are more beautiful than any one,
And yet your body had a flaw:
Your small hands were not beautiful,
And I am afraid that you will run
And paddle to the wrist
In that mysterious, always brimming lake
Where those that have obeyed the holy law
Paddle and are perfect. Leave unchanged
The hands that I have kissed,
For old sake's sake.

The last stroke of midnight dies.
All day in the one chair
From dream to dream and rhyme to rhyme I have ranged
In rambling talk with an image of air:
Vague memories, nothing but memories.

A DEEP-SWORN VOW

Others because you did not keep
That deep-sworn vow have been friends of mine;
Yet always when I look death in the face,
When I clamber to the heights of sleep,
Or when I grow excited with wine,
Suddenly I meet your face.

PRESENCES

This night has been so strange that it seemed
As if the hair stood up on my head.
From going-down of the sun I have dreamed
That women laughing, or timid or wild,
In rustle of lace or silken stuff,
Climbed up my creaking stair. They had read
All I had rhymed of that monstrous thing
Returned and yet unrequited love.
They stood in the door and stood between
My great wood lectern and the fire
Till I could hear their hearts beating:
One is a harlot, and one a child
That never looked upon man with desire,
And one, it may be, a queen.

THE BALLOON OF THE MIND

Hands, do what you're bid:
Bring the balloon of the mind
That bellies and drags in the wind
Into its narrow shed.

TO A SQUIRREL AT KYLE-NA-NO

Come play with me;
Why should you run
Through the shaking tree
As though I'd a gun
To strike you dead?
When all I would do
Is to scratch your head
And let you go.

ON BEING ASKED FOR A WAR POEM

I think it better that in times like these
A poet's mouth be silent, for in truth
We have no gift to set a statesman right;
He has had enough of meddling who can please
A young girl in the indolence of her youth,
Or an old man upon a winter's night.

IN MEMORY OF ALFRED POLLEXFEN

Five-and-twenty years have gone
Since old William Pollexfen
Laid his strong bones down in death
By his wife Elizabeth
In the gray stone tomb he made.

And after twenty years they laid
In that tomb by him and her
His son George, the astrologer;
And Masons drove from miles away
To scatter the Acacia spray
Upon a melancholy man
Who had ended where his breath began.
Many a son and daughter lies
Far from the customary skies,
The Mall and Eades's grammar school,
In London or in Liverpool;
But where is laid the sailor John
That so many lands had known,
Quiet lands or unquiet seas
Where the Indians trade or Japanese?
He never found his rest ashore,
Moping for one voyage more.
Where have they laid the sailor John?
And yesterday the youngest son,
A humorous, unambitious man,
Was buried near the astrologer,
Yesterday in the tenth year
Since he who had been contented long,
A nobody in a great throng,
Decided he would journey home,
Now that his fiftieth year had come,
And 'Mr. Alfred' be again
Upon the lips of common men
Who carried in their memory
His childhood and his family.
At all these death-beds women heard
A visionary white sea-bird
Lamenting that a man should die;
And with that cry I have raised my cry.

UPON A DYING LADY

I

Her Courtesy

With the old kindness, the old distinguished grace,
She lies, her lovely piteous head amid dull red hair
Propped upon pillows, rouge on the pallor of her face.
She would not have us sad because she is lying there,
And when she meets our gaze her eyes are laughter-lit,
Her speech a wicked tale that we may vie with her,
Matching our broken-hearted wit against her wit,
Thinking of saints and of Petronius Arbiter.

II

Certain Artists Bring Her Dolls and Drawings

Bring where our Beauty lies
A new modeled doll, or drawing,
With a friend's or an enemy's
Features, or maybe showing
Her features when a tress
Of dull red hair was flowing
Over some silken dress
Cut in the Turkish fashion,
Or, it may be, like a boy's.
We have given the world our passion,
We have naught for death but toys.

III

She Turns the Dolls' Faces to the Wall

Because today is some religious festival
They had a priest say Mass, and even the Japanese,
Heel up and weight on toe, must face the wall
—Pedant in passion, learned in old courtesies,

Vehement and witty she had seemed—; the Venetian lady
Who had seemed to glide to some intrigue in her red shoes,
Her domino, her panniered skirt copied from Longhi;
The meditative critic; all are on their toes,
Even our Beauty with her Turkish trousers on.
Because the priest must have like every dog his day
Or keep us all awake with baying at the moon,
We and our dolls being but the world were best away.

IV

The End of Day

She is playing like a child
And penance is the play,
Fantastical and wild
Because the end of day
Shows her that some one soon
Will come from the house, and say—
Though play is but half done—
'Come in and leave the play.'

V

Her Race

She has not grown uncivil
As narrow natures would
And called the pleasures evil
Happier days thought good;
She knows herself a woman,
No red and white of a face,
Or rank, raised from a common
Unreckonable race;
And how should her heart fail her
Or sickness break her will
With her dead brother's valor
For an example still?

VI

Her Courage

When her soul flies to the predestined dancing-place
(I have no speech but symbol, the pagan speech I made
Amid the dreams of youth) let her come face to face,
Amid that first astonishment, with Grania's shade,
All but the terrors of the woodland flight forgot
That made her Diarmuid dear, and some old cardinal
Pacing with half-closed eyelids in a sunny spot
Who had murmured of Giorgione at his latest breath—
Aye, and Achilles, Timor, Babar, Barhaim, all
Who have lived in joy and laughed into the face of Death.

VII

Her Friends Bring Her a Christmas Tree

Pardon, great enemy,
Without an angry thought
We've carried in our tree,
And here and there have bought
Till all the boughs are gay,
And she may look from the bed
On pretty things that may
Please a fantastic head.
Give her a little grace,
What if a laughing eye
Have looked into your face?
It is about to die.

EGO DOMINUS TUUS

Hic. On the gray sand beside the shallow stream
    Under your old wind-beaten tower, where still
    A lamp burns on beside the open book

That Michael Robartes left, you walk in the moon,
And, though you have passed the best of life, still trace,
Enthralled by the unconquerable delusion,
Magical shapes.
Ille.   By the help of an image
    I call to my own opposite, summon all
    That I have handled least, least looked upon.
Hic. And I would find myself and not an image.
Ille. That is our modern hope, and by its light
    We have lit upon the gentle, sensitive mind
    And lost the old nonchalance of the hand;
    Whether we have chosen chisel, pen or brush,
    We are but critics, or but half create,
    Timid, entangled, empty and abashed,
    Lacking the countenance of our friends.
Hic.   And yet
    The chief imagination of Christendom,
    Dante Alighieri, so utterly found himself
    That he has made that hollow face of his
    More plain to the mind's eye than any face
    But that of Christ.
Ille.   And did he find himself
    Or was the hunger that had made it hollow
    A hunger for the apple on the bough
    Most out of reach? and is that spectral image
    The man that Lapo and that Guido knew?
    I think he fashioned from his opposite
    An image that might have been a stony face
    Staring upon a Bedouin's horse-hair roof
    From doored and windowed cliff, or half upturned
    Among the coarse grass and the camel-dung.
    He set his chisel to the hardest stone.
    Being mocked by Guido for his lecherous life,
    Derided and deriding, driven out
    To climb that stair and eat that bitter bread,
    He found the unpersuadable justice, he found
    The most exalted lady loved by a man.

Hic. Yet surely there are men who have made their art
    Out of no tragic war, lovers of life,
    Impulsive men that look for happiness
    And sing when they have found it.
Ille.   No, not sing,
    For those that love the world serve it in action,
    Grow rich, popular and full of influence,
    And should they paint or write, still it is action:
    The struggle of the fly in marmalade.
    The rhetorician would deceive his neighbors,
    The sentimentalist himself; while art
    Is but a vision of reality.
    What portion in the world can the artist have
    Who has awakened from the common dream
    But dissipation and despair?
Hic.   And yet
    No one denies to Keats love of the world;
    Remember his deliberate happiness.
Ille. His art is happy, but who knows his mind?
    I see a schoolboy when I think of him,
    With face and nose pressed to a sweet-shop window,
    For certainly he sank into his grave
    His senses and his heart unsatisfied,
    And made—being poor, ailing and ignorant,
    Shut out from all the luxury of the world,
    The coarse-bred son of a livery-stable keeper—
    Luxuriant song.
Hic.   Why should you leave the lamp
    Burning alone beside an open book,
    And trace these characters upon the sands?
    A style is found by sedentary toil
    And by the imitation of great masters.
Ille. Because I seek an image, not a book.
    Those men that in their writings are most wise
    Own nothing but their blind, stupefied hearts.
    I call to the mysterious one who yet
    Shall walk the wet sands by the edge of the stream

And look most like me, being indeed my double,
And prove of all imaginable things
The most unlike, being my anti-self,
And, standing by these characters, disclose
All that I seek; and whisper it as though
He were afraid the birds, who cry aloud
Their momentary cries before it is dawn,
Would carry it away to blasphemous men.

A PRAYER ON GOING INTO MY HOUSE

God grant a blessing on this tower and cottage
And on my heirs, if all remain unspoiled,
No table or chair or stool not simple enough
For shepherd lads in Galilee; and grant
That I myself for portions of the year
May handle nothing and set eyes on nothing
But what the great and passionate have used
Throughout so many varying centuries
We take it for the norm; yet should I dream
Sinbad the sailor's brought a painted chest,
Or image, from beyond the Loadstone Mountain,
That dream is a norm; and should some limb of the Devil
Destroy the view by cutting down an ash
That shades the road, or setting up a cottage
Planned in a government office, shorten his life,
Manacle his soul upon the Red Sea bottom.

THE PHASE OF THE MOON

An old man cocked his ear upon a bridge;
He and his friend, their faces to the South,
Had trod the uneven road. Their boots were soiled,
Their Connemara cloth worn out of shape;

They had kept a steady pace as though their beds,
Despite a dwindling and late-risen moon,
Were distant still. An old man cocked his ear.

Aherne. What made that sound?
Robartes.   A rat or water-hen
   Splashed, or an otter slid into the stream.
   We are on the bridge; that shadow is the tower,
   And the light proves that he is reading still.
   He has found, after the manner of his kind,
   Mere images; chosen this place to live in
   Because, it may be, of the candle-light
   From the far tower where Milton's Platonist
   Sat late, or Shelley's visionary prince:
   The lonely light that Samuel Palmer engraved,
   An image of mysterious wisdom won by toil;
   And now he seeks in book or manuscript
   What he shall never find.
Aherne.   Why should not you
   Who know it all ring at his door, and speak
   Just truth enough to show that his whole life
   Will scarcely find for him a broken crust
   Of all those truths that are your daily bread;
   And when you have spoken take the roads again?
Robartes. He wrote of me in that extravagant style
   He had learnt from Pater, and to round his tale
   Said I was dead; and dead I choose to be.
Aherne. Sing me the changes of the moon once more;
   True song, though speech: 'mine author sung it me.'
Robartes. Twenty-and-eight the phases of the moon,
   The full and the moon's dark and all the crescents,
   Twenty-and-eight, and yet but six-and-twenty
   The cradles that a man must needs be rocked in:
   For there's no human life at the full or the dark.
   From the first crescent to the half, the dream
   But summons to adventure and the man
   Is always happy like a bird or a beast;

But while the moon is rounding towards the full
He follows whatever whim's most difficult
Among whims not impossible, and though scarred,
As with the cat-o'-nine-tails of the mind,
His body molded from within his body
Grows comelier. Eleven pass, and then
Athene takes Achilles by the hair,
Hector is in the dust, Nietzsche is born,
Because the hero's crescent is the twelfth.
And yet, twice born, twice buried, grow he must,
Before the full moon, helpless as a worm,
The thirteenth moon but sets the soul at war
In its own being, and when that war's begun
There is no muscle in the arm; and after,
Under the frenzy of the fourteenth moon,
The soul begins to tremble into stillness,
To die into the labyrinth of itself!

Aherne. Sing out the song; sing to the end, and sing
The strange reward of all that discipline.

Robartes. All thought becomes an image and the soul
Becomes a body: that body and that soul
Too perfect at the full to lie in a cradle,
Too lonely for the traffic of the world:
Body and soul cast out and cast away
Beyond the visible world.

Aherne.   All dreams of the soul
End in a beautiful man's or woman's body.

Robartes. Have you not always known it?

Aherne.   The song will have it
That those we have loved got their long fingers
From death, and wounds, or on Sinai's top,
Or from some bloody whip in their own hands.
They ran from cradle to cradle till at last
Their beauty dropped out of the loneliness
Of body and soul.

Robartes.   The lover's heart knows that.

Aherne. It must be that the terror in their eyes

Is memory or foreknowledge of the hour
When all is fed with light and heaven is bare.
Robartes. When the moon's full those creatures of the full
Are met on the waste hills by countrymen
Who shudder and hurry by: body and soul
Estranged amid the strangeness of themselves,
Caught up in contemplation, the mind's eye
Fixed upon images that once were thought;
For separate, perfect, and immovable
Images can break the solitude
Of lovely, satisfied, indifferent eyes.

*And thereupon with aged, high-pitched voice
Aherne laughed, thinking of the man within,
His sleepless candle and laborious pen.*

Robartes. And after that the crumbling of the moon.
The soul remembering its loneliness
Shudders in many cradles; all is changed,
It would be the world's servant, and as it serves,
Choosing whatever task's most difficult
Among tasks not impossible, it takes
Upon the body and upon the soul
The coarseness of the drudge.
Aherne.   Before the full
It sought itself and afterwards the world.
Robartes. Because you are forgotten, half out of life,
And never wrote a book, your thought is clear.
Reformer, merchant, statesman, learned man,
Dutiful husband, honest wife by turn,
Cradle upon cradle, and all in flight and all
Deformed because there is no deformity
But saves us from a dream.
Aherne.   And what of those
That the last servile crescent has set free?
Robartes. Because all dark, like those that are all light,
They are cast beyond the verge, and in a cloud,

Crying to one another like the bats;
And having no desire they cannot tell
What's good or bad, or what it is to triumph
At the perfection of one's own obedience;
And yet they speak what's blown into the mind;
Deformed beyond deformity, unformed,
Insipid as the dough before it is baked,
They change their bodies at a word.

Aherne.   And then?

Robartes. When all the dough has been so kneaded up
  That it can take what form cook Nature fancies
  The first thin crescent is wheeled round once more.

Aherne. But the escape; the song's not finished yet.

Robartes. Hunchback and Saint and Fool are the last crescents.
  The burning bow that once could shoot an arrow
  Out of the up and down, the wagon-wheel
  Of beauty's cruelty and wisdom's chatter—
  Out of that raving tide—is drawn betwixt
  Deformity of body and of mind.

Aherne. Were not our beds far off I'd ring the bell,
  Stand under the rough roof-timbers of the hall
  Beside the castle door, where all is stark
  Austerity, a place set out for wisdom
  That he will never find; I'd play a part;
  He would never know me after all these years
  But take me for some drunken countryman;
  I'd stand and mutter there until he caught
  'Hunchback and Saint and Fool,' and that they came
  Under the three last crescents of the moon,
  And then I'd stragger out. He'd crack his wits
  Day after day, yet never find the meaning.

And then he laughed to think that what seemed hard
Should be so simple—a bat rose from the hazels
And circled round him with its squeaky cry,
The light in the tower window was put out.

THE CAT AND THE MOON

The cat went here and there
And the moon spun round like a top,
And the nearest kin of the moon,
The creeping cat, looked up.
Black Minnaloushe stared at the moon,
For, wander and wail as he would,
The pure cold light in the sky
Troubled his animal blood.
Minnaloushe runs in the grass
Lifting his delicate feet.
Do you dance, Minnaloushe, do you dance?
When two close kindred meet,
What better than call a dance?
Maybe the moon may learn,
Tired of that courtly fashion,
A new dance turn.
Minnaloushe creeps through the grass
From moonlit place to place,
The sacred moon overhead
Has taken a new phase.
Does Minnaloushe know that his pupils
Will pass from change to change,
And that from round to crescent,
From crescent to round they range?
Minnaloushe creeps through the grass
Alone, important and wise,
And lifts to the changing moon
His changing eyes.

THE SAINT AND THE HUNCHBACK

Hunchback. Stand up and lift your hand and bless
    A man that finds great bitterness
    In thinking of his lost renown.
    A Roman Caesar is held down
    Under this hump.
Saint.   God tries each man
    According to a different plan.
    I shall not cease to bless because
    I lay about me with the taws
    That night and morning I may thrash
    Greek Alexander from my flesh,
    Augustus Caesar, and after these
    That great rogue Alcibiades.
Hunchback. To all that in your flesh have stood
    And blessed, I give my gratitude,
    Honored by all in their degrees.
    But most to Alcibiades.

TWO SONGS OF A FOOL

I

A speckled cat and a tame hare
Eat at my hearthstone
And sleep there;
And both look up to me alone
For learning and defense
As I look up to Providence.

I start out of my sleep to think
Some day I may forget

[312]

Their food and drink;
Or, the house door left unshut,
The hare may run till it's found
The horn's sweet note and the tooth of the hound.

I bear a burden that might well try
Men that do all by rule,
And what can I
That am a wandering-witted fool
But pray to God that He ease
My great responsibilities?

II

I slept on my three-legged stool by the fire,
The speckled cat slept on my knee;
We never thought to inquire
Where the brown hare might be,
And whether the door were shut.
Who knows how she drank the wind
Stretched up on two legs from the mat,
Before she had settled her mind
To drum with her heel and to leap?
Had I but awakened from sleep
And called her name, she had heard,
It may be, and had not stirred,
That now, it may be, has found
The horn's sweet note and the tooth of the hound.

ANOTHER SONG OF A FOOL

This great purple butterfly,
In the prison of my hands,
Has a learning in his eye
Not a poor fool understands.

Once he lived a schoolmaster
With a stark, denying look;
A string of scholars went in fear
Of his great birch and his great book.

Like the clangor of a bell,
Sweet and harsh, harsh and sweet,
That is how he learnt so well
To take the roses for his meat.

THE DOUBLE VISION OF MICHAEL ROBARTES

I

On the gray rock of Cashel the mind's eye
Has called up the cold spirits that are born
When the old moon is vanished from the sky
And the new still hides her horn.

Under blank eyes and fingers never still
The particular is pounded till it is man.
When had I my own will?
O not since life began.

Constrained, arraigned, baffled, bent and unbent
By these wire-jointed jaws and limbs of wood,
Themselves obedient,
Knowing not evil and good;

Obedient to some hidden magical breath.
They do not even feel, so abstract are they,
So dead beyond our death,
Triumph that we obey.

II

On the gray rock of Cashel I suddenly saw
A Sphinx with woman breast and lion paw,

A Buddha, hand at rest,
Hand lifted up that blest;

And right between these two a girl at play
That, it may be, had danced her life away,
For now being dead it seemed
That she of dancing dreamed.

Although I saw it all in the mind's eye
There can be nothing solider till I die;
I saw by the moon's light
Now at its fifteenth night.

One lashed her tail; her eyes lit by the moon
Gazed upon all things known, all things unknown,
In triumph of intellect
With motionless head erect.

That other's moonlit eyeballs never moved,
Being fixed on all things loved, all things unloved,
Yet little peace he had,
For those that love are sad.

O little did they care who danced between,
And little she by whom her dance was seen
So she had outdanced thought.
Body perfection brought,

For what but eye and ear silence the mind
With the minute particulars of mankind?
Mind moved yet seemed to stop
As 'twere a spinning-top.

In contemplation had whose three so wrought
Upon a moment, and so stretched it out
That they, time overthrown,
Were dead yet flesh and bone.

III

I knew that I had seen, had seen at last
That girl my unremembering nights hold fast
Or else my dreams that fly
If I should rub an eye,

And yet in flying fling into my meat
A crazy juice that makes the pulses beat
As though I had been undone
By Homer's Paragon

Who never gave the burning town a thought;
To such a pitch of folly I am brought,
Being caught between the pull
Of the dark moon and the full,

The commonness of thought and images
That have the frenzy of our western seas.
Thereon I made my moan,
And kissed a stone,

And after that arranged it in a song
Seeing that I, ignorant for so long,
Had been rewarded thus
In Cormac's ruined house.

THE TRAGIC GENERATION

By W. B. YEATS

[From *The Trembling of the Veil*]

1

Two or three years after our return to Bedford Park *A Doll's House* had been played at the Royalty Theatre in Dean Street, the first Ibsen play to be played in England, and somebody had given me a seat for the gallery. In the middle of the first act while the heroine was asking for macaroons, a middle-aged washerwoman who sat in front of me, stood up and said to the little boy at her side, "Tommy, if you promise to go home straight, we will go now"; and at the end of the play, as I wandered through the entrance hall, I heard an elderly critic murmur, "A series of conversations terminated by an accident." I was divided in mind, I hated the play; what was it but Carolus Duran, Bastien-Lepage, Huxley and Tyndall all over again; I resented being invited to admire dialogue so close to modern educated speech that music and style were impossible.

"Art is art because it is not nature," I kept repeating to myself, but how could I take the same side with critic and washerwoman? As time passed Ibsen became in my eyes the chosen author of very clever young journalists, who, condemned to their treadmill of abstraction, hated music and style; and yet neither I nor my generation could escape him because, though we and he had not the same friends, we had the same enemies. I bought his collected works in Mr. Archer's translation out of my thirty shillings a week and carried them to and fro upon my journeys to Ireland and Sligo, and Florence Farr, who had but one great gift, the most perfect poetical elocution, became prominent as an Ibsen actress and had almost a success in *Rosmersholm*, where there is symbolism and a stale odor of spilt poetry. She and I and half our friends found ourselves involved in a quarrel with the supporters of old-fashioned melodrama, and conventional romance, in the support of the new dramatists who wrote in what the Daily Press chose to consider the manner of Ibsen. In 1894 she became manageress of the Avenue Theatre with a play of Dr. Todhunter's, called *The Comedy of Sighs,* and Mr. Bernard Shaw's *Arms and the Man.* She asked me to write a one-act play that her niece, Miss Dorothy Paget, a girl of eight or nine, might make her first stage appearance, and I, with my Irish Theatre in mind, wrote *The Land of Heart's Desire,* in some discomfort when the child was theme, for I knew nothing of children, but with an abundant mind when Mary Bruin was, for I knew an Irish woman whose unrest troubled me. When Florence Farr opened her theater she had to meet a hostile audience, almost as violent as that Synge met in

[317]

January 1907, and certainly more brutal, for the Abbey audience had no hatred for the players, and I think but little for Synge himself. Nor had she the certainty of final victory to give her courage. For *The Comedy of Sighs* was a rambling story told with a little paradoxical wit. She had brought the trouble upon herself perhaps, for always in revolt against her own poetical gift, which now seemed obsolete, and against her own Demeter-like face in the mirror, she had tried when interviewed by the Press to shock and startle; and yet, unsure of her own judgment being out of her own trade, had feared to begin with Shaw's athletic wit; and now outraged convention saw its chance. For two hours and a half, pit and gallery drowned the voices of the players with boos and jeers that were meant to be bitter to the author who sat visible to all in his box surrounded by his family, and to the actress struggling bravely through her weary part; and then pit and gallery went home to spread their lying story that the actress had a fit of hysterics in her dressing-room.

Todhunter had sat on to the end, and there were, I think, four acts of it, listening to the howling of his enemies, while his friends slipped out one by one, till one saw everywhere their empty seats, but nothing could arouse the fighting instincts of that melancholy man. Next day I tried to get him to publish his book of words with satirical designs and illustrations, by Beardsley, who was just rising into fame, and an introduction attacking the public, but though petulant and irascible he was incapable of any emotion that could give life to a cause. He shared the superstition still current in the theater, that the public wants sincere drama, but is kept from it by some conspiracy of managers or newspapers, and could not get out of his head that the actors were to blame. Shaw, whose turn came next, had foreseen all months be-

fore, and had planned an opening that would confound his enemies. For the first few minutes *Arms and the Man* is crude melodrama and then just when the audience are thinking how crude it is, it turns into excellent farce. At the dress rehearsal, a dramatist who had his own quarrel with the public, was taken in the noose; at the first laugh he stood up, turned his back on the stage, scowled at the audience, and even when everybody else knew what turn the play had taken, continued to scowl, and order those nearest to be silent.

On the first night the whole pit and gallery, except certain members of the Fabian Society, started to laugh at the author and then, discovering that they themselves were being laughed at, sat there not converted—their hatred was too bitter for that—but dumbfounded, while the rest of the house cheered and laughed. In the silence that greeted the author after the cry for a speech one man did indeed get his courage and boo loudly. "I assure the gentleman in the gallery," was Shaw's answer, "that he and I are of exactly the same opinion, but what can we do against a whole house who are of the contrary opinion?" And from that moment Bernard Shaw became the most formidable man in modern letters, and even the most drunken of medical students knew it. My own play, which had been played with *The Comedy of Sighs,* had roused no passions, but had pleased a sufficient minority for Florence Farr to keep it upon the stage with *Arms and the Man,* and I was in the theater almost every night for some weeks. "Oh yes, the people seem to like *Arms and the Man,*" said one of Mr. Shaw's players to me, "but we have just found out that we are all wrong. Mr. Shaw did really mean it quite seriously, for he has written a letter to say so, and we must not play for laughs any more." Another night I found the manager, triumphant and excited, the Prince of Wales and the Duke of Edinburgh had been there, and the Duke of Edinburgh had spoken his dislike out loud so that the whole stalls could hear, but the Prince of Wales had been "very pleasant" and "got the Duke of Edinburgh away as soon as possible." "They asked for me," he went on, "and the Duke of Edinburgh kept on repeating, 'The man is mad,' meaning Mr. Shaw, and the Prince of Wales asked who Mr. Shaw was, and what he meant by it." I myself was almost as bewildered for though I came mainly to see how my own play went, and for the first fortnight to vex my most patient actors with new lines, I listened to *Arms and the Man* with admiration and hatred. It seemed to me inorganic, logical straightness and not the crooked road of life, yet I stood aghast before its energy as today before that of the Stone Drill by Mr. Epstein or of some design by Mr. Wyndham Lewis. He was right to claim Samuel Butler for his master, for Butler was the first Englishman to make the discovery, that it is possible to write with great effect without music, without style, either good or bad, to eliminate from the mind all emotional implication and to prefer plain water to every vintage, so much metropolitan lead and solder to any tendril of the vine. Presently I had a nightmare that I was haunted by a sewing machine, that clicked and shone, but the incredible thing was that the machine smiled, smiled perpetually. Yet I delighted in Shaw the formidable man. He could hit my enemies and the enemies of all I loved, as I could never hit, as no living author that was dear to me could ever hit.

Florence Farr's way home was mine also for a part of the way, and it was often of this that we talked, and sometimes, though not always, she would share my hesitations, and for years to come I was to wonder whenever Shaw became my topic, whether the cock crowed for my blame or for my praise.

2

Shaw and Wilde, had no catastrophe come, would have long divided the stage between them, though they were most unlike—for Wilde believed himself to value nothing but words in their emotional associations, and he had turned his style to a parade as though it were his show, and he Lord Mayor.

I was at Sligo again and I saw the announcement of his action against Lord Queensberry, when starting from my uncle's home to walk to Knocknarea to dine with Cochrane of the Glen, as he was called, to distinguish him from others of that name, an able old man. He had a relation, a poor mad girl, who shared our meals, and at whom I shuddered. She would take a flower from the vase in front of her and push it along the tablecloth towards any male guest who sat near. The old man himself had strange opinions, born not from any mental eccentricity, but from the solitude of his life; and a freedom from all prejudices that were not of his own discovery. "The world is getting more manly," he would say, "it has begun to drink port again," or "Ireland is going to become prosperous. Divorced couples now choose Ireland for a retreat, just as before Scotland became prosperous they began to go there. There are a divorced wife and her lover living at the other side of the mountain." I remember that I spoke that night of Wilde's kindness to myself, said I did not believe him guilty, quoted the psychologist Bain, who has attributed to every sensualist "a voluminous tenderness," and described Wilde's hard brilliance, his dominating self-possession. I considered him essentially a man of action, that he was a writer by perversity and accident, and would have been more important as soldier or politician; and I was certain that, guilty or not guilty, he would prove himself a man. I was probably excited, and did most of the talking, for if Cochrane had talked, I would have remembered an amusing sentence or two; but he was certainly sympathetic. A couple of days later I received a letter from Lionel Johnson, denouncing Wilde with great bitterness. He had "a cold scientific intellect"; he got a "sense of triumph and power, at every dinner-table he dominated, from the knowledge that he was guilty of that sin which, more than any other possible to man, would turn all those people against him if they but knew." He wrote in the mood of his poem, *To the Destroyer of a Soul,* addressed to Wilde, as I have always believed, though I know nothing of the circumstance that made him write it.

I might have known that Wilde's fantasy had taken some tragic turn, and that he was meditating upon possible disaster, but one took all his words for play—had he not called insincerity "a mere multiplication of the personality" or some such words? I had met a man who had found him in a barber's shop in Venice, and heard him explain, "I am having my hair curled that I may resemble Nero"; and when, as editor of an Irish anthology, I had asked leave to quote "Tread gently, she is near under the snow," he had written that I might do so if I pleased, but his most characteristic poem was that sonnet with the lines

> Lo! with a little rod
> I did but touch the honey's romance—
> And must I lose a soul's inheritance.

When in London for my play I had asked news from an actor who had seen him constantly. "He is in deep melancholy," was the answer. "He says that he tries to sleep away as much of life as possible, only leaving his bed at two or three in the afternoon, and spending the rest of the day at the Café Royal. He has written what he calls the best short story in the world, and will have it that he repeats to himself on getting out of bed and before every meal. 'Christ came from a white plain to a purple city, and as He passed through the first street, He heard voices overheard, and saw a young man lying drunk upon a window-sill, "Why do you waste your soul in drunkenness?" He said. "Lord, I was a leper and You healed me, what else can I do?" A little further through the town He saw a young man following a harlot, and said, "Why do you dissolve your soul in debauchery?" and the young man answered, "Lord, I was blind, and You healed me, what else can I do?" At last in the middle of the city He saw an old man crouching, weeping upon the ground, and when He asked why he wept, the old man answered, "Lord, I was dead and You raised me into life, what else can I do but weep?" ' "

Wilde published that story a little later, but spoiled it with the verbal decoration of his epoch, and I have to repeat it to myself as I first heard it, before I can see its terrible beauty. I no more doubt its sincerity than I doubt that his parade of gloom, all that late rising, and sleeping away his life, that elaborate playing with tragedy, was an attempt to escape from an emotion by its exaggeration. He had three successful plays running at once; he had been almost poor, and now, his head full of Flaubert, found himself with ten thousand a year:—"Lord, I was dead, and You raised me into life, what else can I do but weep." A comedian, he was in the hands of those dramatists who understand nothing but tragedy.

A few days after the first production of my *Land of Heart's Desire,* I had my last conversation with him. He had come into the theater as the curtain fell upon my play, and I knew that it was to ask my pardon that he overwhelmed me with compliments; and yet I wonder if he would have chosen those precise compliments, or spoken so extravagantly, but for the turn his thoughts had taken: "Your story in *The National Observer, The Crucifixion of the Outcast,* is sublime, wonderful, wonderful."

Some business or other brought me to London once more and I asked various Irish writers for letters of sympathy, and I was refused by none but Edward Dowden, who gave me what I considered an irrelevant excuse—his dislike for everything that Wilde had written. I heard that Wilde was at his mother's house in Oakley Street, and I called there, but the Irish servant said, her face drawn and tragic as in the presence of death, that he was not there, but that I could see his brother. Willie Wilde received me with, "Who are you; what do you want?" but became all friendship when I told him that I had brought letters of sympathy. He took the bundle of letters in his hand, but said, "Do these letters urge him to run away? Every friend he has is urging him to, but we have made up our minds that he must stay and take his chance." "No," I said, "I certainly do not think that he should run away, nor do those letters advise it." "Letters from Ireland," he said. "Thank you, thank you. He will be glad to get those letters, but I would keep them from him if they advised him to run away." Then he threw himself back in his chair and began to talk with incoherent emotion, and in phrases that echoed now and again his brother's style at its worst; there were tears in his eyes, and he was, I think, slightly intoxicated. "He could escape, oh, yes, he could escape—there is a yacht in the Thames, and five thousand pounds to pay his bail—well not exactly in the Thames, but there is a yacht—oh, yes, he could escape, even if I had to inflate a balloon in the back-yard with my own hand, but he has resolved to stay, to face it out, to stand the music like Christ. You must have heard—it is not necessary to go into detail—that he and I have not been friends; but he came to me like a wounded stag, and I took him in." "After his release"—after he had been bailed out I suppose—"Stewart Headlam engaged a room at an hotel and brought him there under another name, but the manager came up and said, 'Are you Mr. Wilde?' You know what my brother is, you know how he would answer that. He said, 'Yes, I am Oscar Wilde,' and the manager said he must not stay. The same thing happened in hotel after hotel, and at last he made up his mind to come here. It is his vanity that has brought all this disgrace upon him; they swung incense before him." He dwelt upon the rhythm of the words as his brother would have done—"They swung it before his heart." His first emotion at the thought of the letters over, he became more simple, and explained that his brother considered that his crime was not the vice itself, but that he should have brought such misery upon his wife and children, and that he was bound to accept any chance, however slight, to re-establish his position. "If he is acquitted," he said, "he will stay out of England for a few years, and can then gather his friends about him once more —even if he is condemned he will purge his offense—but if he runs away he will lose every friend that he has." I heard later, from whom I forget now, that Lady Wilde had said, "If you stay, even if you go to prison, you will always be my son, it will make no difference to my affection, but if you go, I will never speak to you again." While I was there, some woman who had just seen him— Willie Wilde's wife, I think—came in, and threw herself in a chair, and said in an exhausted voice, "It is all right now, he has made up his mind to go to prison if necessary." Before his release, two years later, his brother and mother were dead, and a little later his wife, struck by paralysis during his imprisonment, I think, was dead, too; and he himself, his constitution ruined by prison life, followed quickly; but I have never doubted, even for an instant, that he made the right decision, and that he owes to that decision half of his renown.

Cultivated London, that before the action against Lord Queensberry had mocked his pose and his affected style, and refused to acknowledge his wit, was now full of his advocates, though I did not meet a single man who considered him innocent. One old enemy of his overtook me in the street and began to praise his audacity, his self-possession. "He has made," he said, "of infamy a new Thermopylæ." I had written in reply to Lionel Johnson's letter that I regretted Wilde's downfall but not that of his imitators, but Johnson had changed with the rest. "Why do you not regret the fall of Wilde's imitators"—I had but tried to share what I thought his opinion—"They were worthless, but should have been left to criticism." Wilde himself was a martyr in his eyes, and when I said that tragedy might give his art a greater depth, he would not even grant a martyr's enemies that poor merit, and thought Wilde would produce, when it was all over, some comedy exactly like the others, writing from an art where events could leave no trace. Everywhere one met writers and artists who praised his wit and eloquence in the witness-box, or repeated some private saying. Willie Redmond told of finding him, to his astonishment, at the conversazione of some theatrical society, standing amid an infuriated crowd, mocking with more than all his old satirical wit the actors and their country. He had said to a well-known

painter during one or other of the trials, "My poor brother writes to me that he is defending me all over London; my poor, dear brother, he could compromise a steam engine." His brother, too, had suffered a change, for, if rumor did not wrong him, "the wounded stag" had not been at all graciously received. "Thank God my vices were decent," had been his comment, and refusing to sit at the same table, he had dined at some neighboring hotel at his brother's expense. His successful brother who had scorned him for a drunken ne'er-do-well was now at his mercy, and besides, he probably shared, until tragedy awoke another self, the rage and contempt that filled the crowds in the street, and all men and women who had an overabundant normal sexual instinct. "Wilde will never lift his head again," said the art critic, Gleeson White, "for he has against him all men of infamous life." When the verdict was announced the harlots in the street outside danced upon the pavement.

3

Somewhere about 1450, though later in some parts of Europe by a hundred years or so, and in some earlier, men attained to personality in great numbers, "Unity of Being," and became like a "perfectly proportioned human body," and as men so fashioned held places of power, their nations had it too, prince and plowman sharing that thought and feeling. What afterwards showed for rifts and cracks were there already, but imperious impulse held all together. Then the scattering came, the seeding of the poppy, bursting of pea-pod, and for a time personality seemed but the stronger for it. Shakespeare's people make all things serve their passion, and that passion is for the moment the whole energy of their being—birds, beasts, men, women, landscape, society, are but symbols, and metaphors, nothing is studied in itself, the mind is a dark well, no surface, depth only. The men that Titian painted, the men that Jongsen painted, even the men of Van Dyck, seemed at moments like great hawks at rest. In the Dublin National Gallery there hung, perhaps there still hang, upon the same wall, a portrait of some Venetian gentleman by Strozzi and Mr. Sargent's painting of President Wilson. Whatever thought broods in the dark eyes of that Venetian gentleman, has drawn its life from his whole body; it feeds upon it as the flame feeds upon the candle—and should that thought be changed, his pose would change, his very cloak would rustle for his whole body thinks. President Wilson lives only in the eyes, which are steady and intent; the flesh about the mouth is dead, and the hands are dead, and the clothes suggest no movement of his body, nor any movement but that of the valet, who has brushed and folded in mechanical routine. There, all was an energy flowing outward from the nature itself; here, all is the anxious study and slight deflection of external force; there man's mind and body were predominantly subjective; here all is objective, using those words not as philosophy uses them, but as we use them in conversation.

The bright part of the moon's disk, to adopt the symbolism of a certain poem, is subjective mind, and the dark, objective mind, and we have eight and twenty Phases for our classification of mankind, and of the movement of its thought. At the first Phase—the night where there is no moonlight—all is objective, while when, upon the fifteenth night, the moon comes to the full, there is only subjective mind. The mid-renaissance could but approximate to the full moon "For there's no human life at the full or the dark," but we may attribute to the next three nights of the moon the men of Shakespeare, of Titian, of Strozzi, and of Van Dyck, and watch them grow more reasonable, more orderly, less turbulent, as the nights pass; and it is well to find before the fourth—the nineteenth moon counting from the start—a sudden change, as when a cloud becomes rain, or water freezes, for the great transitions are sudden; popular, typical men have grown more ugly and more argumentative; the face that Van Dyck called a fatal face has faded before Cromwell's warty opinionated head. Henceforth no mind made like "a perfectly proportioned human body" shall sway the public, for great men must live in a portion of themselves, become professional and abstract; but seeing that the moon's third quarter is scarce passed; that abstraction has attained but not passed its climax; that a half, as I affirm it, of the twenty-second night still lingers, they may subdue and conquer, cherish even some Utopian dream, spread abstraction ever further till thought is but a film, and there is no dark depth any more, surface only. But men who belong by nature to the nights near to the full are still born, a tragic minority, and how shall they do their work when too ambitious for a private station, except as Wilde of the nineteenth Phase, as my symbolism has it, did his work? He understood his weakness, true personality was impossible, for that is born in solitude, and at his moon one is not solitary; he must project himself before the eyes of others, and, having great ambition, before some great crowd of eyes; but there is no longer any great crowd that cares for his true thought. He must humor and cajole and pose, take wornout stage situations, for he knows that he may be as romantic as he please, so long as he does not believe in his romance, and all that he may get their ears for a few strokes of contemptuous wit in which he does believe.

We Rhymers did not humor and cajole; but it was not wholly from demerit, it was in part because of different merit, that he refused our exile. Shaw, as I understand him, has no true quarrel with his time, its moon and his almost exactly coincide. He is quite content to exchange Narcissus and his Pool for the signalbox at a railway junction, where goods and travelers pass perpetually upon their logical glittering road. Wilde was a monarchist, though content that monarchy should turn demagogue for its own safety, and he held a theater by the means whereby he held a London dinnertable. "He who can dominate a London dinner-table," he had boasted, "can dominate the world." While Shaw has but carried his street-corner socialist eloquence on to the stage, and in him one discovers, in his writing and his public speech, as once—before their outline had been softened by prosperity or the passage of the years—in his clothes and in his stiff joints, the civilization that Sargent's picture has explored. Neither his crowd nor he have yet made a discovery that brought President Wilson so near his death, that the moon draws to its fourth quarter. But what happens to the individual man whose moon has come to that fourth quarter, and what to the civilization . . . ?

I can but remember pipe music tonight, though I can half hear beyond it in the memory a weightier music, but this much at any rate is certain—the dream of my early manhood, that a modern nation can return to Unity of Culture, is false; though it may be we can achieve it for some small circle of men and women, and there leave it till the moon bring round its century.

> The cat went here and there
> And the moon spun round like a top,
> And the nearest kin of the moon
> The creeping cat looked up.
>
> .   .   .   .   .   .

Minnaloushe creeps through the grass
From moonlit place to place;
The sacred moon overhead
Has taken a new phase.

Does Minnaloushe know that his pupils
Will pass from change to change,
And that from round to crescent
From crescent to round they range?
Minnaloushe creeps through the grass
Alone, important and wise,
And lifts to the changing moon
His changing eyes.

4

Henley's troubles and infirmities were growing upon him. He, too, an ambitious, formidable man, who showed alike in his practice and in his theory—in his lack of sympathy for Rossetti and Landor, for instance—that he never understood how small a fragment of our own nature can be brought to perfect expression, nor that even but with great toil, in a much divided civilization; though, doubtless, if our own Phase be right, a fragment may be an image of the whole, the moon's still scarce crumbled image, as it were, in a glass of wine. He would be, and have all poets be, a true epitome of the whole mass, a Herrick and Dr. Johnson in the same body and because this—not so difficult before the Mermaid closed its door—is no longer possible, his work lacks music, is abstract, as even an actor's movement can be when the thought of doing is plainer to his mind than the doing itself: the straight line from cup to lip, let us say, more plain than the hand's own sensation weighed down by that heavy spillable cup. I think he was content, when he had called before our eyes—before the too understanding eyes of his chosen crowd—the violent burly man that he had dreamed, content with the mere suggestion, and so did not work long enough at his verses.

He disliked Victor Hugo as much as he did Rossetti, and yet Rossetti's translation from *Les Burgraves,* because of its mere technical mastery, out-sings Henley in his own song—

My mother is dead; God's patience wears;
It seems my Chaplain will not have done.
      Love on: who cares?
      Who cares? Love on.

I can read his poetry with emotion, but I read it for some glimpse of what he might have been as Border balladist, or Cavalier, or of what he actually was, not as poet but as man. He had what Wilde lacked, even in his ruin, passion, was maybe as passionate as some great man of action, as Parnell, let us say. When he and Stevenson quarreled, he cried over it with some woman or other, and his notorious article was but for vengeance upon Mrs. Stevenson, who had arranged for the public eye, what he considered an imaginary figure, with no resemblance to the gay companion who had founded his life, to that life's injury, upon "The august, the immortal musketeers." She had caused the quarrel, as he believed, and now she had robbed him over again, by blotting from the world's memory the friend of his youth; and because he believed in the robbery I read those angry exaggerated paragraphs with deep sympathy; and I think that the man who has left them out of Henley's collected writings has wronged his memory, as Mrs. Stevenson may have wronged that of Stevenson.

He was no contemplative man, no pleased possessor of wooden models, and paper patterns, but a great passionate man, and no friend of his would have him pictured otherwise. I saw little of him in later years, but I doubt if he was ever the same after the death of his six-year-old daughter. Few passages of his verse touch me as do those few mentions of her though they lack precision of word

and sound. When she is but a hope, he prays that she may have his "gift of life" and his wife's "gift of love," and when she is but a few months old he murmurs over her sleep—

    When you wake in your crib,
    You an inch of experience—
    Vaulted about
    With the wonder of darkness;
    Wailing and striving
    To reach from your feebleness
    Something you feel
    Will be good to and cherish you.

And now he commends some friend "boyish and kind, and shy," who greeted him, and greeted his wife, "that day we brought our beautiful one to lie in the green peace" and who is now dead himself; and after that he speaks of love "turned by death to longing" and so, to an enemy.

When I spoke to him of his child's death he said, "she was a person of genius; she had the genius of the mind, and the genius of the body." And later I heard him talk of her as a man talks of something he cannot keep silence over because it is in all his thoughts. I can remember, too, his talking of some book of natural history he had read, that he might be able to answer her questions.

He had a house now at Mortlake on the Thames with a great ivy tod shadowing door and window, and one night there he shocked and startled a roomful of men by showing that he could be swept beyond our reach in reveries of affection. The dull man, who had tried to put Wilde out of countenance, suddenly said to the whole room, roused by I cannot remember what incautious remark meant for the man at my side: "Yeats believes in magic; what nonsense." Henley said, "No, it may not be nonsense; black magic is all the go in Paris now." And then turning towards me with a changed sound in his voice, "It is just a game, isn't it?" I replied, not noticing till too late his serious tone, and wishing to avoid discussion in the dull man's company, "One has had a vision; one wants to have another, that is all." Then Henley said, speaking in a very low voice, "I want to know how I am to get to my daughter. I was sitting here the other night when she came into the room and played round the table and went out again. Then I saw that the door was shut and I knew that I had seen a vision." There was an embarrassed silence, and then somebody spoke of something else and we began to discuss it hurriedly and eagerly.

5

I came now to be more in London, never missing the meetings of the Rhymers' Club, nor those of the council of the Irish Literary Society, where I constantly fought out our Irish quarrels and pressed upon the unwilling Gavan Duffy the books of our new movement. The Irish members of Parliament looked upon us with some hostility because we had made it a matter of principle never to put a politician in the chair, and upon other grounds. One day, some old Irish member of Parliament made perhaps his only appearance at a gathering of members. He recited with great emotion a ballad of his own composition in the manner of Young Ireland, repeating over his sacred names, Wolfe Tone, Emmet, and Owen Roe, and mourning that new poets and new movements should have taken something of their sacredness away. The ballad had no literary merit, but I went home with a troubled conscience; and for a dozen years perhaps, till I began to see the result of our work in a deepened perception of all those things that strengthen race, that trouble remained. I had in mind that old politician as I wrote but the other day—

Our part
To murmur name upon name
As a mother names her child.

The Rhymers had begun to break up in tragedy, though we did not know that till the play had finished. I have never found a full explanation of that tragedy; sometimes I have remembered that, unlike the Victorian poets, almost all were poor men, and had made it a matter of conscience to turn from every kind of money-making that prevented good writing, and that poverty meant strain, and for the most part, a refusal of domestic life. Then I have remembered that Johnson had private means, and that others who came to tragic ends had wives and families. Another day I think that perhaps our form of lyric, our insistence upon emotion which has no relation to any public interest, gathered together, overwrought, unstable men; and remember, the moment after, that the first to go out of his mind had no lyrical gift, and that we valued him mainly because he seemed a witty man of the world; and that a little later another who seemed, alike as man and writer, dull and formless, went out of his mind, first burning poems which I cannot believe would have proved him as the one man who saw them claims, a man of genius. The meetings were always decorous and often dull; some one would read out a poem and we would comment, too politely for the criticism to have great value; and yet that we read out our poems, and thought that they could be so tested, was a definition of our aims. *Love's Nocturne* is one of the most beautiful poems in the world, but no one can find out its beauty, so intricate its thought and metaphor, till he has read it over several times, or stopped several times to re-read a passage, and the *Faustine* of Swinburne, where much is powerful and musical, could not, were it read out, be understood with pleasure, however clearly it were read, because it has no more logical structure than a bag of shot. I shall, however, remember all my life that evening when Lionel Johnson read or spoke aloud in his musical monotone, where meaning and cadence found the most precise elocution, his poem suggested "by the Statue of King Charles at Charing Cross." It was as though I listened to a great speech. Nor will that poem be to me again what it was that first night. For long I only knew Dowson's *O Mors,* to quote but the first words of its long title, and his *Villanelle of Sunset* from his reading, and it was because of the desire to hold them in my hand that I suggested the first *Book of The Rhymers' Club.* They were not speech but perfect song, though song for the speaking voice. It was perhaps our delight in poetry that was, before all else, speech or song, and could hold the attention of a fitting audience like a good play or good conversation, that made Francis Thompson, whom we admired so much —before the publication of his first poem I had brought to The Cheshire Cheese the proof sheets of his *Ode to the Setting Sun,* his first published poem—come but once and refuse to contribute to our book. Preoccupied with his elaborate verse, he may have seen only that which we renounced, and thought what seemed to us simplicity, mere emptiness. To some members this simplicity was perhaps created by their tumultuous lives, they praised a desired woman and hoped that she would find amid their praise her very self, or at worst, their very passion; and knew that she, ignoramus that she was, would have slept in the middle of *Love's Nocturne,* lofty and tender though it be. Woman herself was still in our eyes, for all that, romantic and mysterious, still the priestess of her shrine, our emotions remembering the *Lilith* and the *Sybilla Palmifera* of Rossetti; for as yet that sense of comedy, which was soon to mold the very fashion plates, and, in the

eyes of men of my generation, to destroy at last the sense of beauty itself, had scarce begun to show here and there, in slight subordinate touches among the designs of great painters and craftsmen. It could not be otherwise, for Johnson's favorite phrase, that life is ritual, expressed something that was in some degree in all our thoughts, and how could life be ritual if woman had not her symbolical place?

If Rossetti was a subconscious influence, and perhaps the most powerful of all, we looked consciously to Pater for our philosophy. Three or four years ago I re-read *Marius the Epicurean,* expecting to find I cared for it no longer, but it still seemed to me, as I think it seemed to us all, the only great prose in modern English, and yet I began to wonder if it, or the attitude of mind of which it was the noblest expression, had not caused the disaster of my friends. It taught us to walk upon a rope, tightly stretched through serene air, and we were left to keep our feet upon a swaying rope in a storm. Pater had made us learned; and, whatever we might be elsewhere, ceremonious and polite, and distant in our relations to one another, and I think none knew as yet that Dowson, who seemed to drink so little and had so much dignity and reserve, was breaking his heart for the daughter of the keeper of an Italian eating house, in dissipation and drink; and that he might that very night sleep upon a six-penny bed in a doss house. It seems to me that even yet, and I am speaking of 1894 and 1895, we knew nothing of one another, but the poems that we read and criticized; perhaps I have forgotten or was too much in Ireland for knowledge, but of this I am certain, we shared nothing but the artistic life. Sometimes Johnson and Symons would visit our sage at Oxford, and I remember Johnson, whose reports however were not always to be trusted, returning with a sentence that long ran in my head. He had noticed books on political economy among Pater's books, and Pater had said, "Everything that has occupied man, for any length of time, is worthy of our study." Perhaps it was because of Pater's influence that we with an affectation of learning, claimed the whole past of literature for our authority, instead of finding it like the young men in the age of comedy that followed us, in some new, and so still unrefuted authority; that we preferred what seemed still uncrumbled rock, to the still unspotted foam; that we were traditional alike in our dress, in our manner, in our opinions, and in our style.

Why should men, who spoke their opinions in low voices, as though they feared to disturb the readers in some ancient library, and timidly as though they knew that all subjects had long since been explored, all questions long since decided in books whereon the dust settled —live lives of such disorder and seek to rediscover in verse the syntax of impulsive common life? Was it that we lived in what is called "an age of transition" and so lacked coherence, or did we but pursue antithesis?

6

All things, apart from love and melancholy, were a study to us; Horne already learned in Botticelli had begun to boast that when he wrote of him there would be no literature, all would be but learning; Symons, as I wrote when I first met him, studied the music halls, as he might have studied the age of Chaucer; while I gave much time to what is called the Christian Cabbala; nor was there any branch of knowledge Johnson did not claim for his own. When I had first gone to see him in 1888 or 1889, at the Charlotte Street house, I had called about five in the afternoon, but the man-servant that he shared with Horne and Image, told me that he was not yet up, adding with effusion "he is always up for dinner at seven." This habit of breakfasting when others dined had been started by insomnia, but he came to defend it for its own sake. When I asked if it did not separate him from men and women he replied, "In my library I have all the knowledge of the world that I need." He had certainly a considerable library, far larger than that of any young man of my acquaintance, so large that he wondered if it might not be possible to find some way of hanging new shelves from the ceiling like chandeliers. That room was always a pleasure to me, with its curtains of gray corduroy over door and window and book case, and its walls covered with brown paper, a fashion invented, I think, by Horne, that was soon to spread. There was a portrait of Cardinal Newman, looking a little like Johnson himself, some religious pictures by Simeon Solomon, and works upon theology in Greek and Latin and a general air of neatness and severity; and talking there by candlelight it never seemed very difficult to murmur Villiers de L'Isle Adam's proud words, "As for living—our servants will do that for us." Yet I can now see that Johnson himself in some half-conscious part of him desired the world he had renounced. I was often puzzled as to when and where he could have met the famous men or beautiful women, whose conversation, often wise, and always appropriate, he quoted so often, and it was not till a little before his death that I discovered that these conversations were imaginary. He never altered a detail of speech, and would quote what he had invented for Gladstone or Newman for years without amplification or amendment, with what seemed a scholar's accuracy. His favorite quotations were from Newman, whom, I believe, he had

never met, though I can remember nothing now but Newman's greeting to Johnson, "I have always considered the profession of a man of letters a third order of the priesthood!" and these quotations became so well known that at Newman's death, the editor of *The Nineteenth Century* asked them for publication. Because of his delight in all that was formal and arranged he objected to the public quotation of private conversation even after death, and this scruple helped his refusal. Perhaps this dreaming was made a necessity by his artificial life, yet before that life began he wrote from Oxford to his Tory but flattered family, that as he stood mounted upon a library ladder in his rooms taking a book from a shelf, Gladstone, about to pass the open door on his way upstairs to some college authority, had stopped, hesitated, come into the room and there spent an hour of talk. Presently it was discovered that Gladstone had not been near Oxford on the date given; yet he quoted that conversation without variation of a word until the end of his life, and I think believed in it as firmly as did his friends. These conversations were always admirable in their drama, but never too dramatic or even too polished to lose their casual accidental character; they were the phantasmagoria through which his philosophy of life found its expression. If he made his knowledge of the world out of his fantasy, his knowledge of tongues and books was certainly very great; and yet was that knowledge as great as he would have us believe? Did he really know Welsh, for instance, had he really as he told me, made his only love song his incomparable *Morfydd* out of three lines in Welsh, heard sung by a woman at her door on a walking tour in Wales, or did he but wish to hide that he shared in their emotion?

> O, what are the winds?
> And what are the waters?
> Mine are your eyes.

He wanted us to believe that all things, his poetry with its Latin weight, his religion with its constant reference to the Fathers of the Church, or to the philosophers of the Church, almost his very courtesy were a study and achievement of the intellect. Arthur Symons' poetry made him angry, because it would substitute for that achievement, Parisian impressionism, "a London fog, the blurred tawny lamplight, the red omnibus, the dreary rain, the depressing mud, the glaring gin shop, the slatternly shivering women, three dexterous stanzas telling you that and nothing more." I, on the other hand, angered him by talking as if art existed for emotion only, and for refutation he would quote the close of the Aeschylean Trilogy, the trial of Orestes on the Acropolis. Yet at moments the thought came to him that intellect, as he conceived it, was too much a thing of many books, that it lacked lively experience. "Yeats," he has said to me, "you need ten years in a library, but I have need of ten years in the wilderness." When he said "Wilderness" I am certain, however, that he thought of some historical, some bookish desert, the Thebaid, or the lands about the Mareotic sea. Though his best poetry is natural and impassioned, he spoke little of it, but much about his prose, and would contend that I had no right to consider words made to read, less natural than words made to be spoken; and he delighted in a sentence in his book on Thomas Hardy, that kept its vitality, as he contended, though two pages long. He punctuated after the manner of the seventeenth century and was always ready to spend an hour discussing the exact use of the colon. "One should use a colon where other people use a semi-colon, a semi-colon where other people use a comma," was, I think, but a condescension to my ignorance for the matter was plainly beset with many subtleties.

7

Not till some time in 1895 did I think he could ever drink too much for his sobriety—though what he drank would certainly be too much for that of most of the men whom I knew—I no more doubted his self-control, though we were very intimate friends, than I doubted his memories of Cardinal Newman. The discovery that he did was a great shock to me, and, I think, altered my general view of the world. I had, by my friendship with O'Leary, by my fight against Gavan Duffy, drawn the attention of a group of men, who at that time controlled what remained of the old Fenian movement in England and Scotland; and at a moment when an attempt, that came to nothing, was being made to combine once more our constitutional and unconstitutional politics, I had been asked to represent this group at some convention in the United States. I went to consult Johnson, whom I found sitting at a table with books about him. I was greatly tempted, because I was promised complete freedom of speech; and I was at the time enraged by some wild articles published by some Irish American newspaper, suggesting the burning down of the houses of Irish landlords. Nine years later I was lecturing in America, and a charming old Irishman came to see me with an interview to write, and we spent, and as I think in entire neglect of his interview, one of the happiest hours I have ever spent, comparing our tales of the Irish fairies, in which he very firmly believed. When he had gone I looked at his card, to discover that he was the writer of that criminal incitement. I told Johnson that if I had a week to decide in I would probably decide to go, but as they had only given me three days, I had refused. He would not hear of my refusal with so much awaiting my condemnation; and

that condemnation would be effective with Catholics, for he would find me passages in the Fathers, condemning every kind of political crime, that of the dynamiter and the incendiary especially. I asked how could the Fathers have condemned weapons they had never heard of, but those weapons, he contended, were merely developments of old methods and weapons; they had decided all in principle; but I need not trouble myself about the matter, for he would put into my hands before I sailed the typewritten statement of their doctrine, dealing with the present situation in the utmost detail. He seemed perfectly logical, though a little more confident and impassioned than usual, and I had, I think, promised to accept—when he rose from his chair, took a step towards me in his eagerness, and fell on to the floor; and I saw that he was drunk. From that on, he began to lose control of his life; he shifted from Charlotte Street, where, I think, there was fear that he would overset lamp or candle and burn the house, to Gray's Inn, and from Gray's Inn to old rambling rooms in Lincoln's Inn Fields, and at last one called to find his outer door shut, the milk on the doorstep sour. Sometimes I would urge him to put himself, as Jack Nettleship had done, into an Institute. One day when I had been very urgent, he spoke of "a craving that made every atom of his body cry out" and said the moment after, "I do not want to be cured," and a moment after that, "In ten years I shall be penniless and shabby, and borrow half-crowns from friends." He seemed to contemplate a vision that gave him pleasure, and now that I look back, I remember that he once said to me that Wilde's pleasure and excitement were perhaps increased by the degradation of that group of beggars and blackmailers where he sought his pathics, and I remember, too, his smile at my surprise, as though he spoke of psychological depths I could never enter. Did the austerity, the melancholy of his thoughts, that spiritual ecstasy which he touched at times, heighten, as complementary colors heighten one another, not only the Vision of Evil, but its fascination? Was it only Villon, or did Dante also feel the fascination of evil, when shown in its horror, and, as it were, judged and lost; and what proud man does not feel temptation strengthened from the certainty that his intellect is not deceived?

8

I began now to hear stories of Dowson, whom I knew only at the Rhymers, or through some chance meeting at Johnson's. I was indolent and procrastinating, and when I thought of asking him to dine, or taking some other step towards better knowledge, he seemed to be in Paris, or at Dieppe. He was drinking, but, unlike Johnson, who, at the autopsy after his death, was discovered never to have grown, except in the brain, after his fifteenth year, he was full of sexual desire. Johnson and he were close friends, and Johnson lectured him out of the Fathers upon chastity, and boasted of the great good done him thereby. But the rest of us counted the glasses emptied in their talk. I began to hear now in some detail of the restaurant-keeper's daughter, and of her marriage to the waiter, and of that weekly game of cards with her that filled so great a share of Dowson's emotional life. Sober, he would look at no other woman, it was said, but drunk, desired whatever woman chance brought, clean or dirty.

Johnson was stern by nature, strong by intellect, and always, I think, deliberately picked his company, but Dowson seemed gentle, affectionate, drifting. His poetry shows how sincerely he felt the fascination of religion, but his religion had certainly no dogmatic outline, being but a desire for a condition of virginal ecstasy. If it is true, as Arthur Symons, his very close friend, has written, that he loved the restaurant-keeper's daughter for her youth, one may be almost certain that he sought from religion some similar quality, something of that which the angels find who move perpetually, as Swedenborg has said, towards "the day-spring of their youth." Johnson's poetry, like Johnson himself before his last decay, conveys an emotion of joy, of intellectual clearness, of hard energy; he gave us of his triumph; while Dowson's poetry is sad, as he himself seemed, and pictures his life of temptation and defeat,

> Unto us they belong
> Us the bitter and gay,
> Wine and women and song.

Their way of looking at their intoxication showed their characters. Johnson, who could not have written *Dark Angel* if he did not suffer from remorse, showed to his friends an impenitent face, and defeated me when I tried to prevent the foundation of an Irish convivial club—it was brought to an end after one meeting by the indignation of the members' wives —whereas the last time I saw Dowson he was pouring out a glass of whiskey for himself in an empty corner of my room and murmuring over and over in what seemed automatic apology "The first today."

9

Two men are always at my side, Lionel Johnson and John Synge whom I was to meet a little later; but Johnson is to me the more vivid in memory, possibly because of the external finish, the clearly-marked lineament of his body, which seemed but to express the clarity of his mind. I think Dowson's best verse immortal, bound, that is, to outlive famous novels and plays and learned histories and other discursive things, but he was too vague and gentle for my affections. I understood him too well, for I had been like him but for the appetite that made me search out strong condiments. Though I cannot explain what brought others of my generation to such misfortune, I think that (falling backward upon my parable of the moon) I can explain some part of Dowson's and Johnson's dissipation—

What portion in the world can the artist have,
Who has awaked from the common dream,
But dissipation and despair?

When Edmund Spenser described the islands of Phædria and of Acrasia he aroused the indignation of Lord Burleigh, "that rugged forehead" and Lord Burleigh was in the right if morality were our only object.

In those islands certain qualities of beauty, certain forms of sensuous loveliness were separated from all the general purposes of life, as they had not been hitherto in European literature—and would not be again, for even the historical process has its ebb and flow, till Keats wrote his *Endymion.* I think that the movement of our thought has more and more so separated certain images and regions of the mind, and that these images grow in beauty as they grow in sterility. Shakespeare leaned, as it were, even as craftsman, upon the general fate of men and nations, had about him the excitement of the playhouse; and all poets, including Spenser in all but a few pages, until our age came, and when it came almost all, have had some propaganda or traditional doctrine to give companionship with their fellows. Had not Matthew Arnold his faith in what he

described as the best thought of his generation? Browning his psychological curiosity, Tennyson, as before him Shelley and Wordsworth, moral values that were not æsthetic values? But Coleridge of the *Ancient Mariner,* and *Kubla Khan,* and Rossetti in all his writing made what Arnold has called that "morbid effort," that search for "perfection of thought and feeling, and to unite this to perfection of form," sought this new, pure beauty, and suffered in their lives because of it. The typical men of the classical age (I think of Commodus, with his half-animal beauty, his cruelty and his caprice), lived public lives, pursuing curiosities of appetite, and so found in Christianity, with its Thebaid and its Mareotic Sea the needed curb. But what can the Christian confessor say to those who more and more must make all out of the privacy of their thought, calling up perpetual images of desire, for he cannot say "Cease to be artist, cease to be poet," where the whole life is art and poetry, nor can he bid men leave the world, who suffer from the terrors that pass before shut-eyes. Coleridge, and Rossetti though his dull brother did once persuade him that he was an agnostic, were devout Christians, and Steinbock and Beardsley were so towards their lives' end, and Dowson and Johnson always, and yet I think it but deepened despair and multiplied temptation.

Dark Angel, with thine aching lust,
To rid the world of penitence:
Malicious angel, who still dost
My soul such subtil violence!

When music sounds, then changest thou
A silvery to a sultry fire:
Nor will thine envious heart allow
Delight untortured by desire.

Through thee, the gracious Muses turn
To Furies, O mine Enemy!
And all the things of beauty burn
With flames of evil ecstasy.

Because of thee, the land of dreams
Becomes a gathering place of fears:
Until tormented slumber seems
One vehemence of useless tears.

Why are these strange souls born everywhere today? with hearts that Christianity, as shaped by history, cannot satisfy. Our love letters wear out our love; no school of painting outlasts its founders, every stroke of the brush exhausts the impulse, pre-Raphaelitism had some twenty years; impressionism thirty perhaps. Why should we believe that religion can never bring round its antithesis? Is it true that our air is disturbed, as Mallarmé said, by "the trembling of the veil of the temple," or "that our whole age is seeking to bring forth a sacred book"? Some of us thought that book near towards the end of last century, but the tide sank again.

10

I do not know whether John Davidson, whose life also was tragic, made that "morbid effort," that search for "perfection of thought and feeling," for he is hidden behind failure, to unite it "to perfection of form." At eleven one morning I met him in the British Museum reading-room, probably in 1894, when I was in London for the production of *The Land of Heart's Desire*, but certainly after some long absence from London. "Are you working here?" I said; "No," he said, "I am loafing, for I have finished my day's work." "What, already?" "I work an hour a day—I cannot work longer without exhaustion, and even as it is, if I meet anybody and get into talk, I cannot write the next day; that is why I loaf when my work is finished." No one had ever doubted his industry; he had supported his wife and family for years by "deviling" many hours a day for some

popular novelist. "What work is it?" I said. "I am writing verse," he answered. "I had been writing prose for a long time, and then one day I thought I might just as well write what I liked, as I must starve in any case. It was the luckiest thought I ever had, for my agent now gets me forty pounds for a ballad, and I made three hundred out of my last book of verse."

He was older by ten years than his fellow Rhymers; a national schoolmaster from Scotland, he had been dismissed, he told us, for asking for a rise in his salary, and had come to London with his wife and children. He looked older than his years. "Ellis," he had said, "how old are you?" "Fifty," Edwin Ellis replied, or whatever his age was. "Then I will take off my wig. I never take off my wig when there is a man under thirty in the room." He had endured and was to endure again, a life of tragic penury, which was made much harder by the conviction that the world was against him, that he was refused for some reason his rightful position. Ellis thought that he pined even for social success, and I that his Scots jealousy kept him provincial and but half articulate.

During the quarrel over Parnell's grave a quotation from Goethe ran through the papers, describing our Irish jealousy: "The Irish seem to me like a pack of hounds, always dragging down some noble stag." But I do not think we object to distinction for its own sake; if we kill the stag, it is that we may carry off his head and antlers. "The Irish people," O'Leary used to say, "do not know good from bad in any art, but they do not hate the good once it is pointed out to them because it is good." An infallible Church, with its Mass in Latin, and its mediæval Philosophy, and our Protestant social prejudice, have kept our ablest men from leveling passions; but Davidson with a jealousy, which may be Scottish, seeing that Carlyle had it, was quick to discover sour grapes. He saw in delicate, laborious, discriminating taste, an effeminate pedantry, and would, when that mood was on him, delight in all that seemed healthy, popular, and bustling. Once when I had praised Herbert Horne for his knowledge and his taste, he burst out, "If a man must be a connoisseur, let him be a connoisseur in women." He, indeed, was accustomed, in the most characteristic phrase of his type, to describe the Rhymers as lacking in "blood and guts," and very nearly brought us to an end by attempting to supply the deficiency by the addition of four Scotsmen. He brought all four upon the same evening, and one read out a poem upon the Life Boat, evidently intended for a recitation; another described how, when gold-digging in Australia, he had fought and knocked down another miner for doubting the rotundity of the earth; while of the remainder I can remember nothing except that they excelled in argument. He insisted upon their immediate election, and the Rhymers, through that complacency of good manners whereby educated Englishmen so often surprise me, obeyed, though secretly resolved never to meet again; and it cost me seven hours' work to get another meeting, and vote the Scotsmen out. A few days later I chanced upon Davidson at some restaurant; he was full of amiability, and when we parted shook my hand, and proclaimed enthusiastically that I had "blood and guts." I think he might have grown to be a successful man had he been enthusiastic instead about Dowson or Johnson, or Horne or Symons, for they had what I still lacked, conscious deliberate craft, and what I must lack always, scholarship. They had taught me that violent energy, which is like a fire of straw, consumes in a few minutes the nervous vitality, and is useless in the arts. Our fire must burn slowly, and we must

constantly turn away to think, constantly analyze what we have done, be content even to have little life outside our work, to show, perhaps, to other men, as little as the watch-mender shows, his magnifying glass caught in his screwed-up eye. Only then do we learn to conserve our vitality, to keep our mind enough under control and to make our technique sufficiently flexible for expression of the emotions of life as they arise. A few months after our meeting in the Museum, Davidson had spent his inspiration. "The fires are out," he said, "and I must hammer the cold iron." When I heard a few years ago that he had drowned himself, I knew that I had always expected some such end. With enough passion to make a great poet, through meeting no man of culture in early life, he lacked intellectual receptivity, and, anarchic and indefinite, lacked pose and gesture, and now no verse of his clings to my memory.

11

Gradually Arthur Symons came to replace in my intimate friendship, Lionel Johnson from whom I was slowly separated by a scruple of conscience. If he came to see me he sat tongue-tied unless I gave him the drink that seemed necessary to bring his vitality to but its normal pitch, and if I called upon him he drank so much that I became his confederate. Once, when a friend and I had sat long after our proper bed-time at his constantly repeated and most earnest entreaty, knowing what black melancholy would descend upon him at our departure, and with the unexpressed hope of getting him to his bed, he fixed upon us a laughing and whimsical look, and said: —"I want you two men to understand that you are merely two men that I am drinking with." That was the only time that I was to hear from him an imaginary conversation that had not an air of the most scrupulous accuracy. He gave two accounts of a conversation with Wilde in prison; in one Wilde wore his hair long, and in the other it had been cropped by the prison barber. He was gradually losing, too, the faculty of experience, and in his prose and verse repeated the old ideas and emotions, but faintly, as though with fading interest. I am certain that he prayed much, and on those rare days that I came upon him dressed and active before mid-day or but little after, I concluded that he had been to morning Mass at Farm Street.

When with Johnson I had turned myself to his mood, but Arthur Symons, more than any man I have ever known, could slip as it were into the mind of another, and my thoughts gained in richness and in clearness from his sympathy, nor shall I ever know how much my practice and my theory owe to the passages that he read me from Catullus and from Verlaine and Mallarmé. I had read *Axel* to myself or was still reading it, so slowly, and with so much difficulty, that certain passages had an exaggerated importance, while all remained so obscure that I could without much effort imagine that here at last was the Sacred Book I longed for. An Irish friend of mine lives in a house where beside a little old tower rises a great new Gothic hall and stair, and I have sometimes got him to extinguish all light but a little Roman lamp, and in that faint light and among great vague shadows, blotting away the unmeaning ornament, have imagined myself partaking in some incredible romance. Half a dozen times, beginning in boyhood with Shelley's *Prometheus Unbound,* I have in that mood possessed for certain hours or months the book that I long for; and Symons, without ever being false to his own impressionist view of art and of life, deepened as I think my longing.

It seems to me, looking backward, that we always discussed life at its most intense moment, that moment which gives a common sacredness to the Song of Songs, and to the Sermon on the Mount, and in which one discovers something supernatural, a stirring as it were of the roots of the hair. He was making those translations from Mallarmé and from Verlaine, from Calderon, from St. John of the Cross, which are the most accomplished metrical translations of our time, and I think that those from Mallarmé may have given elaborate form to my verses of those years, to the later poems of *The Wind Among the Reeds,* to *The Shadowy Waters,* while Villiers de L'Isle Adam had shaped whatever in my *Rosa Alchemica* Pater had not shaped. I can remember the day in Fountain Court when he first read me Herodiade's address to some Sibyl who is her nurse and it may be the moon also:

The horror of my virginity
Delights me, and I would envelope me
In the terror of my tresses, that, by night,
Inviolate reptile, I might feel the white
And glimmering radiance of thy frozen fire,
Thou that are chaste and diest of desire,
White night of ice and of the cruel snow!
Eternal sister, my lone sister, lo
My dreams uplifted before thee! now, apart,
So rare a crystal is my dreaming heart,
And all about me lives but in mine own
Image, the idolatrous mirror of my pride,
Mirroring this Herodiade diamond-eyed.

Yet I am certain that there was something in myself compelling me to attempt creation of an art as separate from everything heterogeneous and casual, from all character and circumstance, as some Herodiade of our theater, dancing seemingly alone in her narrow moving luminous circle. Certainly I had gone a great distance from my first poems, from all that I had copied from the folk-art of Ireland, as from the statue of Mausolus and his Queen, where the luminous circle is motionless and contains the entire popular life; and yet why am I so certain? I can imagine an Aran Islander who had strayed into the Luxembourg Gallery, turning bewildered from Impressionist or Post-Impressionist, but lingering at Moreau's "Jason," to study in mute astonishment the elaborate background, where there are so many jewels, so much wrought stone and molded bronze. Had not lover promised mistress in his own island song, "A ship with a gold and silver mast, gloves of the skin of a fish, and shoes of the skin of a bird, and a suit of the dearest silk in Ireland?"

12

Hitherto when in London I had stayed with my family in Bedford Park, but now I was to live for some twelve months in chambers in the Temple that opened through a little passage into those of Arthur Symons. If anybody rang at either door, one or other would look through a window in the connecting passage, and report. We would then decide whether one or both should receive the visitor, whether his door or mine should be opened, or whether both doors were to remain closed. I have never liked London, but London seemed less disagreeable when one could walk in quiet, empty places after dark, and upon a Sunday morning sit upon the margin of a fountain almost as alone as if in the country. I was already settled there, I imagine, when a publisher called and proposed that Symons should edit a Review or Magazine, and Symons consented on the condition that Beardsley were Art Editor—and I was delighted at his condition, as I think were all his other proposed contributors. Aubrey Beardsley had been dismissed from the Art editorship of *The Yellow Book* under

circumstances that had made us indignant. He had illustrated Wilde's *Salome,* his strange satiric art had raised the popular press to fury, and at the height of the excitement aroused by Wilde's condemnation, a popular novelist, a woman who had great influence among the most conventional part of the British public, had written demanding his dismissal. "She owed it to her position before the British people," she had said. Beardsley was not even a friend of Wilde's—they even disliked each other—he had no sexual abnormality, but he was certainly unpopular, and the moment had come to get rid of unpopular persons. The public at once concluded—they could hardly conclude otherwise, he was dismissed by telegram—that there was evidence against him, and Beardsley, who was some twenty-three years old, being embittered and miserable, plunged into dissipation. We knew that we must face an infuriated press and public, but being all young we delighted in enemies and in everything that had an heroic air.

13

We might have survived but for our association with Beardsley; perhaps, but for his *Under the Hill,* a Rabelaisian fragment promising a literary genius as great maybe as his artistic genius; and for the refusal of the bookseller who controlled the railway bookstalls to display our wares. The bookseller's manager, no doubt looking for a design of Beardsley's, pitched upon Blake's *Anteus setting Virgil and Dante upon the verge of Cocytus* as the ground of refusal, and when Arthur Symons pointed out that Blake was considered "a very spiritual artist," replied, "O, Mr. Symons, you must remember that we have an audience of young ladies as well as an audience of agnostics." However, he called Arthur Symons back from the door to say, "If contrary to our expectations the *Savoy* should have a large sale, we should be very glad to see you again." As Blake's design illustrated an article of mine, I wrote a letter upon that remarkable saying to a principal daily newspaper. But I had mentioned Beardsley, and I was told that the editor had made it a rule that his paper was never to mention Beardsley's name. I said upon meeting him later, "Would you have made the same rule in the case of Hogarth?" against whom much the same objection could be taken, and he replied with what seemed to me a dreamy look, as though suddenly reminded of a lost opportunity—"Ah, there was no popular press in Hogarth's day." We were not allowed to forget that in our own day there was a popular press, and its opinions began to affect our casual acquaintance, and even our comfort in public places. At some well-known house, an elderly man to whom I had just been introduced, got up from my side and walked to the other end of the room; but it was as much my reputation as an Irish rebel as the evil company that I was supposed to keep, that excited some young men in a railway carriage to comment upon my general career in voices raised that they might catch my attention. I discovered, however, one evening that we were perhaps envied as well as despised. I was in the pit at some theater, and had just noticed Arthur Symons a little in front of me, when I heard a young man, who looked like a shop-assistant or clerk, say, "There is Arthur Symons. If he can't get an order, why can't he pay for a stall?" Clearly we were supposed to prosper upon iniquity, and to go to the pit added a sordid parsimony. At another theater I caught sight of a woman that I once liked, the widow of some friend of my father's youth, and tried to attract her attention,

but she had no eyes for anything but the stage curtain; and at some house where I met no hostility to myself, a popular novelist snatched out of my hand a copy of the *Savoy,* and opening it at Beardsley's drawing, called *The Barber,* expounded what he called its bad drawing and wound up with, "Now if you want to admire really great black and white art, admire the *Punch* cartoons of Mr. Lindley Sambourne." Our hostess, after making peace between us, said, "O, Mr. Yeats, why do you not send your poems to the *Spectator* instead of to the *Savoy?*" The answer, "My friends read the *Savoy* and they do not read the *Spectator,*" called up a puzzled, disapproving look.

Yet, even apart from Beardsley, we were a sufficiently distinguished body: Max Beerbohm, Bernard Shaw, Ernest Dowson, Lionel Johnson, Arthur Symons, Charles Conder, Charles Shannon, Havelock Ellis, Selwyn Image, Joseph Conrad; but nothing counted but the one hated name. I think that had we been challenged we might have argued something after this fashion: "Science through much ridicule and some persecution has won its right to explore whatever passes before its corporeal eye, and merely because it passes: to set as it were upon an equality the beetle and the whale though Ben Jonson could find no justification for the entomologist in *The New Inn,* but that he had been crossed in love. Literature now demands the same right of exploration of all that passes before the mind's eye, and merely because it passes." Not a complete defense, for it substitutes a spiritual for a physical objectivity, but sufficient it may be for the moment, and to settle our place in the historical process.

The critic might well reply that certain of my generation delighted in writing with an unscientific partiality for subjects long forbidden. Yet is it not most important to explore especially what has been long forbidden, and to do this not only "with the highest moral purpose," like the followers of Ibsen, but gaily, out of sheer mischief, or sheer delight in that play of the mind? Donne could be as metaphysical as he pleased, and yet never seemed unhuman and hysterical as Shelley often does, because he could be as physical as he pleased; and besides who will thirst for the metaphysical, who have a parched tongue, if we cannot recover the Vision of Evil?

I have felt in certain early works of my own which I have long abandoned, and here and there in the work of others of my generation, a slight, sentimental sensuality which is disagreeable, and does not exist in the work of Donne, let us say, because he, being permitted to say what he pleased, was never tempted to linger, or rather to pretend that we can linger, between spirit and sense. How often had I heard men of my time talk of the meeting of spirit and sense, yet there is no meeting but only change upon the instant, and it is by the perception of a change, like the sudden "blacking out" of the lights of the stage, that passion creates its most violent sensation.

14

Dowson was now at Dieppe, now at a Normandy village. Wilde, too, was at Dieppe; and Symons, Beardsley, and others would cross and recross, returning with many tales, and there were letters and telegrams. Dowson wrote a protest against some friend's too vivid essay upon the disorder of his life, and explained that in reality he was living a life of industry in a little country village; but before the letter arrived that friend received a wire, "arrested, sell watch and send proceeds." Dowson's watch had been left in London—and then another

wire, "Am free." Dowson, or so ran the tale as I heard it ten years after, had got drunk and fought the baker, and a deputation of villagers had gone to the magistrate and pointed out that Monsieur Dowson was one of the most illustrious of English poets. "Quite right to remind me," said the magistrate, "I will imprison the baker."

A Rhymer had seen Dowson at some café in Dieppe with a particularly common harlot, and as he passed, Dowson, who was half drunk, caught him by the sleeve and whispered, "She writes poetry—it is like Browning and Mrs. Browning." Then there came a wonderful tale, repeated by Dowson himself, whether by word of mouth or by letter I do not remember. Wilde had arrived in Dieppe, and Dowson pressed upon him the necessity of acquiring "a more wholesome taste." They emptied their pockets on to the café table, and though there was not much, there was enough if both heaps were put into one. Meanwhile the news had spread, and they set out accompanied by a cheering crowd. Arrived at their destination, Dowson and the crowd remained outside, and presently Wilde returned. He said in a low voice to Dowson, "The first these ten years, and it will be the last. It was like cold mutton" —always, as Henley had said, "a scholar and a gentleman" he now remembered that the Elizabethan dramatists used the words "Cold mutton"—and then aloud so that the crowd might hear him, "But tell it in England, for it will entirely restore my character."

15

When the first few numbers of the *Savoy* had been published, the contributors and the publisher gave themselves a supper, and Symons explained that certain among us were invited afterwards to the publisher's house, and if I went there that once I need never go again. I considered the publisher a scandalous person, and had refused to meet him; we were all agreed as to his character, and only differed as to the distance that should lie between him and us. I had just received two letters, one from T. W. Rolleston protesting with all the conventional moral earnestness of an article in the *Spectator* newspaper, against my writing for such a magazine; and one from A. E. denouncing with the intensity of a personal conviction that magazine, which he called the "Organ of the Incubi and the Succubi." I had forgotten that Arthur Symons had borrowed the letters until as we stood about the supper table waiting for the signal to be seated, I heard the infuriating voice of the publisher shouting, "Give me the letter, give me the letter, I will prosecute that man," and I saw Symons waving Rolleston's letter just out of reach. Then Symons folded it up and put it in his pocket, and began to read out A. E. and the publisher was silent, and I saw Beardsley listening. Presently Beardsley came to me and said, "Yeats, I am going to surprise you very much. I think your friend is right. All my life I have been fascinated by the spiritual life—when a child I saw a vision of a Bleeding Christ over the mantelpiece— but after all to do one's work when there are other things one wants to do so much more, is a kind of religion."

Something, I forget what, delayed me a few minutes after the supper was over, and when I arrived at our publisher's I found Beardsley propped up on a chair in the middle of the room, gray and exhausted, and as I came in he left the chair and went into another room to spit blood, but returned immediately. Our publisher, perspiration pouring from his face, was turning the handle of a hurdy gurdy piano—it worked by electricity, I was told, when the company did not cut off the supply—and very plainly had had enough of it, but Beardsley pressed him to labor on, "The tone is so beautiful," "It gives me such deep pleasure," etc., etc. It was his method of keeping our publisher at a distance.

Another image competes with that image in my memory. Beardsley has arrived at Fountain Court a little after breakfast with a young woman who belongs to our publisher's circle and certainly not to ours, and is called "twopence colored," or is it "penny plain." He is a little drunk and his mind has been running upon his dismissal from *The Yellow Book,* for he puts his hand upon the wall and stares into a mirror. He mutters, "Yes, yes. I look like a Sodomite," which he certainly did not. "But no, I am not that," and then begins railing, against his ancestors, accusing them of that and this, back to and including the great Pitt, from whom he declares himself descended.

16

I can no more justify my convictions in these brief chapters than Shakespeare could justify within the limits of a sonnet his conviction that the soul of the wide world dreams of things to come; and yet as I have set out to describe nature as I see it, I must not only describe events but those patterns into which they fall, when I am the looker-on. A French miracle-working priest once said to Maud Gonne and myself and to an English Catholic who had come with us, that a certain holy woman had been the "victim" for his village, and that another holy woman who had been "victim" for all France, had given him her Crucifix, because he, too, was doomed to become a "victim."

French psychical research has offered

evidence to support the historical proofs that such saints as Lydwine of Schiedam, whose life suggested to Paul Claudel his *L'Annonce fait à Marie,* did really cure disease by taking it upon themselves. As disease was considered the consequence of sin, to take it upon themselves was to copy Christ. All my proof that mind flows into mind, and that we cannot separate mind and body, drives me to accept the thought of victimage in many complex forms, and I ask myself if I cannot so explain the strange, precocious genius of Beardsley. He was in my Lunar metaphor a man of the thirteenth Phase, his nature on the edge of Unity of Being, the understanding of that Unity by the intellect his one overmastering purpose; whereas Lydwine de Schiedam and her like, being of the saints, are at the seven and twentieth Phase, and seek a unity with a life beyond individual being; and so being all subjective he would take upon himself not the consequences, but the knowledge of sin. I surrender myself to the wild thought that by so doing he enabled persons who had never heard his name, to recover innocence. I have so often, too, practiced meditations, or experienced dreams, where the meditations or dreams of two or three persons contrast with and complement one another, in so far as those persons are in themselves complementary or contrasting, that I cannot but see him gathering his knowledge from the saint or potential saint. I see in his fat women and shadowy, pathetic girls, his horrible children, half child, half embryo, in all the lascivious monstrous imagery of the privately published designs, the phantasms that from the beginning have defied the scourge and the hair shirt. I once said to him half seriously, "Beardsley, I was defending you last night in the only way in which it is possible to defend you, by saying that all you draw is inspired by rage against iniquity," and he answered, "If it were so inspired the work would be in no way different," meaning, as I think, that he drew with such sincerity that no change of motive could change the image.

I know that some turn of disease had begun to parade erotic images before his eyes, and I do not doubt that he drew these images. "I make a blot upon the paper," he said to me; "and I begin to shove the ink about and something comes." But I was wrong to say that he drew these things in rage against iniquity, for to know that rage he must needs be objective, concerned with other people, with the Church or the Divinity, with something outside his own head, and responsible not for the knowledge but for the consequence of sin. His preparation had been the exhaustion of sin in act, while the preparation of the Saint is the exhaustion of his pride, and instead of the Saint's humility, he had come to see the images of the mind in a kind of frozen passion, the virginity of the intellect.

Does not all art come when a nature, that never ceases to judge itself, exhausts personal emotion in action or desire so completely that something impersonal, something that has nothing to do with action or desire, suddenly starts into its place, something which is as unforeseen, as completely organized, even as unique, as the images that pass before the mind between sleeping and waking?

But all art is not victimage; and much of the hatred of the art of Beardsley came from the fact that victimage, though familiar under another name to French criticism since the time of Baudelaire, was not known in England. He pictures almost always disillusion, and apart from those privately published drawings which he tried upon his deathbed to have destroyed, there is no representation of desire. Even the beautiful women are exaggerated into doll-like prettiness by a spirit of irony, or are poignant with a thwarted or corrupted innocence. I see his art with more understanding now, than when he lived, for in 1895 or 1896, I was in despair at the new breath of comedy that had begun to wither the beauty that I loved, just when that beauty seemed to have united itself to mystery. I said to him once, "You have never done anything to equal your Salome with the head of John the Baptist." I think, that for the moment he was sincere when he replied, "Yes, yes; but beauty is so difficult." It was for the moment only, for as the popular rage increased and his own disease increased, he became more and more violent in his satire, or created out of a spirit of mockery a form of beauty where his powerful logical intellect eliminated every outline that suggested meditation or even satisfied passion.

The distinction between the Image, between the apparition as it were, and the personal action and desire, took a new form at the approach of death. He made two or three charming and blasphemous designs; I think especially of a Madonna and Child, where the Child has a foolish, doll-like face, and an elaborate modern baby's dress; and of a St. Rose of Lima in an expensive gown decorated with roses, ascending to Heaven upon the bosom of the Madonna, her face enraptured with love, but with that form of it which is least associated with sanctity. I think that his conversion to Catholicism was sincere, but that so much of impulse as could exhaust itself in prayer and ceremony, in formal action and desire, found itself mocked by the antithetical image; and yet I am perhaps mistaken, perhaps it was merely his recognition that historical Christianity had dwindled to a box of toys, and that it might be amusing to empty the whole box on to the counterpane.

17

I had been a good deal in Paris, though never very long at any time; my later visits with a member of the Rhymers' Club whose curiosity or emotion was roused by every pretty girl. He treated me with a now admiring, now mocking wonder, because being in love, and in no way lucky in that love, I had grown exceedingly puritanical so far as my immediate neighborhood was concerned. One night, close to the Luxembourg, a strange young woman in bicycling costume, came out of a side street, threw one arm around his neck, walked beside us in perfect silence for a hundred yards or so, and then darted up another side street. He had a red and white complexion and fair hair, but how she discovered that in the dark I could not understand. I became angry and reproachful, but he defended himself by saying, "You never meet a stray cat without caressing it: I have similar instincts." Presently we found ourselves at some café—the Café D'Harcourt, I think—and when I looked up from my English newspaper, I found myself surrounded with painted ladies and saw that he was taking vengeance. I could not have carried on a conversation in French, but I was able to say, "That gentleman over there has never refused wine or coffee to any lady," and in a little they had all settled about him like greedy pigeons.

I had put my ideal of those years, an ideal that passed away with youth, into my description of *Proud Costello*. "He was of those ascetics of passion, who keep their hearts pure for love or for hatred, as other men for God, for Mary and for the Saints." My friend was not interested in passion. A woman drew him to her by some romantic singularity in her beauty or her circumstance, and drew him the more if the curiosity she aroused were half intellectual. A little after the time I write of, throwing himself into my chair after some visit to a music-hall or hippodrome, he began, "O, Yeats, I was never in love with a serpent-charmer before." He was objective. For him "the visible world existed" as he was fond of quoting, and I suspect him of a Moon that had entered its fourth quarter.

18

At first I used to stay with Macgregor Mathers and his gracious young wife near the Champ de Mars, or in the Rue Mozart, but later by myself in a student's hotel in the Latin Quarter, and I cannot remember always where I stayed when this or that event took place. Macgregor Mathers, or Macgregor, for he had now shed the "Mathers," would come down to breakfast one day with his Horace, the next day with his Macpherson's Ossian, and read out fragments during breakfast, considering both books of equal authenticity. Once when I questioned that of Ossian, he got into a rage—what right had I to take sides with the English enemy—and I found that for him the eighteenth-century controversy still raged. At night he would dress himself in Highland dress, and dance the sword dance, and his mind brooded upon the ramifications of clans and tartans. Yet I have at moments doubted whether he had seen the Highlands, or even, until invited there by some White Rose Society, Scotland itself. Every Sunday he gave to the evocation of Spirits, and I noted that upon that day he would spit blood. That did not matter, he said, because it came from his head, not his lungs; what ailed him I do not know, but I think that he lived under some great strain, and presently I noted that he was drinking too much neat brandy, though not to drunkenness. It was in some mea-

sure a Scottish pose and whether he carried it into later life like his Jacobite opinions I do not know.

He began to foresee changes in the world; announcing in 1893 or 1894, the imminence of immense wars, and was it in 1895 or 1896 that he learned ambulance work, and made others learn it? He had a saber wound on his wrist—or perhaps his forehead, for my memory is not clear—got in some student riot that he had mistaken for the beginning of war. It may have been some talk of his that made me write the poem that begins:

The dews drop slowly and dreams gather;
    unknown spears
Suddenly hurtle before my dream
    awakened eyes,
And then the clash of fallen horsemen
    and the cries
Of unknown perishing armies beat
    about my ears.

Was this prophecy of his, which would shortly be repeated by mediums and clairvoyants all over the world, an unconscious inference taken up into an imagination brooding upon war or was it prevision? An often-repeated statement that anarchy would follow and accompany war suggests prevision, and so too does that unreasoning confidence in his own words. His dream whether prevision or inference was doubtless vague in outline, and as he attempted to make it definite nations and individuals seemed to change into the arbitrary symbols of his desires and fears. He imagined a Napoleonic role for himself, a Europe transformed according to his fancy, Egypt restored, a Highland Principality, and even offered subordinate posts to unlikely people. I was soon to quarrel with him, but up to his death in the middle of the Great War heard of him from time to time. Somewhere in 1914 or 1915 he turned his house into a recruiting office and raised six hundred volunteers for the Foreign Legion—they were used in some other way—from Englishmen or Americans born in France, or from Frenchmen born in England, and had some part in their training. He had lost the small income he had lived on when I first knew him, and had sunk into great poverty, but to set the balance right remembered a title Louis XV had conferred upon a Jacobite ancestor who had fought at Pondicherry and called himself Comte de Glenstrae, and gathered about him Frenchmen and Spaniards whose titles were more shadowy perhaps, an obscure claimant to the French throne among the rest, the most as poor as he and some less honest, and in that dream-court cracked innumerable mechanical jokes—to hide discouragement—and yet remained to the end courageous in thought and kind in act. He had tried to prolong his youthful dream, had mounted into *Hodos Chameliontos,* and I have known none mount there and come to good that lacked philosophy. All that he knew of that was a vague affirmation, a medicinal phrase that he would repeat and have friends repeat in all moments of adversity: "There is no part of me that is not of the Gods."

Once, when Mathers had told me that he met his Teachers in some great crowd, and only knew that they were phantoms by a shock that was like an electric shock to his heart, I asked him how he knew that he was not deceived or hallucinated. He said, "I had been visited by one of them the other night, and I followed him out, and followed him down that little lane to the right. Presently I fell over the milk boy, and the milk boy got in a rage because he said that not only I but the man in front had fallen over him." He like all that I have known, who have given themselves up to images, and to the speech of images, thought that when he had proved that an image could act independently of his mind, he had proved also that neither it, nor what it had

spoken, had originated there. Yet had I need of proof to the contrary, I had it while under his roof. I was eager for news of the Spanish–American War, and went to the Rue Mozart before breakfast to buy a *New York Herald.* As I went out past the young Normandy servant who was laying breakfast, I was telling myself some schoolboy romance, and had just reached a place where I carried my arm in a sling after some remarkable escape. I bought my paper and returned, to find Mathers on the doorstep. "Why, you are all right," he said. "What did the Bonne mean by telling me that you had hurt your arm and carried it in a sling?"

Once when I met him in the street in his Highland clothes, with several knives in his stocking, he said, "When I am dressed like this I feel like a walking flame," and I think that everything he did was but an attempt to feel like a walking flame. Yet at heart he was, I think, gentle, and perhaps even a little timid. He had some impediment in his nose that gave him a great deal of trouble, and it could have been removed had he not shrunk from the slight operation; and once when he was left in a mouse-infested flat with some live traps, he collected his captives into a large birdcage, and to avoid the necessity of their drowning, fed them there for a couple of weeks. Being an un-scholarly, though learned man, he was bound to express the fundamental antithesis in the most crude form, and being arrogant, to prevent as far as possible that alternation between the two natures which is, it may be, necessary to sanity. When the nature turns to its spiritual opposite alone there can be no alternation, but what nature is pure enough for that?

I see Paris in the Eighteen-nineties as a number of events separated from one another, and without cause or consequence, without lot or part in the logical structure of my life; I can often as little find their dates as I can those of events in my early childhood. William Sharp, who came to see me there, may have come in 1895, or on some visit four or five years later, but certainly I was in an hotel in the Boulevard Raspail. When he stood up to go he said, "What is that?" pointing to a geometrical form painted upon a little piece of cardboard that lay upon my window-sill. And then before I could answer, looked out of the window, saying, "There is a funeral passing." I said, "That is curious, as the Death symbol is painted upon the card." I did not look, but I am sure there was no funeral. A few days later he came back and said, "I have been very ill; you must never allow me to see that symbol again." He did not seem anxious to be questioned, but years later he said, "I will now tell you what happened in Paris. I had two rooms at my hotel, a front sitting-room and a bedroom leading out of it. As I passed the threshold of the sitting-room, I saw a woman standing at the bureau writing, and presently she went into my bedroom. I thought somebody had got into the wrong room by mistake, but when I went to the bureau I saw the sheet of paper she had seemed to write upon, and there was no writing upon it. I went into my bedroom and I found nobody, but as there was a door from the bedroom on to the stairs I went down the stairs to see if she had gone that way. When I got out into the street I saw her just turning a corner, but when I turned the corner there was nobody there, and then I saw her at another corner. Constantly seeing her and losing her like that I followed till I came to the Seine, and there I saw her standing at an opening in the wall, looking down into the river. Then she vanished, and I cannot tell why, but I went to the opening in the wall and stood there, just as she had stood, taking just the same attitude. Then I thought I was

in Scotland, and that I heard a sheep bell. After that I must have lost consciousness, for I knew nothing till I found myself lying on my back, dripping wet, and people standing all around. I had thrown myself into the Seine."

I did not believe him, and not because I thought the story impossible, for I knew he had a susceptibility beyond that of any one I had ever known, to symbolic or telepathic influence, but because he never told one anything that was true; the facts of life disturbed him and were forgotten. The story had been created by the influence but it had remained a reverie, though he may in the course of years have come to believe that it happened as an event. The affectionate husband of his admiring and devoted wife, he had created an imaginary beloved, had attributed to her the authorship of all his books that had any talent, and though habitually a sober man, I have known him to get drunk, and at the height of his intoxication when most men speak the truth, to attribute his state to remorse for having been unfaithful to Fiona Macleod.

Paul Verlaine alternated between the two halves of his nature with so little apparent resistance that he seemed like a bad child, though to read his sacred poems is to remember perhaps that the Holy Infant shared His first home with the beasts. In what month was it that I received a note inviting me to "coffee and cigarettes plentifully," and signed "Yours quite cheerfully, Paul Verlaine"? I found him at the top of a tenement house in the Rue St. Jacques, sitting in an easy chair, his bad leg swaddled in many bandages. He asked me, speaking in English, if I knew Paris well, and added, pointing to his leg, that it had scorched his leg for he knew it "well, too well" and "lived in it like a fly in a pot of marmalade." He took up an English dictionary, one of the few books in the room, and began searching for the name of his disease, selecting after a long search and with, as I understood, only comparative accuracy "Erysipelas." Meanwhile his homely middle-aged mistress made the coffee and found the cigarettes; it was obviously she who had given the room its character; her canaries in several cages hanging in the window, and her sentimental lithographs nailed here and there among the nude drawings and newspaper caricatures of her lover as various kinds of monkey, which he had pinned upon the wall. A slovenly, ragged man came in, his trousers belted with a piece of rope and an opera hat upon his head. She drew a box over to the fire, and he sat down, now holding the opera hat upon his knees, and I think he must have acquired it very lately for he kept constantly closing and opening it. Verlaine introduced him by saying, "He is a poor man, but a good fellow, and is so like Louis XI to look at that we call him Louis the XIth." I remember that Verlaine talked of Victor Hugo who was "a supreme poet, but a volcano of mud as well as of flame," and of Villiers de L'Isle Adam who was "exalté" and wrote excellent French; and of *In Memoriam*, which he had tried to translate and could not. "Tennyson is too noble, too Anglais; when he should have been broken-hearted, he had many reminiscences."

At Verlaine's burial, but a few months after, his mistress quarreled with a publisher at the graveside as to who owned the sheet by which the body had been covered, and Louis XI stole fourteen umbrellas that he found leaning against a tree in the Cemetery.

19

I am certain of one date, for I have gone to much trouble to get it right. I met John Synge for the first time in the Autumn of 1896, when I was one and thirty, and he four and twenty. I was at the Hotel Corneille instead of my usual lodging, and why I cannot remember for I thought it expensive. Synge's biographer says that you boarded there for a pound a week, but I was accustomed to cook my own breakfast, and dine at an anarchist restaurant in the Boulevard St. Jacques for little over a shilling. Some one, whose name I forget, told me there was a poor Irishman at the top of the house, and presently introduced us. Synge had come lately from Italy, and had played his fiddle to peasants in the Black Forest; six months of travel upon fifty pounds; and was now reading French literature and writing morbid and melancholy verse. He told me that he had learned Irish at Trinity College, so I urged him to go to the Aran Islands and find a life that had never been expressed in literature, instead of a life where all had been expressed. I did not divine his genius, but I felt he needed something to take him out of his morbidity and melancholy. Perhaps I would have given the same advice to any young Irish writer who knew Irish, for I had been that summer upon Inishmaan and Inishmore, and was full of the subject. My friends and I had landed from a fishing boat to find ourselves among a group of islanders, one of whom said he would bring us to the oldest man upon Inishmaan. This old man, speaking very slowly, but with laughing eyes, had said, "If any gentleman has done a crime, we'll hide him. There was a gentleman that killed his father, and I had him in my own house six months till he got away to America."

From that on I saw much of Synge, and brought him to Maud Gonne's, under whose persuasion perhaps, he joined the "Young Ireland Society of Paris," the name we gave to half a dozen Parisian Irish, but resigned after a few months because "it wanted to stir up

Continental nations against England, and England will never give us freedom until she feels she is safe," the one political sentence I ever heard him speak. Over a year was to pass before he took my advice and settled for a while in an Aran cottage, and became happy, having escaped at last, as he wrote, "from the squalor of the poor and the nullity of the rich." I almost forget the prose and verse he showed me in Paris, though I read it all through again when after his death I decided, at his written request, what was to be published and what not. Indeed, I have but a vague impression, as of a man trying to look out of a window and blurring all that he sees by breathing upon the window. According to my Lunar parable, he was a man of the twenty-third Phase; a man whose subjective lives—for a constant return to our life is a part of my dream—were over; who must not pursue an image, but fly from it, all that subjective dreaming, that had once been power and joy, now corrupting within him. He had to take the first plunge into the world beyond himself, the first plunge away from himself that is always pure technique, the delight in doing, not because one would or should, but merely because one can do.

He once said to me, "a man has to bring up his family and be as virtuous as is compatible with so doing, and if he does more than that he is a puritan; a dramatist has to express his subject and to find as much beauty as is compatible with that, and if he does more he is an æsthete," that is to say, he was consciously objective. Whenever he tried to write drama without dialect he wrote badly, and he made several attempts, because only through dialect could he escape self-expression, see all that he did from without, allow his intellect to judge the images of his mind as if they had been created by some other mind. His objectivity was, however, technical only, for in those images paraded all the desires of his heart. He was timid, too shy for general conversation, an invalid and full of moral scruple, and he was to create now some ranting braggadocio, now some tipsy hag full of poetical speech, and now some young man or girl full of the most abounding health. He never spoke an unkind word, had admirable manners, and yet his art was to fill the streets with rioters, and to bring upon his dearest friends enemies that may last their lifetime.

No mind can engender till divided into two, but that of a Keats or a Shelley falls into an intellectual part that follows, and a hidden emotional flying image, whereas in a mind like that of Synge the emotional part is dreaded and stagnant, while the intellectual part is a clear mirror-like technical achievement.

But in writing of Synge I have run far ahead, for in 1896 he was but one picture among many. I am often astonished when I think that we can meet unmoved some person, or pass some house, that in later years is to bear a chief part in our life. Should there not be some flutter of the nerve or stopping of the heart like that Macgregor Mathers experienced at the first meeting with a phantom?

20

Many pictures come before me without date or order. I am walking somewhere near the Luxembourg Gardens when Synge, who seldom generalizes and only after much thought, says, "There are three things any two of which have often come together but never all three; ecstasy, asceticism, austerity; I wish to bring all three together."

.   .   .

I notice that Macgregor Mathers considers William Sharp vague and sentimental, while Sharp is repelled by Mathers' hardness and arrogance. William Sharp met Mathers in the Louvre, and said, "No doubt considering your studies you live upon milk and fruit." And Mathers replied, "No, not exactly milk and fruit, but very nearly so"; and now Sharp has lunched with Mathers and been given nothing but brandy and radishes.

. . .

Mathers is much troubled by ladies who seek spiritual advice, and one has called to ask his help against phantoms who have the appearance of decayed corpses, and try to get into bed with her at night. He has driven her away with one furious sentence, "Very bad taste on both sides."

. . .

I take hashish with some followers of the eighteenth-century mystic Saint-Martin. At one in the morning, while we are talking wildly, and some are dancing, there is a tap at the shuttered window; we open it and three ladies enter, the wife of a man of letters who thought to find no one but a confederate, and her husband's two young sisters whom she has brought secretly to some disreputable dance. She is very confused at seeing us, but as she looks from one to another understands that we have taken some drug and laughs; caught in our dream we know vaguely that she is scandalous according to our code and to all codes, but smile at her benevolently and laugh.

. . .

I am at Stuart Merrill's, and I meet there a young Jewish Persian scholar. He has a large gold ring, seemingly very rough, made by some amateur, and he shows me that it has shaped itself to his finger, and says, "That is because it contains no alloy—it is alchemical gold." I

ask who made the gold, and he says a certain Rabbi, and begins to talk of the Rabbi's miracles. We do not question him—perhaps it is true—perhaps he has imagined it all—we are inclined to accept every historical belief once more.

. . .

I am sitting in a café with two French Americans, a German poet Douchenday, and a silent man whom I discover to be Strindberg, and who is looking for the Philosopher's Stone. The French American reads out a manifesto he is about to issue to the Latin Quarter; it proposes to establish a communistic colony of artists in Virginia, and there is a footnote to explain why he selects Virginia, "Art has never flourished twice in the same place. Art has never flourished in Virginia."

Douchenday, who has some reputation as a poet, explains that his poems are without verbs, as the verb is the root of all evil in the world. He wishes for an art where all things are immovable, as though the clouds should be made of marble. I turn over the page of one of his books which he shows me, and find there a poem in dramatic form, but when I ask if he hopes to have it played he says: "It could only be played by actors before a black marble wall, with masks in their hands. They must not wear the masks for that would not express my scorn for reality."

. . .

I go to the first performance of Alfred Jarry's *Ubu Roi*, at the Théâtre de L'Œuvre, with the Rhymer who had been so attractive to the girl in the bicycling costume. The audience shake their fists at one another, and the Rhymer whispers to me, "There are often duels after these performances," and he explains to me what is happening on the stage. The players are supposed to be dolls, toys, marionettes, and now they are all hopping like wooden frogs, and I can see for myself that the chief personage, who is some kind of King, carries for Scepter a brush of the kind that we use to clean a closet. Feeling bound to support the most spirited party, we have shouted for the play, but that night at the Hotel Corneille I am very sad, for comedy, objectivity, has displayed its growing power once more. I say, "After Stephane Mallarmé, after Paul Verlaine, after Gustave Moreau, after Puvis de Chavannes, after our own verse, after all our subtle color and nervous rhythm, after the faint mixed tints of Conder, what more is possible? After us the Savage God."

THE LIFE AND WORKS OF
WILLIAM BUTLER YEATS

By FRANK KERMODE

YEATS, most autobiographical of poets, refers again and again to his family background and the places where he lived in early days. Through his father he was descended from well-to-do Anglo-Irish merchants, well known in the Dublin of Swift and Grattan and related by marriage to the powerful family of Butler, Earls of Ormonde.

Their fortune did not outlast the eighteenth century, and the poet's grandfather was the first of several Yeatses to take orders. He was rector of Drumcliff, County Sligo, from 1805 to 1846. It was there, in Drumcliff churchyard, that Yeats's own remains were interred a century later, for though he was born in Dublin and spent much of his life in Galway, in London, and abroad, Sligo is the center of the Yeats country and Drumcliff its terminal point.

Sligo, the county town, was the haven of Yeats's youth, and thereabouts are many familiar places: the mountain of Knocknarea, where according to local folklore Queen Maeve is buried; the Ox Mountains, drab and uninviting; the great heathlands, with Rosses Point; and Lissadell, the fine estate of the Gore-Booths.

William Butler Yeats, the poet's grandfather, had been both a scholar and an athlete. His father, John Butler Yeats, was born in 1839. He was a true Yeats, with the proud and aristocratic manners of the best Anglo-Irish families. He was one of the most brilliant men of his time. In 1863, he married Susan Pollexfen, of a well-to-do merchant family whose mill still straddles the road at Ballisodare, a few miles from Sligo, a name that often recurs in Yeats's writings. John Butler Yeats refused to take orders and preferred painting to reading for the bar, so he did not yet enjoy a very secure position when his first son, William Butler Yeats, was born in Dublin on June 13, 1865. When the boy was only three years old, his parents moved to London. In the space of six years they had four more children, three of whom lived and distinguished themselves in the arts: the girls Lily and Lolly, and Jack, the painter.

John Butler Yeats never earned much money. He was not a successful painter, for he rarely finished a picture, and his son had known him to say: "When I was young, the definition of a gentleman was a man not wholly occupied in getting on." The result of all this was that his son's education, though all very well for a poet, remained sketchy. The boy spent the summer months in Sligo, in the house of the Pollexfen family, which he

[349]

thought of as home; and in London, where his parents lived in the artists' quarter at Bedford Park, he was in daily contact with cultivated people, poets, theatrical folk, and painters.

His father, an eccentric but a strong personality, gave him lessons at home, and this was the start of an intense and fruitful understanding between the two, which years later still filled the old man's remarkable letters to his son. But the lack of a formal education was a drawback that Yeats never overcame. He had little Latin and even less French, and he never learned Gaelic; he translated Sophocles without knowing any Greek, he floundered in his occult dabblings at Hebrew and Arabic, having no knowledge of either language.

Although he read very widely with a ready understanding, one might say of him what he said of Macgregor Mathers, that he "had much learning but little scholarship." He moved, however, among the leading spirits of the day, the intellectual elite, and what Sligo brought him in the way of myth and atmosphere partly made up for the gaps in his education. His debt to Sligo is quite clear in his *Reveries over Childhood and Youth* (1915), which later went to form the first part of his *Autobiographies* (1955).

When Yeats was fifteen the family moved back to Dublin. Two years later he began writing verse. He was much influenced by Shelley, and in the traditional atmosphere of Ireland he took quite naturally to the study of magic and occultism. In 1884, he enrolled in a Dublin art school where he met George ("Æ") Russell, the poet, mystic, and painter. Henceforth the trend of his mind, the trend most congenial to it, was firmly marked out: "It was only when I began to study psychical research and mystical philosophy," he wrote, "that I broke away from my father's influence." John Butler Yeats, a staunch disciple of

Mill, would have scorned such books as A. P. Sinnett's *Esoteric Buddhism* or the theosophical manual *Light on the Path*. But his son, like many poets of this period, needed a loophole to escape from the hateful, all-pervading pall of science. He found it in occultism and theosophy, in Irish patriotism and legend. Of these matters Yeats's mind was so full that he distilled his ideas of history and philosophy into a sort of secret, mystical theory of history, of the human personality, even of theology. All this fostered the writing of a magnificent and original poetry, not by providing material for it but by enlarging the poet's expression and imagination. It was of the very nature of Yeats's intelligence to transform everything with a view to poetry, and Yeats, like all great poets, had his share of luck. Even his shyness turned into protective arrogance, and the elements of rationalism taken over from his father mellowed into self-criticism and self-irony, thus enabling him to reach the necessary level of self-defense. The enthralling account he gives of his visit to Verlaine and his own memories of the "tragic generation"—those friends of his who had not enough decency or faith in poetry to survive into their maturity—show how far he surpassed them.

In 1885, some of his poems, notably *Mosada,* which his father had shown to Gerard Manley Hopkins, appeared in the *Dublin University Review.* The same year he founded the Hermetic Society and declared at the first meeting that "whatever the great poets had affirmed in their finest moments was the nearest we could come to an authoritative religion." This view was in keeping with the belief he expressed in a famous essay written nearly thirteen years later, to the effect that poets are simply the modern heirs of the magicians who ruled in more primitive and more secret societies.

With magic and poetry he now combined politics, joining the Young Ireland Society, whose president was John O'Leary. "From these debates," he wrote, "from O'Leary's conversation, and from the Irish books he lent or gave me has come all I have set my hand to since." O'Leary he particularly admired and respected, and thanks to his influence Yeats understood from the start that his own participation in Ireland's struggle would be literary, and he set to work with a certain envy of those more active men who were to shape the future. When he had achieved more than anyone else could have given to Irish literature, he still felt some rancor against his vocation.

Yeats was poor, yet his life in Dublin was a full one. Then, in 1887, his father moved back to London, and he began his life of incessant crossings between the two countries—London, Sligo, Oxford, Galway. Pursuing his dual path of poetry and magic, he joined Madame Blavatsky's Theosophical Society and later the Hermetic Students of the Golden Dawn founded by Macgregor Mathers, while working on his ambitious long poem *The Wanderings of Oisin* (1890). Yeats became friendly with William Morris and through him met Shaw; he also met T. H. Huxley and Oscar Wilde; the latter was particularly kind to him. Theatrical performances in the red-brick clubhouse at Bedford Park brought him the acquaintance of John Todhunter, a pioneer in the writing of poetical plays, and that of the actress Florence Farr. His imagination was stirred, and his interest in the theater dates from this time.

Early in 1889 he began collaborating with Edwin Ellis, a friend of his father's, on a large edition of Blake, which it took them four years to produce. And about this time he fell in love with the actress Maud Gonne. His meeting with her was the most important of all, for she determined his private life as well as his poetry, and kept him in touch, willy-nilly, with extremist Irish nationalism. He never forgot that first meeting: "In that day she seemed a classical personification of the Spring, the Virgilian commendation 'She walks like a goddess' made for her alone."

At twenty-five, Yeats published his novel *John Sherman* (1890), founded the Rhymers' Club and the Irish Literary Society, and published his first important poem. *The Wanderings of Oisin* counts for little in the final evaluation of the poet's work, but at every point it attempted—what Yeats felt to be necessary in any symbolic poem—to break away from mechanical rhymes, and to use symbols in a highly personal manner. The interest of *Oisin* lies chiefly in the fact that it foreshadows the later Yeats. Already, though his manner was still slow and painful, he had begun working toward a more rigorous diction. Although *The Wanderings of Oisin* seems to confine its author in a romantic, pre-Raphaelite context, and in a late nineteenth-century vogue for occultism and national mythography, this poem has qualities which finally bring it to maturity and make it modern.

From this time on, Yeats was active in the literary societies of London and Dublin. He lived for a time with Arthur Symons and was thereby associated with the brilliant, short-lived career of *The Savoy,* successor of *The Yellow Book.* At this time he was working on *The Trembling of the Veil* (1920), one of the greatest of modern autobiographies. A quarter of a century later he featured the friends of these years in *A Vision* (1925), in which he classified human personality in a series of types. This was a period when, given free rein in a culture cut loose, as it seemed, from the sources that had quickened it, "abstraction" had attained its highest pitch. "Abstraction" was for Yeats synonymous with the decay of soul, and under its sway even the best of men were "bonds-men" condemned to a tragic fate. His friends Lionel Johnson, Beardsley, Dow-son, and Synge he called the "tragic generation." They later took their place in Yeats's private mythology alongside the "ancient heroes."

It was not, however, till a few years later that Yeats wrote of this period in London. At that time he was working hard; Maud Gonne, who had refused to marry him in 1891 (and refused again in 1916), inspired him to write *The Countess Cathleen* (1892). As an aspirant for recognition as an Irish poet, he had once again chosen as his theme an Irish myth. In 1893, he published *The Celtic Twilight,* a collection of mannered essays, well suited to such a title, and in 1895 his *Poems.* The latter contained all of his early verse which he wished to preserve.

Revisiting Ireland with Arthur Symons in 1896, Yeats met Lady Gregory. She not only represented one more character to be added to his heroic collection, but she also had a decisive influence on his life. For years her house at Coole, in Galway, was the poet's house, and her name and that of her son Robert are closely connected with his work in verse. At first she looked after him, and he needed the care she lavished upon him for he had been reckless of his health and had overworked. She organized the household so as best to guard him against intrusion. Later she became his collabo-rator and a perpetual stimulus. Her dig-nity and the social position she enjoyed as a great lady suited Yeats's aristocratic penchant. They read Castiglione's *Book of the Courtier* together and years later even visited Urbino. When she nearly died in 1909, he wrote: "All Wednesday I heard Castiglione's phrase ringing in my memory, 'Never be it spoken without tears, the Duchess, too, is dead.'" Like the landscape of Coole and the Burren Hills, she was absorbed into the Yeatsian

myth. The first poem in which the full force of the poet's mature talent burst forth was an elegy to her son; and the tower which became the dominant sym-bol of his most brilliant period stood near Coole and was closely associated with the Gregory family. Poem after poem cele-brates its grandeur; her house, her woods, her lake gave their names to Yeats's books.

The impetus given by Lady Gregory also took effect on the poet's public life. By 1899 he had begun the movement for an Irish national theater, while that same year he scored a great success with the poems in *The Wind among the Reeds.* But now he concentrated all his efforts on the stage. In Dublin, his play *The Countess Cathleen,* with Maud Gonne in the role of the Countess, was followed by *Diarmuid and Grania* (1901), written in collaboration with George Moore, a new and dangerous friend. The Irish Literary Theatre was founded, soon to be super-seded by the Irish National Theatre So-ciety, of which Yeats became president. A very talented group of actors was brought together, and Yeats proceeded to write for them his first important plays. With the help of Florence Farr, he began trying his hand at the art of writing verse plays. Out of this ferment came the Abbey Theatre in 1904.

The Abbey Theatre was financed by Miss Annie Horniman, and, after an ex-periment in democratic management, full control was placed in the hands of Lady Gregory, Yeats, and Synge. Yeats did not want it to be run on an ordinary com-mercial basis; he meant to use it instead as a testing ground for his experiments in poetic drama. Habitual notions of speech, acting, and scenery were to be discarded.

Yeats became a skilled and resourceful stage manager. His greatest success was obtained when he spoke in defense of Synge's *Playboy of the Western World* in

1907. He was absent on the first night when the audience protested violently against the use of the word "shift." Returning from Scotland he confronted the "howling mob": "The author of *Cathleen ni Houlihan* (1902) [a very patriotic play] addresses you." It was a victory but Synge's play continued to stir up controversy and even caused trouble during a tour of the Abbey Players in America in 1912.

Meanwhile, other events of great importance were taking place outside the theater. In 1903, Yeats suffered the great moral shock of his life when he learned of Maud Gonne's marriage with John MacBride, a man he despised. That same year he published his first volume of criticism, *Ideas of Good and Evil,* which included the two essays *Symbolism in Painting* (1899) and *The Symbolism of Poetry* (1900); the latter also contained long essays on Blake and Shelley.

This book and *The Cutting of an Agate* (1912), together with subsequent essays, established Yeats as a critic. His prose—which Yeats never abandoned— is not altogether to the liking of modern readers, and on this point justice has not been done to Yeats. Admittedly, here as elsewhere he sacrificed everything to his requirements as a poet; the books he loved he regarded as "sacred," the others he ignored. But he was never far removed from the centers of interest of modern literature, and sometimes his insights were prophetic. His essay on Shelley was far in advance of modern research, and no one has written more acutely on the modernism of Blake, that "realist of imagination."

The philosophy underlying Yeats's literary criticism is almost entirely pure symbolism; through symbols, imagination rebuilds the world that reason destroys; and not only the cabbalistic symbols of magic or the conventional symbols of the Rose or the Cross but also landscapes and people may contribute to restore that lost unity. Taken as a whole, however, Yeats's theory of criticism, with its yearning for a return to the initial scheme of things, its adhesion to a shared knowledge of symbols, its historical myth of break-up and decline, is not peculiar to him, it is also in line with the critical and literary theories of our time.

Noteworthy, too, in connection with this part of Yeats's work, is the fact that anyone reading through it often has the pleasant surprise of meeting his poetry in its latent state, for again and again some passage from his prose was taken up and recast, often years later, into a masterly poem. His was a memory ever on the alert, and essentially self-centered, which lost nothing that might serve his imagination.

The poems of this period were brought together in *The Green Helmet* (1910). Yeats had already revised his early work for publication in the eight-volume collected edition of 1908, but these new poems, collected in *The Green Helmet,* were various, not only in their voracity and force, but also in the closeness of their relation to contemporary affairs. They were not many in number, for "all things can tempt me from this craft of verse," but they were important ones. They include the first great poems on Maud Gonne (now mythologically converted into Helen of Troy) and some violent epigrams on the affairs of the Abbey Theatre.

Though a great poet might be expected to produce more than this in the space of six years, it must be remembered that Yeats continued to develop his mind and perfect his talent. His public life was identified with the Abbey Theatre and all the worries connected with it, while his private life continued to be rich and full. In London he became friendly with Ezra Pound and met Miss Georgie Hyde-Lees, whom he was to marry a few years later.

Two reminiscences written at this time, *Estrangement* (written in 1909, published in 1926) and *The Death of Synge* (written in 1909, published in 1926) are the most moving and revealing of his prose works.

By now he was recognized as one of the leading men of letters in Dublin and London. In 1910 he was awarded a Civil List pension of 150 pounds; he accepted it on the understanding that he would still be free to speak or act as he saw fit on political issues. But Yeats was not happy, and in 1914 he published a volume of lyrics, *Responsibilities*. This is the book of a man living in two worlds, trying—as he put it himself—"to unite in one thought reality and justice." Reality was the petty animosities of Dublin, the goad that set him writing bitter epigrams. He was full of contempt for the "shop-keeping logicians" of this "blind and ignorant town."

This volume also contains some sensitive and forcible poems dedicated to Lady Gregory and Maud Gonne. Even more remarkable are the poems that flowed out of his continuing concern with magic and mysticism: "The Cold Heaven," so powerful and impassioned, or "The Magi," evoking the Nativity, a theme he interpreted several times.

Yeats was arriving at the full maturity of his powers. *Responsibilities* ended with "A Coat," a poem in which he gave up his old coat embroidered with mythologies. But he was not to be "walking naked" for long, for the modern world offered him heroes of tragedy and myth in abundance.

At first World War I did not much preoccupy Yeats; the Irish had troubles of their own. He spent the first winter of the war in England, with Ezra Pound, who was acting as his secretary. It was undoubtedly under Pound's influence that Yeats came to enter a new phase of his literary life as a playwright; but it is not known how far that influence may have affected the technique of his versification.

Pound, as the literary executor of Ernest Fenollosa, had the latter's manuscripts in his possession and introduced Yeats to the plays of the Japanese Noh theater. Yeats found in them a remarkable confirmation of his own aristocratic theory of tragedy, which he had already set forth in an essay, *The Tragic Theatre* (1911). He contributed a fine introduction to *Certain Noble Plays of Japan,* chosen by Pound from Fenollosa's manuscripts, and in 1916 he wrote a play in the Japanese style with masked players and dancing. A private performance of *At the Hawk's Well,* for an essentially aristocratic audience, was given in the London drawing room of Lady Cunard. It was a memorable evening, with the Japanese dancer Ito, masked and costumed by Edmund Dulac, as the guardian of the well, dancing to music also composed by Dulac. That performance was attended by the young T. S. Eliot, who realized then and there that Yeats in his fifties represented a new force in modern poetry.

For many years to come Yeats kept on writing plays of this kind: *The Only Jealousy of Emer* (1918), *The Dreaming of the Bones* (1919), *Calvary* (1920), *The Cat and the Moon* (1926), and still others in the closing years of his life. All these plays were written according to the "system," but were equally far removed from didacticism and naturalism.

Yeats was soon to feel the impact of the war. In 1915, Hugh Lane, the great collector and a nephew of Lady Gregory, went down on the *Lusitania.* In 1916 came the Easter Rebellion in Dublin, followed by the execution of sixteen of its leaders by the British. Among them was John MacBride, Maud Gonne's husband. This event had many consequences for Yeats. It was, first of all, a national tragedy, and one in which he was personally involved; it also had a kind of liberating effect on him. He crossed to France where Maud Gonne was living and proposed to her; she refused him. He then fell in love with her adopted daughter Iseult and proposed to her, but she too refused him. He returned to England with them. It was in 1917, shortly after he bought Thoor Ballylee, a Norman tower near Lady Gregory's estate in Galway, that he married Georgie Hyde-Lees. He set about restoring the tower and the neighboring cottage, intending to make his summer home there.

Early in 1918, shortly before he and his wife settled at Thoor Ballylee, Lady Gregory's son Robert, a squadron leader in the Royal Flying Corps, was killed in action on the Italian front. This was the period of Yeats's greatest moral crisis. He still wrote new plays and pursued his occult researches, which were about to reach their first quasi-systematic formulation in *Per Amica Silentia Lunae* (1918). The death of Robert Gregory came as a blow to Yeats, and his marriage had been a step he could not help taking with apprehension. And the political situation in Ireland was tense. From this tumult of events and emotions, Yeats suddenly emerged as a poet of new and unsuspected powers.

Shortly after his marriage Yeats discovered that his wife had a psychic gift —the power of "automatic writing." Through her "communicators" sent messages destined to organize the poet's mystical philosophy into a system and provide him with "metaphors for poetry." So his marriage became not only the end of a long torment, it was the beginning of a new philosophical orientation.

In 1919, Yeats published *The Wild Swans at Coole,* an outstanding collection of poems full of the eager breath of life, of the vigor that age and wisdom are apt to quell, and pervaded by an intimate sense of the high moral value of effort in a degenerate world. The poem "Upon a Dying Lady," unlike anything Yeats had written hitherto, is proof of his virtuoso powers. Now he was able to control the passion of his imaginative thought; but it was not until the early 1920s that he reached the point where his vigorous technique counterbalanced the slow expansion of his imaginative power.

His first child, Anne Butler Yeats, was born in February 1919, while Yeats was living at Oxford. The family spent that summer in their cottage at Ballylee, while work on the tower was still in progress. Yeats lived a few years longer at Oxford, where he saw much of his old friends John Masefield, Robert Bridges, Sturge Moore and Edmund Dulac; and he was a frequent visitor to Garsington, near Oxford, where Lady Ottoline Morrell held open house to men of letters. He worked on *The Trembling of the Veil* and on *Michael Robartes and the Dancer* (1921). His search for "unity of being" —an almost untenable position in our post-Renaissance history—is represented in his poems by the combination of reason and passion. Of all the other philosophical fantasies in *Michael Robartes and the Dancer,* the most famous is certainly "The Second Coming." It is based on a magic symbol evoked thirty years before by Macgregor Mathers, which combined the imagery of the Christian Apocalypse with the *Anima Mundi* of Neoplatonism. Yeats's own "theory of gyres" included the idea that the Christian era was drawing to a hideous close and would be superseded by an antithetical civilization. This was taken by everyone to be a prophecy of events then taking place. *Michael Robartes and the Dancer* also contained a long meditation called "A Prayer for My Daughter" which movingly combines simplicity and grandiloquence.

Yeats was at Oxford when the English

forces, the notorious Black and Tans, went into action against Irish patriots, and Lady Gregory wrote to him of the atrocities committed in the neighborhood of Gort. His absence from Ireland at this time no doubt enabled him to write his greatest poem, "Nineteen Hundred and Nineteen." He continued to work on his "system," classifying all his Oxford friends—so J. M. Hone tells us—in accordance with the twenty-eight phases into which he had divided the human personality.

In the summer of 1921, while Yeats and his wife were living in Oxfordshire, a son was born and christened William Michael. Early in 1922 the whole family returned to Dublin and they took a house in Merrion Square. This was the first year of Ireland's independence; Yeats was recognized as the Free State's foremost man of letters and invited to become a member of the Senate. But the political situation worsened, and in the spring of 1922 the opponents of the treaty with England took up arms and attacked Dublin. This was the beginning of civil war. Yeats was fifty-seven, and though he looked and felt younger he complained continually of "being old." He read and worked unceasingly, and though opposed to the insurgents he avoided the subject of politics. He incorporated the civil war, like everything else, into his myth. For him it represented the first phase of the general downfall of the West. The firing and bombing in Dublin, and the blowing up of the bridges at Ballylee which placed his children in some danger, brought no change in his habits.

All the events in Yeats's life during these years were but a prelude to *The Tower* (1928).

In December 1923 he went to Stockholm to receive the Nobel Prize. On his return he wrote his magnificent essay "The Bounty of Sweden"; he wrote it not only out of common courtesy, but out of habit, for he was always working. As Professor Melchiori has said, he assimilated in his own way the architecture of the Stockholm Town Hall and turned it into poetry.

Then in 1925 he traveled to Sicily where he took a keen interest in Byzantine antiquities. That year the first version of *A Vision* was at last finished and published. The poet thought that by this time he could settle down to the writing of easier, simpler things, but his powers had suffered no decline—on the contrary.

The theater and public life continued to interest him. His versions of the *Oedipus* plays, with their remarkable choruses, were performed at the Abbey Theatre.

In 1926 he was again involved in a riot at the Abbey Theatre, touched off this time by Sean O'Casey's play *The Plough and the Stars*. He delivered a brilliant speech in the Irish Senate during a debate on divorce. He went on reading voraciously: Gibbon, Joyce, Croce, Giovanni Gentile, Hegel, "profound MacTaggart," Bergson, etc. In 1925 the doctors warned him against overwork, and in 1927 he fell seriously ill. He recovered and in 1928 went out to Rapallo for convalescence. That year he published *The Tower,* unquestionably his finest book of poetry. Rereading it, he wrote to Olivia Shakespear: "I was astonished at its bitterness, and long to live out of Ireland that I may find some new vintage. Yet that bitterness gave the book its power and it is the best book I have written." Now that his health was breaking down, he seemed to yearn more than ever for physical beauty and physical activity; heroic action and positive sexuality seemed to him still more precious. He wrote at the beginning of "Sailing to Byzantium":

That is no country for old men. The
    young
In one another's arms, birds in the trees
—Those dying generations—at their
    song,
The salmon-falls, the mackerel-
    crowded seas,
Fish, flesh, or fowl, commend all sum-
    mer long
Whatever is begotten, born, and dies.
Caught in that sensual music all neglect
Monuments of unageing intellect.

"Sailing to Byzantium" is the introductory poem of *The Tower,* a long sequence turning in a more personal and more poignant manner on the same theme. Again and again, in *The Tower,* history and systematic philosophy are seen to flare up into poetic fire, as in the songs from his play *The Resurrection* or as in the sonnet "Leda and the Swan." Among the rest, mention must be made of "Among the School Children," which to my mind is the finest of all his meditative poems. It begins with graceful irony which brings him, once more, to compare the value of flesh and blood with that of "bronze and marble," and the work ends in a dazzling vision of the "Unity of Being" in the artifice of eternity.

Yeats was sixty-three when *The Tower* was published, but he was by no means disposed to take a rest. In spite of age and failing health, he threw himself with fresh ardor into a round of life and study, and took on the appearance of an old man still hale and hearty. Entering on an entirely new life, financially independent, he wrote more freely than before. Then, in December 1929, he suffered a breakdown at Rapallo and was gravely ill throughout the winter. But the following spring found him at Coole writing a powerful and quite unexpected play in prose, *The Worlds Upon the Window Pane* (published in 1934).

Lady Gregory died in 1932. "A queer Dublin sculptor . . . came . . . 'to pay his respects.' He walked from room to room and then stood where hang the mezzotints and engravings of those under or with whom . . . the Gregorys have served, Fox, Burke and so on, and after standing silent said 'All the nobility of earth.' I felt he did not mean it for that room alone but for lost tradition. How much of my own verse has not been but the repetition of those words."

In 1932 Yeats published *Words for Music Perhaps,* which shortly afterward was added to his volume of poems published in 1933, *The Winding Stair.* This volume bears witness to his new passion for eighteenth-century Ireland, with Swift, Grattan, and Burke as its ruling minds. The central poem of this collection is "Byzantium," but more complex, more occult, more impersonal. Again the antitheses are being and becoming, the fury and the mire; and again the groundwork is a welter of images, and the emotion they generate implies that the poet longs for the flux of growth and change, for the bitter forces of complexity.

For some time Yeats wondered if the death of Lady Gregory in 1932 would not mark the end of his creative life. But in 1934 he underwent the so-called Steinach operation for rejuvenation and felt it to be successful. He found himself now, in fact, at the beginning of one of the most fantastic phases of his career; embarking on fresh studies and new friendships, defying recurrent illnesses, he went on writing and philosophizing with indomitable ardor and intellectual excitement. A volume of plays, *Wheels and Butterflies,* appeared in 1934 and in 1935 he published *A Full Moon in March,* containing two dance plays, *A Full Moon in March* and *The King of the Great Clock Tower,* together with a strange, half-mystical, half-political poem, "Parnell's Funeral." Politics was finding new expression in his poetry.

Dramatis Personae (1936), the continuation of his autobiography, contained a moving account of Lady Gregory and a satirical portrait of George Moore, which was in effect a long-deferred revenge.

He spent the winter of 1935–1936 in Majorca with Swami Shri Purohit, helping the Swami to translate the *Upanishads*. There he was again taken ill but slowly recovered. He wrote a series of ballads on Cromwell, Parnell, and Roger Casement, and began *The Herne's Egg* (published in 1938), a Rabelaisian play with occult implications, whose dramatic verse has a new and at times magnificent purity.

Late in 1936 appeared *The Oxford Book of Modern Verse,* an anthology compiled by Yeats at the request of the Clarendon Press. It had cost him many months of wide reading and reflection. A bold, eccentric, highly personal anthology, it contains a long introduction whose importance was not to be appreciated until some years had passed.

Always keenly interested in the spoken word, in 1937 he was persuaded by the British Broadcasting Company to take part in a series of poetry recitals, two of them devoted to his own work. Still composing indefatigably, he completed in 1937 his last, revised version of *A Vision*. Despite the "stylistic arrangement of experience" which he had achieved, W. B. Yeats's craving for life was still unsatisfied.

Early in 1938 he went out to Menton, intending henceforth to spend his winters on the Riviera, and there a new phase of activity began. He planned a series of pamphlets which he called *On the Boiler*. Only the first was published—an outspoken medley of Yeats's opinions on politics, eugenics, and poetry, written in the manner of a wild old man railing at the state of the world. If the world was content to muddle along regardless of its approaching doom, the poet could do likewise! At the same time he wrote in his new manner what his admirers think his finest play, *Purgatory,* a masterpiece of construction and versification, concealing under the outer husk a wealth of occult and religious ideas. The first performance of *Purgatory* took place in Dublin in August 1938: there he made his last appearance in public, declaring in a short speech that this play contained "his own convictions about this world and the next." The poems of his old age were published regularly in the *London Mercury,* giving new life and unprecedented prestige to this all but defunct periodical.

The last poem he wrote finally turns away from the problems of the world's future to deal with those of a dying man, for though "Cuchulain Comforted" reverts to an old myth and assumes the accents of Dante, it is a profoundly personal poem.

This ultimate union of Irish myth, heterodox theology, and introspection emphasizes the lifelong continuity of the poet's efforts: "Hammer your thoughts into unity."

Frank Kermode is professor of literature at the University of Manchester in England. Translated by James Emmons.

THE 1923 PRIZE

By GUNNAR AHLSTRÖM

AT THE END of World War I, Great Britain had had only one Nobel Prizewinner for Literature, Germany had received four, and France three.

At the time, the name of Thomas Hardy was particularly prominent and had rallied a fair number of supporters in the Swedish press. It had accepted as certain that this leading personality of the literary world, fully qualified to receive the Prize, would soon do so. His candidacy had been put forward on several occasions by competent English authorities. The master of the tragic novel had also, in his old age, added to his prestige by composing a series of poems of undeniable perfection. In his own country, he deservedly enjoyed an Olympian reputation. In 1923, it was therefore expected that the Prize would be awarded to the author of *Tess of the D'Urbervilles* and *Jude the Obscure*. Among possible rivals, there was mention of Thomas Mann, Sigrid Undset, and John Galsworthy; even so, it seemed fairly certain that England would get the Prize that year. Great was the astonishment when the Prize went to William Butler Yeats of Ireland.

"Anglophobia is not dead," a liberal Swedish newspaper commented, "and when finally one cannot help turning toward the West, one goes to its farthest periphery." The critics also added that this choice had disagreeable political implications: in view of the tension then existing between England and Ireland, the Swedish Academy's decision could be interpreted as taking a stand and making a gesture in favor of *Suorstat Eireann* and other controversies of a Celtic nature, whose doings could be followed in the press articles on foreign politics. Added to this was the fact that William Butler Yeats was unknown to the general public. There was also some gnashing of teeth in England; but the dissatisfaction was more the result of Thomas Hardy having been passed over once again, than from any doubt as to the merits of Yeats.

Researches were made in Sweden, documentary works were consulted; publications were thumbed through; poems translated; and well before Christmas, a whole collection of Yeats's dramatic works had been published in translation. Everything helped to confirm the impression that this time the Prize had been awarded to an important and original writer who, in addition, was the mouthpiece of the new literature of a newly freed country.

Actually, the decision was not the result of a sudden caprice. The case book on W. B. Yeats had been building up ever since 1902, the year which marked

Theodore Mommsen's winning of the Prize. In that year, Yeats had been proposed by a very much older compatriot, W. E. H. Lecky, the liberal historian whose book, *A History of England in the XVIIIth Century,* had also found readers in France. Lecky represented Dublin University in the House of Commons from 1895 until his death in 1903. He had done his utmost to draw the attention of readers abroad to the Irish poet W. B. Yeats, "young and mystical, it is true, but remarkably gifted. I do not pretend that he is the greatest of our living poets, nor even that he is the most popular among them; but I know of no other who combines sound poetic gifts with the idealistic tendency which you appreciate so truly, or who does so much to stimulate this tendency in contemporary English literature."

The years passed, and the young mystic poet finally acquired a well-founded reputation. Since 1914 he had been on the list, recommended by G. M. Plunket of the Royal Society of Literature. When Yeats's name reappeared on the agenda after the war, it was on the initiative of the Nobel Committee, where he had an ardent admirer in the person of the Nobel Committee chairman, Per Hallström, who looked upon Thomas Hardy as a dubious determinist, whereas Yeats answered to his taste for the idealistic. A candidate of this kind, moreover, stood a very good chance of winning sympathy in the heart of the Academy which was to make the decision.

In an essay called "The Bounty of Sweden" which was first printed in the *London Mercury* in 1924, and afterward published in book form, and finally incorporated in the author's posthumous autobiography, he recorded his impressions of his experience in Stockholm: Let us quote: "When I received from the hands of your King the great honor your Academy has conferred upon me, I felt that a young man's ghost should have stood upon one side of me and at the other a living woman in her vigorous old age." This concept throws a gleam of Celtic poetry on to the 1923 ceremony, when the lecturer was presented with the Prize which he had won "for his always inspired poetry, which in a highly artistic form gives expression to the spirit of a whole nation."

Translated by Camilla Sykes.